EARLY BEHAVIOR

EARLY BEHAVIOR

Comparative and Developmental Approaches

Editors

HAROLD W. STEVENSON

Professor of Child Psychology and
Director, Institute of Child Development,
University of Minnesota

ECKHARD H. HESS

Professor of Psychology and Chairman,
Department of Psychology,
University of Chicago

HARRIET L. RHEINGOLD

Research Professor of Psychology and
Director, Laboratory of Infant Behavior,
University of North Carolina

JOHN WILEY & SONS, INC.

New York · London · Sydney

Contributors

ERICH KLINGHAMMER
Assistant Professor of Psychology,
The University of Chicago.

BYRON A. CAMPBELL
Associate Professor of Psychology,
Princeton University.

J. M. WARREN
Professor of Psychology,
Pennsylvania State University.

WILLIAM A. MASON
Professor of Psychology and Head, Behavioral Sciences,
Delta Regional Primate Research Center,
Tulane University.

IRENÄUS EIBL-EIBESFELDT
a member of the staff,
Max Planck Institut für Verhaltensphysiologie,
Seewiesen, West Germany,
and Dozent, University of Munich.

WILLIAM KESSEN
Professor of Psychology and Research Associate in Pediatrics,
Yale University.

ROBERT L. FANTZ
Associate Clinical Professor of Psychology,
Western Reserve University.

LEWIS P. LIPSITT
Professor of Psychology,
Brown University.

HANUŠ PAPOUŠEK
Senior Research Scientist and Chief of the
Department of Infant Physiology and Pathology,
Institute for the Care of Mother and Child, Prague.

Acknowledgments

THE activities of the Social Science Research Council's Committee on Comparative-Developmental Behavior and the preparation of this volume were supported by a grant from the National Science Foundation (G 9687). We acknowledge this support and the interest of Henry Odbert, Program Director in Psychobiology, with gratitude. Staff members of the Social Science Research Council, notably Francis H. Palmer, the late Ben Willerman, and Paul Webbink, facilitated the work of the Committee in many ways during its five years of operation.

We are indebted to the individuals whose long-term and enthusiastic participation in the Committee's conferences resulted in the essays presented here. Without such participation the publication of this volume would have been impossible. The death of Bernard Greenberg, an initial participant, robbed us of a stimulating chapter. Three other persons attended our conferences, Walter S. Stanley, Robert Zimmerman, and Milton Trapold, and their contributions are gratefully acknowledged. We were assisted by Sylvia W. Rosen in preparing the material for publication.

The publication of this volume concludes the activities of the Committee. It is hoped that the Committee's work will have helped to stimulate interest in the comparative and developmental study of behavior, a neglected but important area of investigation.

Harold W. Stevenson
Eckhard H. Hess
Harriet L. Rheingold

Contents

EARLY BEHAVIOR

∾ 1 ∾

Introduction

Eckhard H. Hess

THIS book originated in the efforts of Francis H. Palmer, formerly of the staff of the Social Science Research Council, to initiate discussion of the development of behavior in a comparative manner. His first step was to organize a conference in January 1961 on the "Critical Period Hypothesis." Working papers were presented by Harry F. Harlow, Eckhard H. Hess, William Mason, and Austin Riesen. The papers dealt with the importance for normal development of the affectional systems between infant and mother monkeys and among infant monkeys (Harlow), variables affecting imprinting in animals (Hess), the significance of experiences in the first year of life for socialization in the monkey (Mason), and the role of sensory stimulation in perceptual and behavioral development (Riesen). The discussion pointed out the difficulties of generalizing results of research, not only from one member of a phylogenetic family to another but even between breeds of the same species. The conclusion reached by the majority of the participants was that at our present state of knowledge the concept of 'critical period' was not a useful one for looking at the behavior of the young organism.

As a result of this conference, the Social Science Research Council organized the Committee on Comparative-Developmental Behavior. Members were Harold W. Stevenson (Chairman), Harry F. Harlow, Eckhard H. Hess, Harriet L. Rheingold, and Robert R. Sears. Francis Palmer represented the Council on the Committee. The late Ben Willerman later took Palmer's place as Council representative. To our regret, Harry F. Harlow and Robert R. Sears resigned from the Committee because of the pressure of other obligations before its activities were concluded.

The Committee was asked to take appropriate steps to stimulate research on the development of social processes across phylogenetic levels. Several activities were considered and relevant literature was reviewed. On the basis of these reviews, it was decided to concentrate on the topic of early development. As a final step, two research confer-

1

ences were held, one in 1963, the other in 1965. The participants were chosen as representatives of differing approaches to the topic of early development; all were studying the development of young organisms, ranging from birds to man. The first version of their reports was presented in 1963 and their final papers were discussed in 1965. This book is the result of the two conferences.

The average American psychologist is almost fanatic in his insistence that the concept of "innate" behavior is useless. A corollary of this very clear theoretical position is that "critical periods" in development are somehow related to the concept of "innate" and are therefore also suspect and useless. It has often occurred to me, and I am sure this is not an original idea, that our national or political climate has something to do in determining this point of view. The notion that all men are created equal seems to have seeped into the consideration of behavior and its genesis, not only in the human but in the animal as well. Indeed, it is unfashionable today to consider the possibility that there are innate differences in persons of various genetic backgrounds. We would like to assume instead that everyone is equal, provided he has the proper environmental opportunities. It is clear, of course, that such a point of view can have a profound influence on the manner in which the development of infants and young children will be studied.

There is, however, a second point of view. This way utilizes some of the methodologies and concepts of ethology and applies them to psychological problems in a rigorous fashion. I feel that such an approach is becoming inevitable and have decided that *Ethological Psychology* is a most apt term for it. One of the consequences of such a viewpoint is that we once again discover that the infant is a biological organism and that it brings into the world, as part of its genetically determined structure, potential avenues of development. Such a point of view would lead in some instances to concepts, research designs, and conclusions diametrically opposed to those engendered by the first point of view. These, in turn, would influence any attempt to apply human behavior research to making the world a better place in which to live.

It is because of my concern with scientific progress that I am happy with this book. The papers do not represent isolated viewpoints. The investigators who contributed to this volume are wide ranging in their ideas and theoretical positions regarding such concepts. I think in many ways this marks the first instance in which such a wide spectrum of thought has been directed to a study of the basic problem of the development of young organisms. An additional good feature of this compilation is the subject matter of study: animals from the lower vertebrates to man and behavior processes from the simplest kind of association learning to complex problem solving are considered. Even within categories of the organisms to be studied, the approaches differ widely. As you will see, for example, the approaches of Eibl-Eibesfeldt, Fantz, and Lipsitt clearly differ from one another not only in orientation but in the theoretical views brought to bear on the problem of the development of behavior in young organisms. This is good. Among other things, the volume exhibits diverse viewpoints to the reader and gives him a much better understanding of the multifaceted approach to the study of behavior that is representative of science in the world today. In this one volume the reader may expose himself to points of view that vary from one in which genetic and innate organizations of perception and behavior are considered to be critical to those in which these considerations are not only disregarded but an attempt is made to demonstrate that conditioning and learning are sufficient for the understanding of behavior. For this reason, if for no other, reading this book should be a stimulating experience.

2

Factors Influencing Choice of Mate in Altricial Birds

ERICH KLINGHAMMER

The University of Chicago

IN 1935 the Austrian zoologist Konrad Lorenz published a pioneer paper entitled "Der Kumpan in der Umwelt des Vogels" (The Companion in the Birds' World) in which he described how young birds of some species form a social attachment to their parents. This phenomenon he called "imprinting." Most young birds do not innately recognize their own species but must acquire this knowledge early in life. Although Heinroth (1910), Heinroth and Heinroth (1924–1933), Portielje (1921), and Spaulding (1873) had already reported this phenomenon, it was Lorenz who first discussed it specifically. For example, the grey-lag gosling (*Anser anser*) flees from a human when a few days old but follows him readily if he is the first moving object the gosling sees as soon as it has hatched. Furthermore, having once followed the person, it will no longer follow its own natural parents.

Based on these observations and on others in different species, Lorenz (1935) saw the imprinting process to be different in essence from ordinary learning for the following reasons:

1. "This acquisition of the object of innate behavior patterns can take place only in a closely restricted time period of the individual life." (p. 167)

2. "The imprinted knowledge of the object to which species-specific behavior patterns are normally directed appears, after the passing of the species-specific physiologically determined imprinting period, as if it were inborn. It can, henceforth, not be forgotten." (p. 167)

3. "Imprinting selects, as it were, supra-individual, species-specific cues from the picture of the parents and siblings." (p. 172)

4. Not the whole animal becomes imprinted to a specific object, but only a single reaction.

5. The determination of the imprinting object occurs when the appropriate reaction itself is not performed.

One must always keep in mind the important distinction between imprinting of the following response and imprinting of sexual reactions. This difference was pointed out by Lorenz (1935) and further analyzed experimentally by Polt and Hess (1964) and Schutz (1965). From reading Lorenz (1935) one gains the impression that the criteria of imprinting are not to be regarded as an all-inclusive definition, but as primary characteristics of the phenomenon. This view is supported by the fact that throughout his paper Lorenz gave examples of many species that only approximate or do not even fit his classical model of the grey-lag goose. Thus the example par excellence of irreversible imprinting cited by Lorenz is not the grey-lag goose but a musk drake (*Cairina moschata*). His awareness of many different ways in which social bonds become established in different species indicates that the criteria of imprinting were not meant to apply to all species.

Following this initial study, imprinting research in birds was not undertaken during the next 15 years. The literature contains only one report by Raeber (1948) on a turkey (*Meleagris gallopavo*), and not until 1951 were imprinting studies in precocial birds again reported.

Independently, Ramsay (1951), in the United States, and Fabricius (1951), in Sweden, reported some important factors operating in imprinting. Ramsay's experiment dealt with imprinting on models as well as with an exchange of the young of one species of waterfowl with the young of another. The importance of auditory components and the effect of color changes in the recognition of parents by the young were also studied. Fabricius investigated several species of ducks and was able to approximate the critical age during which imprinting is the strongest. Following these two investigations and some observations on ducklings by Nice (1953), Ramsay and Hess (1954) conducted the first controlled laboratory experiment of the imprinting phenomenon with mallard ducklings. Ducklings (*Anas platyrhynchos*) of various ages were exposed to a male mallard decoy in a circular runway under uniform conditions for a specified time and various following distances. Testing for the effect of imprinting was standardized and degrees of responsiveness were objectively scored. The critical imprinting age for mallards tested under these conditions was found to be between 13 and 16 hours.

Following this experiment, more imprinting investigations based on similarly standardized methods were reported in the United States and Europe. These experiments were done with precocial birds, that is, those able to follow their parent(s) shortly after hatching, mainly chicks of various races of *Gallus gallus* and various species of ducks. These experiments were performed under controlled conditions, but almost all spanned only the early following-response period of the animals' lives; the tests for imprinting took place within one week after the initial exposure to the imprinting object.

For a reasonably complete summary in the rapidly expanding area of imprinting in precocial birds, the reader is referred to Gray (1963), Hess (1959; 1964), Moltz (1960), and Sluckin (1965).

As a result of research with precocial birds many persons equate the concept of imprinting with the following response of the young to their parent(s), foster parent(s), or models used in the laboratory. Indeed, Moltz (1963), who stressed an epigenetic approach to imprinting, was primarily concerned with this phase of the imprinting process. Meanwhile, the effect of early experience on adult sexual behavior has not received the attention it should. Schutz (1965), working with various species of ducks, was the first recent investigator to depart from this trend with precocial birds.

Although many examples in this chapter would fall into the category of "sexual imprinting," our increasing knowledge of specific experiences and their possible role in affecting adult behavior has led me to think more in terms of the factors that determine the choice of sexual partner. In the following sections many examples illustrating these factors are cited and discussed. All the examples given deal with altricial birds.

Altricial birds comprise all species whose young are born in a relatively helpless state, that is, they require prolonged care in the nest. This consists of brooding, protecting, and especially feeding them while in the nest and for some time after fledging. There is no following response as in precocial birds. Because these young birds spend a varying number of days on the nest—less than two weeks in song-birds to more than a month in the large birds of prey—they can be expected to learn certain necessary things about their environment in ways that differ from precocial birds that must follow their parents about within hours, or at most days, after hatching in order to be led to food.

In the examples that follow, we shall see that altricial birds must also learn at some time during their lives to recognize the objects toward which they will direct social and sexual responses. In the natural situation this is usually the species' member. However, it is in unnatural

Male

(a) Rush attack

(b) Bow–coo

(c) Ritualized preening

(e) Copulation

(d) Mounting

Fig. 2-1 Sketches of courting and mating behavior of a male ring dove towards the human hand (drawn after frames of cine film).

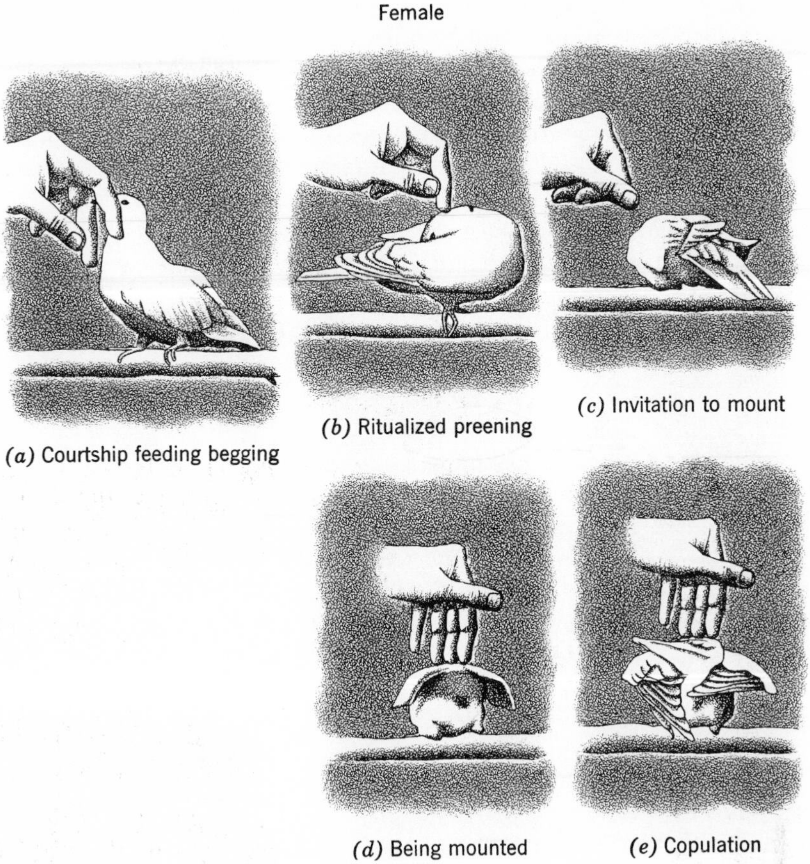

Female

(a) Courtship feeding begging

(b) Ritualized preening

(c) Invitation to mount

(d) Being mounted

(e) Copulation

Fig. 2-2 Sketches of courting and mating behavior of a female ring dove towards the human hand (drawn after frames of cine film).

situations, in captivity and in the laboratory, in which we gain some insight into the factors that ensure that male and female will meet to propagate the species.

Before I proceed to the description of the examples listed in Table 2-1, a word about the seeming "anecdotal" nature of some of the examples must be given. In all instances the overt behavior of the birds described by the authors consists largely of the species-specific fixed-action patterns (see Hess, 1962) that normal parent-raised birds perform during courtship and mating activities with species' members. As can be seen in Figs. 2-1 and 2-2, the degree of identifiability of these fixed-action patterns, with due consideration to individual differences within a species, rivals the objectivity attained by the use of sophisticated measuring instruments in many other areas of science.

The reliance on a single case in some instances to demonstrate the presence of a process in a species, such as imprinting or taming, stems from the knowledge that no unlearned, highly unique behavior pattern or process is exhibited in an intact single animal unless it is a part of the behavior repertoire or physiological organization of the species to which the animal belongs. This is not to say that additional verification and further detailed investigation is unnecessary. However, if at least one animal of a species does show a capacity to imprint, we can expect that further research will verify this initial conclusion.

PASSERIFORMES

Nicolai (1964) discussed imprinting phenomena as factors in the formation of races and species in the parasitic Viduinae, the widow birds that are a subfamily of the weaverbirds (Ploceidae). These birds live in the grassland regions of Africa in an area that extends from the southern edge of the Sahara Desert in the north to the cape region in the south, and from Somalia in the east to the coastal regions of Senegal in the west.

During the course of investigations spanning eight years, Nicolai maintained more than 500 Estrildine finches belonging to 48 species, 82 Viduines belonging to 10 species, and 50 Ploceids belonging to 5 species.

The Viduinae parasitize the Estrildidae. The females of a particular species, for example, *Vidua macroura* lay their eggs in the nest of only one species, in this case *Estrilda astrild*. The foster parents then raise the parasite's young. This is made possible by the fact that during the course of evolution the young Viduines of one particular species mimicked the juvenile plumage, gape markings in the mouth, and bill papilla of the particular Estrildidae host species. About adult Viduine behavior Nicolai (1964) wrote the following:

The songs of adult Viduinae are composed of two groups of elements; in each case one is weaverlike, while the other encompasses the entire vocal repertoire of a particular species of Estrildid. Song elements of both groups can follow one another in unpredictable sequence: in sexual motivation the imitations of Estrildid notes predominate, in aggressive motivation the innate, phylogentically older Euplectinelike song components. Thus the songs of the Viduinae reveal the identity of the host species on which they parasitize. (p. 200)

The imitated songs so perfectly match the Estrildid song that neither the host species, the human ear, nor sound spectrographic analysis can detect differences that are greater than individual variability existing within the Estrildine species. Nicolai continued:

Host specificity has been forced on the Viduinae in the course of their evolution by the selectivity of the Estrildids. The fixation on the host species has its origin in imprinting phenomena and is maintained by this means. Pairing between sex partners of the same adaptive type expresses itself in the males in the adoption of the entire vocabulary of the host species, and in the females in that they can come into breeding condition and ovulate only through stimulation by observing the brood preparations of a pair of the host species. The perfection of the host phrases in the songs of the Viduine males was subject from the beginning of the development of brood parasitism to a rigorous sexual selection, in that the females preferred those copulation partners whose song contained the most complete and accurate imitations of the notes of their joint host species. (p. 201)

We are not so much concerned here with the part imprinting played in the evolution of brood parasitism in the Viduinae as we are in the role of imprinting during the ontogenetic development of the young Viduines while in the Estrildid nest. Thus as the young Viduines grow up in the nest of their foster parents, they become imprinted on the latter's appearance and especially on their songs. The male Viduines learn the song of their foster fathers, whereas the females learn to remember it. In addition to learning the song of their foster species, the Viduines innately produce and recognize their own species-specific song. When, during the breeding season, the male Viduines have acquired their striking plumage and long tail feathers, they sing, alternating between components of their own song and those of their foster species. When perceiving a male or female of their foster species in the process of nest building, the Viduine male will suddenly sing only nest calls of the foster species and orient its body in that direction. This combination of species-specific and host-species song serves the function of showing a female the foster-species' pair. It is this observation of the foster-species' pair by the Viduine female that stimulates her sexually to copulate with the Viduine male and causes ovulation. The result is that her physiological state is synchronized with that of the foster species' female she is observing and the eggs she lays in her nest will develop at the same time. The incubation time for the eggs of host and parasite are the same.

This, then, is the biological function of imprinting in the host-parasite relationship between Viduinae and Estrildidae. When and how this imprinting takes place has not yet been analyzed.

The same author (Nicolai, 1956) also reported his observations on European bullfinches (*Pyrrhula pyrrhula L.*) that were hand-raised in isolation from species' members for varying periods of time. When bullfinches are hand-raised by humans in the company of siblings, they never court humans. In other words, the presence of siblings determines the later choice of sexual partner.

In bullfinches raised by their own parents, Nicolai observed that the young, after weaning, form what he calls "sibling pairs," which may be either homo- or heterosexual. In addition, individual members of these "betrothed" pairs may have similar relationships simultaneously with other siblings. This, Nicolai called "double betrothal." During this period, which lasts slightly longer than one year, the birds show various forms of the innate courtship behavior patterns without actually mating and breeding. After a year or more, when the gonads begin to develop, these sibling pairs break up rather suddenly. The partner is now attacked, except that males will not attack females but merely avoid or ignore them. This aggressiveness is directed primarily against the siblings and seems to prevent inbreeding.

When a male bullfinch is hand-raised by man, the latter is regarded as a "sibling partner." If a normal female is provided the male will accept and mate with her when he breaks off the "betrothal" with the human sibling partner.

If, on the other hand, no female is present, then the bird becomes irreversibly imprinted on man and henceforth directs all his social and sexual behavior toward him. Although no systematic experiment has yet been carried out, Nicolai suspected that the sensitive period during which final sexual imprinting can take place is terminated before the end of the second year of life. This sensitive period also varied in length in different individuals.

Another report of abnormal sexual behavior in finches is that of a hawfinch (*Coccothraustes coccothraustes*) reported by Kear (1960). This female hawfinch was removed from the nest when 5 days old and raised with other nestlings for six weeks. Although the bird lived with a male hawfinch for two years, she courted Miss Kear after the male died.

Immelmann (1965) reported some experiments with zebra finches (*Taeniopygia guttata castanotis*). He placed their eggs in the nests of society finches (*Lonchura striata* f. *domestica*) which readily accept hatchling finches among their own young. Between 33 and 66 days of age the zebra finches were removed from their foster parents and housed individually until about 4 months of age, when they were sexually mature. They were then tested in standardized situations in their own cages and were offered a choice between a species' member and a society finch, the latter of the opposite sex from the experimental bird. All zebra finch males that were raised by society finches directed all their social and sexual behavior to society finches and formed pairs with them. The zebra finch females, present at the same time, were either ignored or attacked.

The results with zebra finch females raised by society finches were entirely different; the female first approached the society finch but then turned to the zebra finch male as soon as he began to court her. From then on she only reacted to the zebra finch and pair formation took place. The differences in imprinting between male and female zebra finches could be correlated with the sexual dimorphism of zebra finches: the female possesses few, the males many, releasers (color patterns, song, courtship dance). Apparently the female can innately react to some of the releasers presented by the males, but the male's knowledge of the female's appearance must be acquired by imprinting.

CORVIDAE

We now turn to members of the family of Corvidae. Many crows, ravens, jackdaws, and jays have been hand-raised and became quite tame to man. However, the accounts that are often published in newspapers, sports and hunting magazines usually do not contain the pertinent observations and data on life history that are necessary to permit a meaningful evaluation. Fortunately, there are a few, well-documented reports in the literature from which we can gain some insight about choice of mate in this group.

Lorenz (1935) observed that jackdaws (*Coloeus monedula*) at the age of 14 days already recognize their parents but will still accept human caretakers as parent-companions, although initially they show some fear. After 20 more days the young are fledged, and, as far as the childhood instinctive behavior is concerned, it is now no longer possible for jackdaws to return to it. Likewise, young jackdaws raised by their parents up to this age will no longer accept humans. Lorenz reported that he hand-raised three jackdaws from the time they had no feathers—when they were quite young—and six more when they were about to be fledged. All the birds were quite tame when they were still begging for food. However, after childhood behavior patterns waned, the second six birds became shy, whereas the first three began to direct sexual behavior to Lorenz. Apparently the birds were hand-raised together.

Lorenz discussed a number of factors that affected this choice. The species' member recognition must be learned during ontogeny. He stated that there are two subperiods in the development of some behavior patterns that are initially not directed toward a specific object. One is usually a short period in which the bird "seeks" the object to which it will direct its inherited behavior, and a second, longer period, in which this object has already been found but acceptance of another object is still possible.

In 1961 I removed a young crow (*Corvus brachyrhynchos*) from a nest when it was about 2 weeks old. It was then hand-raised by a colleague in the exclusive company of humans. After fledging, the bird followed humans about, flying free until it was about 5 months old, when it was placed in a large flight cage. After ignoring and avoiding two crows of the same species, the bird eventually paired with one of them and built a nest. Today, four years later, the crow is still tame to humans, especially to the person who raised it and to others whom it knew. All humans, however, are greeted whenever they come near the cage.

A recent thorough study of the raven (*Corax c. corax L.*) by Gwinner (1964) provides a wealth of material and throws light on the factors that affect choice of mate, since all 18 ravens of this study were hand-raised and observed for several years in aviaries and at semi-liberty.

Young ravens leave the nest when approximately 50 days old, and at an age of about 75 days they are self-sufficient. At this time the parent-young bond loosens, and the young join other sibling groups that may contain as many as 25 individuals, or they may join a flock of birds born the preceding year. During the winter flocks of ravens numbering as high as 150 birds may be seen at sites of abundant food.

In such a flock pairs are formed. Late in the fall courtship begins, and shortly before the third year of life the pair leaves the flock and selects a breeding territory, which, from then on, is rarely left. Gwinner extensively studied the social behavior of his ravens and illustrated their various postures with good photographs and line drawings. He cited several cases of birds that had regarded humans as mates but, under certain conditions, also selected species' members as permanent mates. His observations are summarized as follows:

All males and females that received special attention during the hand-raising period (from various ages on) and the months after weaning courted Gwinner later. One female exhibited a progressively more complete courting and nest-building activity that was directed at him from the first to the third seasons, despite the presence of a male raven that courted her at the same time. The female either ignored him or attacked him when he attacked her chosen human "mate." At the end of the third season Gwinner withdrew from her and restricted his contact to routine care and observations; in the same year the female paired with the male, although she laid no eggs.

Gwinner stated earlier that all ravens eventually select a mate of their own species. The question therefore arises of whether it is possible to speak of imprinting, or if it even occurs in this species. He observed that in the social flocks of ravens individual bonds are of equal importance as is the case in some highly developed mammals. A raven can become so closely attached to his human foster parent that he will court only him, even if the raven grows up among species' members that are ready to mate. However, the recognition of innate behavior patterns along with the withdrawal of the human companion enables the raven to pair with a species' member. Such equivalence of raven-human seems indicated in the example of a male that alternately courted Gwinner and females. One necessary precondition for courting a human seems to be that the ravens be tamed, which in Gwinner's study took place while the birds were being hand-raised.

PSITTACIFORMES

Since birds of the order of Psittaciformes (the parrots, macaws, etc.) are so popular as pets and are frequently kept exclusively in human company, cases in which sexual behavior is directed to humans are undoubtedly numerous. At the same time, accurate and detailed information is rare and not readily available. However, the examples presented below do indicate that an imprinting process does exist in this group.

Thorpe (1963) discussed Hellman's and Lorenz's observations on budgerigars (*Melopsittacus undulatus*).

. . . Budgerigars (were) imprinted to humans and then isolated for two years from humans, being fed, watered, and cleaned in such a manner that the human attendant was never visible to the birds. Under these conditions they bred and reared young normally. But when, after these two years, they were first re-exposed to humans, they immediately courted Hellman and Lorenz again and neglected their own species.

One of my acquaintances obtained a Senegal parrot (*Poicephalus senegalus senegalus*) that was hand-raised with a sibling from the time it was 4 days old in March of 1964. The bird was purchased in

October and lived away from other parrots. Its sex was not determined. When about 9 months old, the bird, which showed a decided preference for the man in the house, began to court him or his wife in his absence. The bird regurgitated food and attempted to feed the person, offered his head for scratching, and, after several minutes of this, would squat, drop his wings, and spread his tail feathers. In addition, the bird was aggressive to other persons except the one it was courting. No free-choice situation that included species' members was ever offered.

CICONIIFORMES

Portielje (1921) was cited by Thorpe (1963) as reporting imprinting in the American bittern (*Botaurus stellaris*). The male would drive his female from the nest whenever the preferred human appeared, then would try to entice the human into the nest.

A very well-documented instance of imprinting is provided by O. von Frisch (1957) who hand-raised a young purple heron (*Ardea pupurea*) from the time it was 10 days old. When mature, the bird treated him as a female, attempting to copulate with him when he was crouched, building a nest with him, and in short exhibiting all the behavior a heron normally directs to his mate.

Löhrl (1961) hand-raised a European white stork (*Ciconia ciconia*) from the eighth day of life until sexual maturity. The bird was allowed to fly free and search for much of its food. When mature, the stork began to show the nest site to Löhrl, clapped the bill, which seems to be part of the greeting ceremony, and presented the female copulation posture to him, which led Löhrl to the conclusion that the bird was a female.

STRIGIFORMES

Among their experiences with countless numbers of birds, O. and M. Heinroth (1924–1933) described the courting of two eagle owl siblings (*Bubo bubo*), which were hand-raised together. The male courted Heinroth; the female, however, preferred his wife, and all attempts to withdraw from the owls and induce them to mate with one another ended in failure. Each courted only its own human "mate."

FALCONIFORMES

Fairly complete records on hand-raised sparrowhawks (*Accipiter n. nisus L.*) are given by Mohr (1960), who studied their behavior development. If removed from the nest between 1 to 8 days of age, the young become tame and accept man as parent and later as sexual companion. Once they are 20 days old, they will no longer accept the human but only adult sparrowhawks. Between 10 to 14 days of age the young will still accept the human as parent if much time is spent with them, but they remain shy and will not respond sexually to man. When 30 days old, they leave the nest in captivity.

A human-imprinted female sparrowhawk was heard to give a series of faint calls whenever she saw people. Later on these calls occurred only when the author came into view. As the breeding season progressed, the female showed a typical posture that is normally only seen as an "invitation to copulate" among mates. If the author approached her, she would fly off a short distance and repeat this behavior. At the same time she began to build a nest.

A young male that had been initially hand-raised with this female was then gradually introduced, but the female continued to court Mohr. When the two birds were left alone after two days, the female killed, plucked, and proceeded to eat the male. During the first winter another juvenile male was placed into a cage next to the female, which avoided Mohr outside the breeding season. In April of the next spring she became tame from one day to the next and again courted him while ignoring two stuffed sparrowhawk males in juvenile and adult plumage. The courting behavior of the female was much more pronounced during this second season. While in the copulation posture she permitted a hand to be placed on her back, after which she raised her tail up and to the side and turned her head away. This quite clearly is the female copulatory behavior. Male courtship behavior was not observed.

Mohr further cites Waller (1942), whose paper was not available for review, who succeeded in breeding peregrine falcons (*Falco peregrinus*) in captivity. Of that pair, the female had been human-imprinted during the first years of her life. Unfortunately, details on the manner of keeping and degree of contact with humans versus species' member were not available.

COLUMBIFORMES

Although bird hybrids in 18 bird families have been reported by Gray (1958) in her book *Bird Hybrids,* we are concerned here primarily with the Columbidae. Gray listed all published records of hybrids occurring in nature as well as under artificial conditions in captivity. One hundred fifty different hybrid combinations were reported in 23 genera among pigeons and doves, with 40 of the cases in the genera *Columba* and 58 in *Streptopelia,* which reflects either that more birds of this group are maintained in captivity or the ease with which they may be crossed. The first may be the more likely reason.

Whitman's (1919) extensive studies on the evolution of color patterns in pigeons, carried out at The University of Chicago and the Woodshole Marine Biological station from around the turn of the century until his death in 1910, were successful to a large measure because he was able to produce hybrids from a great number of different species and races of wild and domesticated pigeons.

It will be useful to quote some passages written by Carr, the editor of the third volume of Whitman's posthumous works *The Behavior of Pigeons,* as they pertain to mate selection.

In the chapter on mating preferences Carr observes that the birds' previous social environment is a factor and that there is a preference for the species' member at maturity which is an acquired function of the social environment in which the birds were reared.

We are told that young birds raised under foster-parents of a different species are very apt to prefer a mating not with their own kind, but with a member of the species among which they were reared. The author's (Whitman's) phrase "very apt to prefer" indicates that such means of social education are not always efficacious, and this fact shows that some degree of innate preference probably exists. Adult preferences must thus be regarded as the result of two factors, instinct, and experience. (p. 98)

One sentence deserves particular attention.

It is possible that previous experience is efficacious in part by removing fear and distrust or indifference and substituting therefore a more positive attitude of familiarity. (p. 99)

In further consideration of the influence of social environment, Whitman came to use the cross-fostering technique for producing hybrids of different species. He wrote the following:

If a bird of one species is hatched and reared by a wholly different species, it is very apt, when fully grown, to mate with the species under which it has been reared. For example, a male passenger pigeon that was reared by ring doves and had remained with that species was ever ready, when fully grown, to mate with any ring dove but could never be induced to mate with one of his own species. I kept him away from ring doves a whole season, in order to see what could be accomplished in the way of getting him mated finally with his own species, but he would never make any advances to the females, and whenever a ring dove was seen or heard in the yard he was at once attentive. (p. 28)

Carr's comment on this statement is as follows:

It may be remarked by the editor that the discovery of this principle furnishes the key to Professor Whitman's success in hybridizing the various species of pigeons. A novel and important principle of behavior is here involved. The range of stimuli to which an instinctive tendency will respond may be modified by habits acquired long before the expression of the instinct. The first expression of a delayed instinctive tendency may thus be in part a function of all that the organism has previously acquired. (p. 28)

Nicolai (1962) reported a case of a mourning dove that was parent-raised but later courted him when she found no available mate. The bird came from a small population of birds that had been raised for a number of generations in captivity.

K. Heinroth (1961) recalled how a male domestic pigeon (*Columba livia* L.) had courted her late husband in preference to all species' members.

Goodwin (1948) observed that the reactions of a pigeon to species "which it habitually sees" may influence the direction its sexual behavior will take. He cited examples in which a male turtle dove (*Turtur turtur*), a male wood pigeon (*Columba palumbus*), and a male and a female domestic pigeon, which had all been hand-raised from the seventh to twelfth days on, courted only domestic pigeons, stock doves (*Columba oenas*), and people, but never their own species. Thus even hand-raised pigeons would court the species they habitually saw if they were removed from their parents before a certain age. This suggests that not only the nestling period but the time after fledging is susceptible to lasting influences.

A personal observation confirms this. In the spring of 1963 a homing pigeon (Y30) (*C. livia*) was abandoned by its parents and was hand-raised from the time it was 23 days old. Although the bird accepted the human foster-parent only with some struggling, it permitted hand-feeding until it became independent at 29 days. When the bird was 38 days old, it was placed into a community cage that contained mourning doves, several species of *Streptopelia,* and one pair of picazuro pigeons (*Columba picazuro*). When the bird was 6 months old, six more homing pigeons were added to the loft. During the entire spring the bird remained close to the picazuros and would not perch near its own species' members. It courted the picazuros, but they did not respond. The other homing pigeons formed three pairs and raised young, of which, by the end of the year, there were 14. These juvenile birds were placed into a separate loft in November of 1964 and allowed to fly free; later they were taken 10 miles away from the loft and released. All returned. Although the hand-raised bird lived in the loft with them, he could be recognized at once because he always perched by himself. When released away from home, he did not join the flock but would circle it at a distance of about 50 to 100 feet on the way home. Gradually this changed, and by February of 1965 he seemed to have become a full-fledged member; he no longer sat by himself, and he flew with the flock. In March of 1965 he mated with a *C. livia* hen and was incubating two eggs and helped to raise the young. The picazuro pigeons, a mated pair, were occasionally visible to Y30, but he showed no further interest.

Goodwin (1958) reviewed some of his observations of domesticated *Columba livia* which indicated to him that the color pattern of parents as well as of other pigeons living in the cage after a young pigeon has become a fledgling affect its choice of sexual partner at sexual maturity.

Conditioning for such preferences probably takes place in the later fledgling period and/or the early days after leaving the nest.

In this species (*C. livia*), where the nest is often in darkness, one would indeed expect this, but I think it probably holds for other pigeons as well. . . . (p. 139)

Because in large populations of pigeons consisting of pied, red, and blue pigeons, pairs were primarily of similar colors, Goodwin concluded that two mechanisms account for such preferences. First, the young remain near their birthplace and there is then a tendency to pair with relatives who would be similarly colored; and second, imprinting on parents and/or nest mates causes a preference for their colors. This hypothesis seems supported by the observations that free-flying German toy pigeons did not mix with blue dove-cote pigeons; and in Egypt little or no inbreeding occurs between dove-cote and blue rock pigeons or with the larger pied, white, or red domestic pigeons. Sympatric species of closely related wild pigeons exist, for example, snow pigeon (*C. leuconata*) and the blue hill pigeon (*C. campestris*), and the white-crowned and red-necked pigeons (*C. leucocephala* and *C. squamosa*). Goodwin suspected that in addition to ecological factors and voice, color preferences influenced by imprinting have been important factors in the speciation of wild forms.

In a systematic study, in which early experience was a variable in mate selection among pigeons, Warriner (1960) studied the effect of the interaction of parents and young on mating behavior at maturity in king pigeons, a domesticated race of *Columba livia*. He raised 32 black king pigeons and 32 white king pigeons in the following manner: 16 black kings were raised by their own parents and 16 were raised by white king foster parents; and 16 white kings were raised by their own parents and 16 more by black king foster parents. Each group consisted of half males and half females. After raising the birds with their respective parents and foster parents for 40 days, each bird was placed into visual isolation until sexual maturity. Then, two males and two females of each of the four possible combinations were placed into a mating pen, and observations were made of which birds mated. The results showed that males mated with females that were similar in characteristics (color) with their own parents or with their foster parents, respectively. The conclusion is that the early experience, at least in males, has an effect on the choice of mate at maturity.

Warriner evaluated his results as follows. First, he convinced himself that the presence or absence of a sibling in the nest had no effect on choice of mate and, second, that there was no difference in mating preferences between breeds. He interpreted the sex differences in his results on mating preference in terms of the greater aggressiveness and related variables of males. This alone could account for the fact that males showed an effect of early experience in mate selection although females did not.

Craig (1914) isolated parent-raised ring doves (*S. risoria*) from all other doves at ages varying from 32 to 110 days. After some time, they began to show courting behavior directed toward Craig. Later, when he placed the birds again with ring doves, normal nesting took place. Thus in the absence of species' members a human was chosen as a mate.

In experiments dealing with dove songs as innately coded patterns of specific behavior Lade and Thorpe (1964) crossed the following species of doves.[1]

Miss Lade (personal communication) explained how these pairings

---

[1] The classification used by Lade and Thorpe (1964) and Gray (1958) is given here, although Delacour (1959) referred to *Stigmatopelia* and *Spilopelia* as *Streptopelia*.

were obtained: On arrival in July to October the birds were visually isolated from their species, some auditorily by distance. In the middle of winter they were set up in interspecies pairs in individual cages. In the first breeding season the following spring no pairs attempted nesting or produced young until the following July, when one pair did so. After this failure eggs were exchanged between *Spilopelia chinensis* and *Streptopelia risoria,* and the young resulting from this cross-fostering procedure mated with the foster species. It was found,

	Male		Female
1.	*Spilopelia chinensis tigrina*	x	*Streptopelia risoria*
2.	*Streptopelia risoria*	x	*S. decaocto*
3.	*S. decaocto*	x	*S. risoria*
4.	*Stigmatopelia senegalensis*	x	*S. risoria*
5.	*Streptopelia turtur*	x	*S. risoria*
6.	*Spilopelia chinensis tigrina*	x	*S. decaocto*

however, that matings could also be effected by the simple expedient of leaving the pairs together all winter, as a result of which nearly all the pairs set up previously nested successfully in the following spring.

Thus prolonged exposure to another species in the absence of one's own also resulted in pair formation.

The hybrids showed no reluctance to attempt nesting with either parent species or with their own hybrid types. This, perhaps, because imprinting occurred to both, and in Lade's experiments the hybrids were imprinted to hybrid siblings as well. The effects of sibling presence are discussed later in work with mourning doves, in which it was also discovered.

In the preceding pages we have reviewed a number of cases in some detail that elucidate factors which affect choice of mate in birds of the orders of Galliformes (turkeys, chickens), Gruiformes (rails), Columbiformes (pigeons and doves), Anseriformes (ducks, geese, etc.), Passeriformes (the perching birds that include the *Corvidae* (crows, etc.), Ploceidae (weaver finches), Psittaciformes (parrots), Ciconiiformes (storks, herons, etc.), Strigiformes (owls), and Falconiformes (hawks, etc.) (see Table 2-1).

TERMS

In this chapter I have used the term "innate" on several occasions. Because this term is frequently misunderstood and has been criticized by Beach (1955), Hebb (1953), Lehrman (1953; 1956), and Schneirla (1956; 1957), the reasons for retaining it should be given.

TABLE 2-1

Summary of Altricial Birds Discussed in Respect to Sexual Imprinting

Page			PASSERIFORMES	
13, 14	Lorenz	1935	Jackdaws	*Coloeus monedula spermologous*
12	Nicolai	1956	Bullfinch	*Pyrrhula pyrrhula* L.
12, 13	Immelmann	1965	Zebra finch	*Taeniopygia guttata castanotis*
12	Kear	1960	Hawfinch	*Coccothraustes coccothraustes*
10, 11	Nicolai	1964	Widow birds	*Viduinae*
14	Gwinner	1964	Raven	*Corax corax corax* L.
14	Klinghammer	1961	Crow	*Corvus brachrynchos*
			PSITTACIFORMES	
15	Hellman	1954	Budgerigar	*Melopsittacus undulatus*
15	Klinghammer	1964	Senegal parrot	*Poicephalus s. senegalus*
			CICONIIFORMES	
16	Portielje	1921	Am. Bittern	*Botauris stellaris*
16	O. v. Frisch	1957	Purple Heron	*Ardea purpurea*
16	Löhrl	1961	White Stork	*Ciconia ciconia*
			STRIGIFORMES	
16	Heinroth, O. & M.	1924–1933	Eagle Owl	*Bubo bubo*
			FALCONIFORMES	
17	Waller	1942	Peregrine Falcon	*Falco peregrinus*
17	Mohr	1960	Sparrowhawk	*Accipiter n. nisus* L.
			COLUMBIFORMES	
21	Craig	1914	Ring Dove	*Streptopelia risoria*
18	Whitman	1919	Doves & Pigeons	*Columbidae*
19, 20, 21	Goodwin	1948, 1958	Pigeons & Doves	*Columbidae*
21	Warriner	1960	King Pigeons	*Columba livia*
19	Heinroth K.	1961	Pigeon	*C. livia*
19	Nicolai	1962	Mourning Dove	*Zenaidura macroura*
21, 22	Lade & Thorpe	1964	Doves	*Streptopelia*
28	Klinghammer & Hess	1964	Ring Doves	*S. risoria*
19	Klinghammer	1966	Pigeon	*Columba livia*
28			Mourning Dove	*Zenaidura macroura*
29, 30			Grayson's Dove	*Zenaida graysoni*
35			Dwarf Turtle Dove	*Streptopelia tranquebarica*
35			Spotted Dove	*S. chinensis*

The use of terms like "innate," "inherited," "inborn," "instinctive," as applied to behavior, appears usually in opposition to "learned" behavior. The authors cited hold that this dichotomy has no merit, since it does not consider the interactions between genetic and environmental factors during ontogenetic development. Lorenz (1956; 1965) has stated his view on the usefulness of distinguishing how information about the environment can get into the organism: (a) during the life of the individual organism, and (b) by natural selection in the species during the course of evolution. In the first example we speak of learning, in the second of innate behavior in which the information is ultimately stored in the genome. Furthermore, Lorenz was concerned exclusively with adapted behavior that serves the animal in the normal environment of the species. Ethologists have at all times been aware of the complex interactions between the organism and its environment, which includes the embryonic environment as well as, for example, climatic factors to which the organism is exposed after birth. What is important for an understanding of adapted behavior in an organism is not only how, during ontogenetic development from the time of conception onward, various genetic and environmental factors interact to produce an adapted organism, but whether the relevant information for such behavior is acquired during phylogeny or ontogeny and how innate and learned components become linked into the appropriate, species-specific behavior patterns of adaptive behavior. An awareness of these two sources of information has implications for research. Failure to consider them can result in an inappropriate design of experiments, as pointed out by Klinghammer and Hess (1964a).

THE EXPERIMENTAL ANALYSIS OF MATE SELECTION IN SEVERAL SPECIES OF THE COLUMBIDAE

I have been interested in altricial birds for two reasons: first, because it is my view that imprinting phenomena in altricial birds can and ought to be discussed separately since the adaptive requirements to which a newborn altricial bird is exposed and to which a particular species has become adapted during the course of evolution are substantially different from those that precocial animals encounter; and second, because precocial birds have been extensively reviewed by others.

These differences between altricial and precocial birds must be considered in the design of experiments to study the various early experiences on later behavior, especially courting and mating behavior. The very nature of development in altricial young also places certain limitations on the scope of such investigations. Experimental subjects are fewer because of the large amount of time that must be spent raising each individual, and because the birds must be kept until maturity if effects of early experiences on sexual behavior are to be distinguished from taming. A following response meaningfully analogous to that found in precocial birds does not exist and hence cannot be taken as an indicator that imprinting has occurred during the first days of life.

Such considerations undoubtedly account for the relative dearth of experimental work with altricial birds. In addition, space requirements for isolating the birds from species' members are substantial, and testing for the effects of early experience is complex. Furthermore, the long time span between birth and maturity allows for more experiences to have an effect than is possible in the few days in which the great majority of precocial birds are imprinted and tested.

In view of these considerations, it is not surprising that the foster parent of an altricial young bird has often been a human. One of the main reasons is the desire to have a tame animal that will remain near humans of its own accord and can thus be studied with a degree of thoroughness not possible with wild birds. In addition, human beings can, with the necessary skill and knowledge, take the place of foster parents and successfully raise such young when many birds would not be suitable as foster parents. In the case of many of the small passerines, especially finches, some species are often used successfully as foster parents. Thus the society finch (*Lonchura striata*) will accept and raise many other finches that normally do not readily breed in captivity because they usually have a longer incubation period than those species whose eggs they are given and because the releasers eliciting their parental care need not be very specific. Therefore they will respond to young quite different from their own.

As a corollary to what has already been said, the use of models presents certain problems. A model cannot feed a young altricial bird, whereas precocial birds can follow models and be fed and watered separately. The task of hand-feeding also requires that one can see what he is doing, although, with some skill, pigeons and doves can be fed in the dark. Furthermore, when models can be used, a bird of a related species is perhaps as good or better. But cross-fostering requires a large number of potential foster parents of various species, and the requirement of synchronizing several breeding pairs in respect to incubation period and brooding is very time consuming and in many instances cannot be met. Usually facilities that can meet all the necessary prerequisites on a large scale are not available, and breeding colonies take time to establish.

One important reason for using a human foster parent is that one can obtain information otherwise readily overlooked, since under this condition there is such intimate contact with the experimental animal. When it would be desirable to eliminate human contact as a variable, the experiments can be repeated by cross-fostering between different species. Only then does one have the information that permits the design of experiments with a minimal waste of birds, time, and effort.

A question may be raised of how objective one can be in observing and evaluating an animal with which one has had such intimate contact. This is really not a problem, however, because the responses are so clearly identifiable. In addition, the usual precautions are taken, such as the double-blind technique, in which the tester does not know to which experimental group an animal belongs.

In order to select meaningful criteria for the evaluation of the effects of early experience, one should always have a detailed knowledge of the behavior repertoire of a species. When life histories and ethograms (a behavior inventory of the species) are not available, raising and studying normal animals is a necessary prerequisite. Ecological information is extremely helpful, since in too many cases there are references to the "selective" advantage of a behavior in the natural situation and the adaptiveness of behavior, although the actual conditions under which the species lives or has evolved are not known.

Next, it is important to know the normal course of ontogenetic development or morphological characteristics and behavior. When do eyes open? What is the time of feather development, onset of fear, leaving the nest, weaning? This kind of information makes possible an efficient design of an experiment. For example, if visual isolation is desired, it is not necessary to remove the young from their parents before their eyes open, for in the time they are fed by their parents their physical development is usually better than if they were hand-raised.

When selecting criteria of imprinting, one should use those that are biologically meaningful and appropriate for the particular species; for example, ring doves begin to court and mate with a species' member or foster species usually in less than one hour; mourning doves, on the other hand, take days to exhibit all the same behavior patterns. It would be wrong, therefore, to set the testing period arbitrarily for one hour for both species. In this case uniformity of testing conditions would actually be a fault of the experimental design.

Having selected the criteria of imprinting to be used, one must then make certain that the test situation contains all those stimuli and releasers that are necessary to elicit the behavior that is expected. Thus a bare test cage may never elicit all the courtship behavior in a dove, whereas the presence of a nest bowl and nesting material will facilitate the behavior greatly.

THE FREE-CHOICE SITUATION

Mate preferences in doves, as well as in all other birds, should always be assessed in a free-choice situation between the imprinting object and a species' member of the opposite sex. It is important that the species' member be a parent-raised bird that shows normal preferences for his own species but is also habituated to the experimental situation, including the imprinting object. If it is not, the new environment and the closeness to the strange imprinting object, especially when it is a human, may so inhibit the behavior of the bird that it will not court or respond to the experimental bird. In that case, copulation, or precopulatory behavior, one of the criteria of choice of mate, cannot be achieved. Usually birds habituated to living in cages and to human caretakers will perform in a free-choice test, especially if the test cage is large enough so that the bird can maintain some distance from the stranger.

AUDITORY ISOLATION

In our ring dove and mourning dove experiments the birds were, when necessary, isolated visually from species' members but not auditorily. The reason was partly practical. Voices of doves carry hundreds of yards and can be heard even from adjacent rooms when the doors are closed. Auditory isolation would either be very costly or require separation of birds in distant buildings. Fortunately, it is not necessary in these experiments. Observations have shown that choice of mate does not depend on hearing the voice of another bird, although it may have a function in recognition of mates already acquainted. Lehrman (1958) provided an answer to this question experimentally when he placed a pair of birds in a cage where the male and female were separated by an opaque partition. Seven days later the nest, eggs, and nesting material were introduced and the partition removed. After five to seven days the birds began with incubation. In another group in which the pair was together from the beginning and was provided with nest, eggs, and nesting material, incubation began after seven days. If we assume that the birds separated by the partition were also calling, which they usually do in the laboratory, then we can conclude that the effect of hearing the other birds was negligible.

Ring Doves, Mourning Doves, and Grayson's Dove

In our laboratory we have developed procedures for analyzing sexual preferences in altricial birds, keeping in mind the above considerations. Our experimental animals are ring doves (*Streptopelia risoria*), mourning doves (*Zenaidura macroura*), and related species. The procedures and results of experiments with ring doves (Klinghammer & Hess, 1964b) are summarized as follows:

Young ring doves were removed from the nest from the age of 4 days (eyes begin to open) to 14 days and raised by hand in visual isolation from other doves. When sexually mature, eight to nine months later, they were tested for preference of sexual partner in a free-choice situation between a human and a species member of the opposite sex. The birds were divided into four groups: AA, 25 birds in individual cages from the time they were removed from the nest until tested; AB, 11 birds isolated only while hand-raised until weaning and then placed into a community cage with other ring doves; BA, six birds raised by their parents until weaning and then placed into isolation; BB, six birds raised by their parents and remaining with ring doves until tested. In group AA there was a strong preference for the human among birds removed from the nest between 4 to 9 days with an optimum effectiveness in birds between 6 to 9 days old at time of isolation. Groups AB and BB all chose species members, whereas in group BA two birds chose the human, two chose species members, one chose both, and one ignored both.

The results indicated that imprinting in this species is reversible (groups AB and BA), although the effects of early experience are not lost in some birds. Furthermore, not only early experiences during the nestling and fledging period, but subsequent experiences as well, affect the choice of sexual partner. It appears that two mechanisms which either cooperate or singly result in pair formation at sexual maturity are at work here.

Ring doves have been domesticated for almost a thousand years, and their behavior may have undergone some changes during this time. For example, they are much less wild and are well adjusted to living in small cages. It seemed desirable for this reason to study imprinting problems in a species still under natural-selection pressure and for which ecological information was available by direct field observations. The mourning dove, readily available in Northern Illinois and Indiana, proved to be ideally suitable as an experimental animal (Klinghammer, in preparation).

In order to investigate factors affecting mate selection in mourning doves, 18 mourning doves were removed at various ages from the nest and hand-raised (a) in isolation from species' members until sexually mature, (b) isolated and raised by hand until 22 and 52 days old, and (c) hand-raised with siblings until weaning and placed into community cages with other mourning doves.

When sexually mature, the birds were tested for mating preferences in a free-choice situation between humans and mourning doves. Criteria were sexual responses directed to one or the other choice object.

The following results were obtained:

1. There is a critical period around the eighth day of life. If birds are removed to be hand-raised before that time, they remain tame to humans. After that time they show fear of them when they are mature.

2. Mourning doves hand-raised in isolation until sexual maturity will select a human as mate if they were removed from their parents on or before the eighth day of life. In these birds there is a progressive shift of preference from human, to human and mourning dove, to mourning dove and human, and finally to mourning dove as sexual partner in the fourth breeding season.

3. If hand-raised with a sibling, regardless of when they were removed from the nest, mourning doves will always select a species' member as mate.

4. When birds were removed from their parents on or before the eighth day of life and were maintained in isolation until 52 days of age, at which time they were placed in a community cage with other mourning doves, then they mated with mourning doves. This indicates that experiences with species' members after 52 days of age will still result in selection of a mourning dove mate.

5. Sexual and parental functional cycles are separate since both can be performed by single birds that have no permanent mate.

6. In regard to taming, the effect of early experience on later behavior is permanent.

Based on these findings, the following hypothesis was proposed to explain the process of mate selection in mourning doves:

Early experience on the nest before the eighth day of life may be a prerequisite for keeping mourning doves together, and learning experiences that result in the choice of species' members as mates can still take place until sometime after 52 days of age.

Some initial observations on *Zenaida graysoni*, a dove from the island of Socorro in the Pacific Ocean off the coast of Mexico, indicate that both in the absence and presence of species' members, other species—in this case ring doves—are courted. One parent-raised female, that had copulated successfully with a species' member, solicited ring doves in the characteristic "invitation to copulate" posture when she was isolated from species' members. Furthermore, she jointly occupied a nest with a ring-dove pair and laid her own eggs into the nest.

A male *Z. graysoni*, which had raised several broods of young with a female of his species, courted ring doves persistently after living for about one year in an aviary with them. This is the more remarkable since his former mate had died, but additional species' members of both sexes in breeding condition were present in the loft. In addition, his daughter, parent-raised and living under the same conditions, solicited ring doves repeatedly. Investigations concerned with mate selection in this species using the cross-fostering technique with other species, for example, the white-winged dove *Zenaida asiatica,* are now in progress.

CRITICAL PERIODS

The term "critical period," that is, the period during which a particular exposure to a stimulus is most effective (Ramsay & Hess, 1954), must be re-examined when we deal with altricial birds.

It is obvious from the enumeration of examples in this chapter that a critical period, if it exists, is not too precisely circumscribed and covers at least a day in respect to taming in mourning doves (Klinghammer, in preparation) or weeks in jackdaws (Lorenz, 1935). In many other examples a critical period has either not been discovered or was not experimentally examined (Nicolai, 1964; Warriner, 1960). In ring doves a period optimum for choosing the human in a free-choice situation was discovered to be between the seventh to ninth days of life (Klinghammer & Hess, 1964b). But because subsequent exposure to species' members during the juvenile stage was also effective in determining choice of sexual partner, the term "optimum" was selected as more fitting than "critical."

Gwinner (1964) showed quite convincingly that in ravens the choice of human or species' member is not dependent on exposure to either one during a critical period, but depends on the amount of time spent continuously with one or the other, as well as on individual ties, rather than supra-individual characters. The possible role of taming in this process is discussed in a later section.

Finally, there are clear-cut examples in bullfinches (Nicolai, 1956) and in mourning doves (Klinghammer, in preparation) in which a critical period *during* which something happens is absent and instead there is a "critical point" *after* which bullfinches no longer choose species' members as mates or mourning doves can no longer be tamed.

To think in terms of a "critical period" certainly has its value, as it impresses on us that certain behaviors occur only when a bird is subjected to a particular experience at a specific time—not sooner and not later. However, although such a concept as "critical period" has been accepted as one of several criteria of imprinting and has been extensively employed in discussions, the over-all process of ontogenetic development and maturation of behavior must nevertheless be considered, especially in altricial birds.

TAMING

In some altricial species of birds, for example, mourning doves (Klinghammer, in preparation), we observe the more or less familiar process of "taming" as a factor influencing choice of mate, at least when the human is the imprinting object. It will be useful to discuss taming and related matters in some detail. One author who has written at some length on the subject is H. Hediger (1964), whose observations while director of the Basel and Zurich zoos in Switzerland are important in this context.

With many mammals and altricial birds, any interpretation of social and sexual behavior directed to humans or other animals in terms of imprinting must first consider the problem of "taming." Since the onset of fear has been found to terminate the critical period for imprinting in chicks and ducklings (Hess, 1959), it is possible that the mere absence of fear, for example, toward man, would enable a tame animal to respond socially and sexually to him.

Hediger (1964) defines tameness:

Taming means artificial removal of the flight tendency by man, and this intermediate stage leads to tameness. Tameness means lack of flight tendency and thus of flight distance; that is, it means emotional stability. The flight distance of the tame animal is zero. (p. 156)

In addition to tameness to man, however, many more complex interactions take place between man and animals. For example, a dog licking his master's hand or face is greeting him in the same manner in which one dog greets another. A cat rubbing its head against a person's leg is showing some part of courting behavior, and a lion attacking its trainer may be challenging his position in the dominance hierarchy of the group. Hediger (1964) discusses such interactions in more detail.

A characteristic of men as well as animals is the tendency to regard animals of different species, between which there are intimate relations, as if they belonged to the same species. This is particularly so the more primitive the type of man in question. This tendency to assimilation, appearing in man in the form of a variety of anthropomorphisms, occurs in the corresponding form of zoomorphism in animals. (p. 163)

Very little needs to be said about anthropomorphism. Many examples exist in which an animal's true motives and behavior are misinterpreted.

The reciprocal interactions between animals and man have also another side. Hediger (1964) has this to say about zoomorphisms:

The humanizing tendency of man, as we have said, corresponds to an animalizing tendency of the animal; thus the animal sometimes considers a man as one of its kind, and consequently treats him as a member of the same species. The man then enters into the social organization of the corresponding animal group. Whether he likes it or not, he must play the part thrust upon him in accordance with the ceremonial peculiar to the species. It goes without saying that among the larger animals man must at all costs assume the alpha position and always keep it. He must be ready for social disputes, even with completely tame, harmless individuals. A great deal of so-called incalculability, cunning, etc., is in reality nothing but a social crisis induced in the animal by biological impulse. The animal must know whether it is socially inferior to its partner or vice versa; without a definite decision the animal is not, and cannot be, at ease. If the man puts off, or, through mistakenly misinterpreting the facts, intentionally neglects a decision on the social situation between himself and his animal partner at the proper moment, he at once gives the initiative to the animal, and it will then take it at the least expected moment. (p. 166)

Zoomorphism in animals can also take a form closely akin to what occurs in imprinted animals. Hediger (1964) continues:

In practice, an unpleasant result of the animal's tendency to assimilation is that the favored man is not only accepted by them as one of their own species, but is considered and treated as a fellow member of a particular sex; thus, during the breeding season they either try to fight over him or mate with him. The animal is often wrong, too, in its diagnosis of sex. When a tame roebuck has a tendency to drive off every rival, he will fight fiercely during the rutting season to remove all rivals of his own sex. The roebuck always regards man as a rival of the same sex so he tries to attack him vigorously. This is the reason for the so-called viciousness of all tame roebuck. Other species sometimes mistake the man they have accepted for a female of their species and try to mate with him. A tame emu in the Basle Zoo regularly tries to mate with its keeper during the mating season in winter. If, as was once observed, it happens with a moose, the man concerned is in some danger. Here the tame and most trusty animals can become a danger to man. This behavior has nothing at all to do with viciousness. (p. 168)

In the absence of a detailed life history of an animal, we do not know whether it has been imprinted to humans, nor can we positively conclude from the cited behavior, specifically that of the emu, whether imprinting occurs in the species. Then, since animals do behave toward man "as if they have been imprinted," any imprinting studies that are not restricted to employing lifeless models must take into account this tendency of animals to "animalize" humans (Hediger, 1964). Therefore we must look more closely at the role taming plays in imprinting studies in altricial birds.

Gwinner's (1964) work on ravens, which were all tame, unfortunately does not discuss tameness specifically. Lorenz (1935), on the other hand, describes his experiences with jackdaws:

A second difficulty in determining the precise time period of imprinting is that the time for the imprinting of an object to which one instinctive action is directed, overlaps the object-imprinting of another. This peculiar behavior does not seem to be rare in altricial birds. Especially in the perching birds I have observed that individuals, which one took into care comparatively late, may still respond to the human in their childhood instinctive acts, but may later on direct their likewise object-less inherited sexual responses to species' members. (p. 170–171)

Lorenz went on to describe how six young jackdaws, removed shortly before they normally would have left the nest, gaped to be fed by him for a while but later became shy toward him. Taming in the latter case was very transitory. He concluded that "in jackdaws it seems that the object-imprinting for sexual behavior occurs before the final fixation of childhood behavior patterns, although this too does not seem to be complete."

This description agrees with observations in mourning doves, among which birds removed on the ninth and thirteenth days from their parents readily accepted their human foster parent after some hours and begged to be fed by him; after they became able to feed themselves, they became wild and avoided people. In the mourning-dove study (Klinghammer, in preparation) it was found that birds removed from their parents before the eighth day of life always remained tame to humans whether they chose the human or the species' member as sexual object. Birds removed on or after the eighth day would always, even after initial begging behavior toward humans, become wild and subsequently avoid them.

These observations, based on information in respect to age (accurate within one day) and life history, for example, time spent with parents, time of removal from nest, conditions of hand-raising, and subsequent living conditions, permit us to overcome the ". . . difficulty in determining the precise period of imprinting (in altricial birds), . . ." Lorenz (1935).

Mourning doves never selected the human foster species as sexual partners in a free-choice situation if the bird had been removed *after* the eighth day of life and subsequently raised in isolation from birds until adulthood. One exception (Nicolai, 1962) is discussed separately. In addition, mourning doves hand-raised with siblings always chose mourning doves as sexual partners regardless of when they were removed from their parents, but they remained tame throughout their lives if they were removed before the eighth day, and became wild again when hand-raised after the eighth day. This eighth day (at most) is seen as a critical point in the life of a mourning dove. However, the removal alone before day 8 does not result in the subsequent choice of humans by individually isolated birds, although it would be evidence for imprinting during that period. This is indicated by the behavior of birds that were isolated before day 8 and hand-raised only until days 22 and 52, respectively, when they were again placed in a community cage with mourning doves. All the birds mated with mourning doves. Hence the period before the eighth day of life cannot be the sole determinant of later choice of sexual partner.

Because it is difficult, if not impossible, to detect tameness or its equivalent between two species of birds but it is easy to see in respect to humans, the following hypothesis for the role of taming in mate selection based on mourning doves (Klinghammer, in preparation) was advanced: during the first eight days on the nest, and only then, can mourning doves (eggs from wild populations) become tame to humans. Once they have become tame, exposure to humans, during a period some time after they have become independent, will result in the choice of the human as sexual partner, provided no other doves have been seen for any length of time. Thus at least in mourning doves, if not in many other altricial birds, the period on the nest establishes the initial ties with the parents. After leaving the nest the young must follow the parents before becoming self-sufficient. During the winter months, when aggregation in flocks occurs, and when the juvenile feathers have moulted into adult plumage, the kind of learning experience takes place that results in pair formation with species' members during the breeding season in the following spring. Since there is no external force compelling a young mourning dove to be near species' members, this aggregation of doves would most likely not occur without the initial taming period before day 8 on the nest. To what degree innate components play a role in the recognition of adult species members, as far as choice of sexual partner is concerned, remains to be seen. Their significance, however, cannot be great, as is demonstrated by the observations that human-imprinted mourning doves take four breeding seasons before they are able to normally pair with a species' member.

This taming hypothesis is strengthened by the observations of Lade and Thorpe (1964), who attempted to cross doves of different species. If they kept a male and female of different species together from the fall on, successful copulation and rearing of young took place in the following spring. Before pairings were effected in this manner, however, cross-fostering of young was the only successful method. Thus the enforced proximity plus the prolonged exposure to one another (taming?) overcame the early experience of being raised by their own parents. The lowering of threshold for mating behavior, resulting in the acceptance of another bird as a substitute or because the mating behavior patterns in many doves are so similar, made copulation possible. Nest building and responses to eggs and young, all part of the separate functional cycle of parental behavior, then could be engaged in individually by each bird, for the responses to eggs and young are innate (Klinghammer & Hess, 1964a), without requiring more than a minimum of actual cooperation among the birds. The confinement in the cage alone seemed to be sufficient in these cases to insure the exposure of the birds to those stimuli, that is, nest, eggs, or young, that innately release the appropriate parental behavior.

There is also some evidence, however, that intraspecies pairs can be formed when a dove can still see conspecifics although none is available as a prospective mate. Nicolai (1962) related the behavior of a female mourning dove that was parent-raised in an aviary and later allowed to fly free. When all other mourning doves had paired, this female had no mate. She then proceeded to fly after Nicolai and exhibited courting behavior directed toward him.

This behavior agrees with some observations in our aviaries. In one year there were more male dwarf turtle doves (*Streptopelia tranquebarica*) than females. However, one spotted turtle dove (*Streptopelia chinensis*) female had lost her mate the year before. One of the male *S. tranquebarica* began to court the *S. chinensis* female, and they formed a pair, produced fertile eggs that hatched, and raised their young successfully. This took place in a large flight cage also containing several other species of doves, as well as conspecific females that were mated to other *S. tranquebarica* males.

We see then that doves of different species will mate with one another even when females of their species can be seen. Mere visual exposure to a conspecific does not seem to prevent mating with a member of another species. If actual participation in courtship activities with a conspecific does not take place, a member of another species that can be engaged in such activities is an acceptable substitute. Once such an interspecific pair has been formed, the individual bond can overcome the attraction for a conspecific, especially when an attachment to nest, eggs, or young has developed. We do not know, of course, whether this would occur in the natural situation as well.

These considerations indicate the fruitfulness of thinking not only in terms of a critical period for sexual imprinting in these and perhaps other species but also in terms of *all behavior and experiences that occur during the life span of the experimental birds*. In this way integrations of more than one process may be discovered, if indeed they should exist, thus giving ultimately a more complete understanding of the problems under investigation.

The behavior of ring doves raised by their own parents until weaning, at which time they were visually isolated from species' members and henceforth exposed to humans (Klinghammer & Hess, 1964b), and who preferred the human as sexual partner in the free-choice test, provides an analogous case to Craig's (1914) ring doves, and Lade and Thorpe's (1964) *Streptopelia* species. In both instances enforced proximity in the absence of species' members resulted in acceptance of the human or another species as sexual partner. An interesting observation in our ring doves was that they chose humans as sexual partners in a free-choice situation and were quite tame to them, but in strange surroundings they would avoid them and never approach or follow. This seems further evidence for the hypothesis proposed about mourning doves that the early taming on the nest establishes the bond that insures subsequent aggregation of birds with members of their own, rather than other, species. Subsequent taming after weaning does not establish bonds so complete and lasting as the experience in the first half of the nestling period.

This work with doves may also provide an explanation for the difficulties that Lorenz (1935) described in separating sexual imprinting from acceptance of a parent substitute without the later choice of a human as courting object. However, the individual bonds between the human as foster species and jackdaws and ravens are apparently more readily established in the Corvidae than in the Columbidae. Among the Corvidae humans were chosen even if the birds were raised with conspecific nest mates, whereas in mourning doves this was not the case.

THE FUNCTION OF THE CRITICAL PERIOD

From what has been said so far, we can make some reasonable guesses about the biological function of a critical period in the acquisition of information needed to insure mating between male and female in some species of birds. Although many of the species discussed possess an extensive species-specific behavior repertoire that requires no or a minimum of individual learning during ontogeny, there is already a certain degree of flexibility in the mechanisms that insure that certain behavior patterns will be directed to the appropriate objects at the right time. This individual learning permits adaptation to slightly different environmental conditions, for example, a change in the plumage pattern of parents or other species' members, when innate recognition would impose a limitation on the further evolution of a species. In sexually dimorphic birds this learning mechanism takes the place of separate unlearned recognition of each sex at least in males of some species of ducks (Schutz, 1965). At the same time, the relative shortness of the critical period permits a maximum of learning in the shortest possible time; that is, it is efficient for learning and its strong resistance to extinction nevertheless gives it all the stability of inherited behavior.

In some altricial species reviewed, but by no means in all, a sharply defined critical period for sexual imprinting does not exist. At the present time we have no data that would allow us to explain this absence in terms of adaptive advantage or disadvantage for a species, or to account for it from an evolutionary point of view.

Taming to the appropriate species and recognition of parents, however, must occur during the short time the young remain on the nest. We have seen that there is in most instances a critical cut-off point after which taming no longer occurs.

THE QUESTION OF "IRREVERSIBILITY"

In a number of publications this criterion of imprinting has received special attention (Hinde, Thorpe, & Vince, 1956; Steven, 1955; Thorpe,

1956, referring to Craig, 1914). Sometimes the impression is given that if an imprinted bird should ever follow another species or model than the one to which it was first exposed, then the entire concept of imprinting loses its significance. A few remarks may put this matter into its proper perspective. First, only a free-choice situation is the real test of preference for an imprinting object or mate. Second, even Lorenz (1935), who first used the term "imprinting," did not always attach as much importance to it, but rather frequently spoke of "the experience (that) cannot be forgotten." There is no question that this is a more appropriate phrase. Yet examples of "irreversibility" exist, for example, budgerigars (Hellman in Thorpe, 1953b) and bullfinches (Nicolai, 1956). So do cases of so-called "reversibility," for example, ring doves (Craig, 1914; Klinghammer & Hess, 1964b).

The process of taming that takes place before the critical cut-off age on the nest, for example, mourning doves, is irreversible; while in other cases taming by withholding food may again be lost.

Such concern with irreversibility and reversibility diverts attention from the real problems, namely, from an analysis of *all* the factors that affect the choice of mate at sexual maturity.

SUBSTITUTE OBJECTS

To the question of what happens when a bird, such as the budgerigar, accepts a species' member as mate although he has been hand-raised and is imprinted to humans, Lorenz (1955) commented as follows:

> I would not say that imprinting is not related to other types of learning or that there are no intermediates between them. But still, consider those budgerigars that had *learned* to accept each other as substitute objects, but still remained object-fixated in the human species, with which they could never attain the reinforcement of a consummatory act. (p. 209)

Because the motor patterns involved in courting and mating behavior are innate in all species discussed and are exhibited even by isolated birds, it is easy to see that when biologically meaningful behavior patterns are performed and "fit" together, they can lead to a successful pairing with a species' member to which the birds had not been previously exposed. The term "reversal of imprinting" does not accurately describe this acceptance of the species' member as substitute object. At the same time, calling a species' member a "substitute object" when the biological functions can be fulfilled perfectly in the absence of the "imprinting" (taming) object also seems rather unsatisfactory.

Clearly we have here a case in which experimental procedures have so affected the normal, species-specific course of events that such animals have been provided with additional experiences that they would never have had in a natural situation. In other words, having a mate of one's species *and* an imprinting object from another species is bound to have a disruptive effect on behavior. The question of who is the substitute, it appears, cannot be decided simply by saying that the substitute is obviously the one to which the bird was not imprinted during the imprinting period. One might argue with equal justification that the nonspecies' imprinting object is a substitute for the species' member.

CONCLUSIONS

From the observations and experiments reviewed in this chapter, we have seen the following:

1. Sexual imprinting occurs relatively early during the nestling period or shortly thereafter in the following species: jackdaw, zebrafinch, hawfinch, and possibly the budgerigar.

2. Choice of sexual partner can still be influenced long after the young have become independent of their parents. This has been found in all the pigeons and doves reviewed in this chapter.

3. The final choice of sexual partner occurs close to or at sexual maturity in the bullfinch, crow, and raven.

4. Sexual partners can belong to more than one species, either successively or in some cases simultaneously, in pigeons, doves, ravens, peregrine falcons, hawfinch, and budgerigar.

5. Evidence that early experience with another species had a lasting effect on the choice of sexual partner, that is, was not forgotten in spite of contact or even mating with species' members, exists in jackdaw, bullfinch, zebra finch, hawfinch, widow birds, raven, crow, budgerigar, American bittern, all doves, and pigeons.

When we consider these five points and look over those examples from which they were drawn, several factors emerge that all affect, either singly or interacting in various degrees, the choice of sexual partner in the sexually mature bird.

The amount of a bird's exposure to its own versus another species is important, so is early versus later exposure in the life of the bird. It matters in some species whether siblings are present when the bird is raised away from its natural parents, while in others it does not. The same holds for the free-choice test. Finally, releasers for sexual behavior for example, postures and calls, innate or acquired, undoubtedly have an affect on choice of mate, although analysis of these factors was made in only a few instances.

One common element seems to be essential in all the examples reported: Before a bird will direct courting behavior to humans it must be tame to them. Furthermore, this taming is most effective and lasting when the birds are removed from their parents at a very early age while still on the nest. Although we do not know at this time whether taming exists between two species of birds, something like taming or just a certain amount of exposure is a prerequisite for preference of a sexual partner of another species.

A very important point emerges in regard to the choice of mate in altricial birds: At the level of organization that we have examined, that is, the overt behavior patterns of courting and mating birds, there is no *one* way in which the final choice of mate is achieved. Various species have solved this problem in unique ways under the pressures of selection during the course of evolution.

These conclusions have implications for future research in the general area of mate selection in altricial birds. First, there is a great need for careful, well-documented studies of the factors that influence choice of mate *throughout* a bird's entire life. Second, these investigations should be extended over as many species as possible. Finally, the adaptive advantage of the varied solutions that result in choice of mate should also be studied in the natural environment when possible or under experimental conditions that contain the essential elements required for the normal development of these functions.

REFERENCES

Beach, F. A. (1955) The descent of instinct. *Psychol. Rev.* 62, 401–410.

Craig, W. (1914) Male doves reared in isolation. *J. anim. Behav.* 4, 121–133.

Delacour, J. (1959) *Wild pigeons and doves.* Fond du Lac, Wis.: All-Pets Books.

Fabricius, E. (1951) Zur Ethologie junger Anatiden. *Acta Zool. Fennica.* 68, 1–178.

Frisch, O. v. (1957) Mit einem Purpurreiher verheiratet. *Z. Tierpsychol.* 14, 233–237.

Goodwin, D. (1948) Some abnormal sexual fixations in birds. *Ibis* 90, 45–48.

Goodwin, D. (1958) The existence and causation of colour preference in the pairing of feral and domestic pigeons. *Bull. Brit. Ornithol. Club* 78, 136–139.

Gray, A. P. (1958) *Bird hybrids. Commonwealth Agricult. Bur. Farnham Royal.* Bucks.

Gray, P. H. (1963) A checklist of papers since 1951 dealing with imprinting in birds. *Psychol. Rec.* 13, 445–454.

Gwinner, E. (1964) Untersuchungen ueber das Ausdrucks—und Sozialverhalten des Kolkraben (*Corvus corax corax* L.). *Z. Tierpsychol.* 21, 657–748.

Hebb, D. O. (1953) Heredity and environment in mammalian behavior. *Brit. J. anim. Behav.* **1**, 43–47.

Hediger, H. (1964) *Wild animals in captivity.* New York: Dover.

Heinroth, K. (1961) Personal communication.

Heinroth, O. (1910) Beitraege zur Biologie, namentlich Ethologie und Psychologie der Anatiden. *Verh. 5th Int. Ornith. Kongr.* Pp. 589–702.

Heinroth, O., & Heinroth, M. (1924–1933) *Die Voegel Mitteleuropas.* Berlin: Lichterfelde.

Hess, E. H. (1959) Imprinting, an effect of early experience. *Science* **130**, 133–141.

Hess, E. H. (1962) Ethology. In R. Brown, E. Galanter, E. H. Hess, & G. Mandler, *New directions in psychology.* New York: Holt, Rinehart, and Winston. Pp. 157–266.

Hess, E. H. (1964) Imprinting in birds. *Science* **146**, 1128–1139.

Hinde, R. A., Thorpe, W. H., & Vince, M. A. (1956) The following responses of young coots and moorhens. *Behaviour* **9**, 214–242.

Immelmann, K. (1965) Objektfixierung geschlechtlicher Triebhandlungen bei Prachtfinken. *Die Naturwissenschaften* **52**, 169.

Kear, J. (1960) Abnormal sexual behavior in the hawfinch, *Coccothraustes coccothraustes. Ibis* **102**, 614–616.

Klinghammer, E. (In preparation) Imprinting in an altricial bird: the mourning dove (*Zenaidura macroura*).

Klinghammer, E., & Hess, E. H. (1964) Parental feeding in ring doves (*Streptopelia roseogrisea*): innate or learned? *Z. Tierpsychol.* **21**, 338–347. (a)

Klinghammer, E., & Hess, E. H. (1964) Imprinting in an altricial bird: the blond ring dove (*Streptopelia risoria*). *Science* **146**, 265–266. (b)

Lade, B. I., & Thorpe, W. H. (1964) Dove songs as innately coded patterns of specific behaviour. *Nature* **202**, 366–368.

Lehrman, D. S. (1953) A critique of Konrad Lorenz's theory of instinctive behavior. *Quart. Rev. Biol.* **28**, 337–363.

Lehrman, D. S. (1956) On the organization of maternal behavior and the problem of instinct. In P. P. Grassé, *L'instinct dans le comportement des animaux et de l'homme.* Paris: Masson.

Lehrman, D. S. (1958) Induction of broodiness by participation in courtship and nest-building in the ring dove (*Streptopelia risoria*). *J. comp. physiol. Psychol.* **51**, 32–36.

Löhrl, H. (1961) Verhaltensweisen eines erfahrungslosen Weissen Storches. *Die Vogelwarte* **21**, 137–142.

Lorenz, K. (1935) Der Kumpan in der Umwelt des Vogels. *J. Ornithol.* **83**, 137–213, 289–413.

Lorenz, K. (1955) Behavior patterns in allied species. In B. Schaffner (Ed.), *Conferences on group processes: transactions of the first conference, 1954.* New York: Josiah Macy, Jr. Foundation.

Lorenz, K. (1956) The objectivistic theory of instinct. In P. P. Grassé, *L'instinct dans le comportement des animaux et de l'homme.* Paris: Masson.

Lorenz, K. (1965) *Evolution and modification of behavior.* Chicago: Univer. Chicago Press.

Mohr, H. (1960) Ueber die Entwicklung einiger Verhaltensweisen bei handaufgezogenen Sperbern (*Accipiter n. nisus* L.) und Baumfalken (*Falco s. subbutteo* L.). *Z. Tierpsychol.* **17**, 700–727.

Moltz, H. (1960) Imprinting: empirical and theoretical significance. *Psychol. Bull.* **57**, 291–314.

Moltz, H. (1963) Imprinting: an epigenetic approach. *Psychol. Rev.* **70**, 123–138.

Nice, M. M. (1953) Some experiences in imprinting ducklings. *Condor* **55**, 33–37.

Nicolai, J. (1956) Zur Biologie und Ethologie des Gimpels (*Pyrrhula pyrrhula L.*). *Z. Tierpsychol.* **13**, 93–132.

Nicolai, J. (1962) Personal communication.

Nicolai, J. (1964) Der Brutparasitismus als ethologisches Problem. *Z. Tierpsychol.* **21**, 129–204.

Polt, J. M., & Hess, E. H. (1964) Following and imprinting: effects of light and social experience. *Science* **143**, 1185.

Portielje, A. F. J. (1921) Zur Ethologie bezw. Psychologie von *Botauris stellaris*. *Ardea* **15**, 1–15.

Raeber, H. (1948) Analyse des Balzverhaltens eines domestizierten Truthahns (*Meleagris*). *Behavior* **1**, 237–266.

Ramsay, O. (1951) Familial recognition in domestic birds. *The Auk* **68**, 1–16.

Ramsay, O., & Hess, E. H. (1954) A laboratory approach to the study of imprinting. *Wilson Bull.* **66**, 196–206.

Schneirla, T. C. (1956) Interrelationships of the "innate" and the "acquired" in instinctive behavior. In P. P. Grassé, *L'instinct dans le comportement des animaux et de l'homme*. Paris: Masson.

Schneirla, T. C. (1957) The concept of development in comparative psychology. In D. B. Harris (Ed.), *The concept of development*. Minneapolis: Univer. Minn. Press.

Schutz, F. (1965) Sexuelle Prägung bei Anatiden. *Z. Tierpsychol.* **22**, 50–103.

Sluckin, W. (1965) *Imprinting and early learning*. Chicago: Aldine.

Spaulding, D. A. (1873) Instinct, with original observations on young animals. Reprinted in *Brit. J. anim. Behav.* (1954) **2**, 2–11.

Steven, M. D. (1955) Transference of "imprinting" in a wild gosling. *Brit. J. anim. Behav.* **3**, 14–16.

Thorpe, W. H. (1956) *Learning and instinct in animals*. Cambridge: Harvard Univer. Press.

Thorpe, W. H. (1963) *Learning and instinct in animals*. (2nd ed.) Cambridge: Harvard Univer. Press.

Waller, R. (1942) Die erste geglueckte Wanderfalkenzucht in der Gefangenschaft. *Deutscher Falkenorden* **24**.

Warriner, C. C. (1960) *Early experience as a variable in mate selection among pigeons*. Ann Arbor, Mich.: Univer. Microfilms, Inc.

Whitman, C. O. (1919) The behavior of pigeons. In H. A. Carr (Ed.), *Posthumous works of Charles Otis Whitman*, III. Washington: Carnegie Inst.

❦ 3 ❦

Development Studies of Learning and Motivation in Infra-Primate Mammals

BYRON A. CAMPBELL

Princeton University

Is it true that the young can learn new behavior more readily and retain it longer than adults?

The belief that this is true originated in folklore and has been accepted and made the basis of important decisions in our increasingly complex world. Since the nineteenth century it has been the basis of much of the concern over child-labor practices and slum conditions; it has been the basis for the ideas that childhood is the period in which adulthood is structured and the battles of the world are won and lost on the playing fields of schools; and always it has been the foundation of educational practices. In the latter part of the nineteenth century Freud made this belief the rock on which psychoanalytic theory was built.

But the belief is not rock. It is shifting sand. The evidence that learning is easier or better in youth in either animals or men is grossly deficient, both in scope and excellence. Most of the evidence is mere mythology, though like many myths it may be true. How astonishing that this publicly important assumption about behavior is so unilluminated by careful research. I am not trying to imply that the long-standing belief is necessarily false but rather that is it uninvestigated, not sorted out in a scientific fashion, and that its very popular acceptance and the moral progressive movements based on it seem to have numbed criticism and frightened off investigation of its credibility. Then, too, the many studies, often of excellent quality, on

This research was supported by Public Health Research Grant M-1562 from the National Institute of Mental Health and by National Science Foundation Grant GB235. I should also like to acknowledge the enthusiastic support and assistance of a number of colleagues and students without whom the research would have foundered long ago. These include James R. Misanin, George A. Cicala, Raymond H. Kirby, Ruth Ann Williams, Nelson F. Smith, Joseph Gnandt, Stephie Orsi, and Julian Jaynes.

the effects of early experience on adult behavior are frequently so intriguing that we forget that we have no glimmer into how these effects occur.

My concern here, then, is not with what is learned at different ages (which may be found in the literature on critical periods), nor with the effects of particular learning on later behavior (which may be found in the literature on the effects of early experience), but with the development of learning abilities themselves and how their basic dimensions and parameters may change with age. My goal in this chapter is to review briefly previous research on this problem, explain why it is of little substance, state the requirements of a proper solution to the problem, and then describe some attempts at solution.

EARLY STUDIES: CONFLICT AND CONFUSION

When comparative psychology emerged as an experimental science at about the turn of the century, one of the first problems considered was whether young animals learned more or less readily than older ones. None other than Watson began the confusion that followed. He concluded that the young of white rats formed motor habits much more readily than the adults but manipulated puzzle boxes far less well (Watson, 1903). But, by the time he came to write his textbook in comparative psychology, he hedged because he felt that his conclusions were "not based upon a sufficiently large number of tests" (Watson, 1914). Yerkes (1907) somewhat confirmed the idea that young animals learned faster by showing that the dancing mouse at 1 month of age could learn a black-white discrimination faster than adults, although his particular animals were scarcely very representative of the mammalian group. Hubbert (1915) next entered the conflict; she received the blessing of Watson for what he announced as "a thorough study upon the effect of age upon the formation of maze habits in rats" (Watson, 1914).

Using Watson's circular maze and five groups of 12 to 28 rats aged, respectively, 25, 65, 200, 300, and 500 days, she found that the younger rats learned more readily than the older ones. Perhaps because of some of the concurrent antipathy to Watson's personality, quarrels immediately arose over her studies. Paterson (1917) painfully proved that Miss Hubbert's study had no statistical reliability whatsoever. And a decade later, she was still being criticized by Liu (1928) who, using a Carr maze, set out to do the study correctly.

It was far worse. He trained seven groups of rats ranging in age from 30 to 250 days, that is, 30, 45, 60, 75, 100, 150, and 250 days. He reported that learning ability in the white rat increased from 30 to 75 days, and then slowly decreased up to 250 days. Now this is a very concrete finding and a most interesting result. Liu's graph summarizing his data was reprinted in many an early text of psychology and, had his study been carefully done, much of the later confusion might have been precluded. Unfortunately, however, in his study of rats learning to obtain food under conditions of hunger, he weighed neither a single animal nor a single amount of food, nor did he keep the time of feeding constant, and, heaping naïveté upon naïveté, he changed the diet occasionally in the middle of the experiment.

If the early studies on this problem have a hero, it is C. P. Stone (1929a, 1929b). He was the first investigator to regulate the weight of his subjects carefully by increasing or decreasing the daily food allowance, to try to control the genetic constitution by the split-litter technique, to equate his groups for sex, and to keep as constant as possible all other conditions surrounding the experiments. He was not satisfied with just one apparatus but tested age differences in learning ability by using a simple-platform escape box, a triple-platform escape box, a modified Carr maze, and a multiple T-maze. He also studied the reliability of his apparatus and found that the most reliable data were obtained with the multiple T-maze. He studied the learning abilities with these various apparatus in groups of rats ranging in age from 30 days to sometimes 700 or more days. The general finding was that what differences appeared were not in any learning ability, but in performance, and were probably the result of unequal motivation—a factor, Stone emphasized, that was not sufficiently controlled. Even using the same maze as Liu, he found no maximal age for learning ability whatever. In some of these extensive studies he occasionally found a significant but small superiority in young rats, but always attributed it to increased activity or to his own inadequate control of motivation, rather than to any real age difference.

In the second study (Stone, 1929b) he tried following up Yerkes' earlier discrimination study in a better way. He used a multiple-light discrimination maze and found that no significant age differences appeared when the rats of various ages were under high motivation, thus contradicting the generality of Yerkes' finding. But in further tests, sometimes with different and more complex conditions, such as training animals on two problems at once, Stone refuted his own earlier clarity on the problem. Often he found that young adult animals were able to break up discriminations more easily than year-old animals, that when multiple-discrimination and triple-platform escape problems were taught at the same time, younger animals were better in the early stages of discrimination and retained the teaching slightly better 70 days later. But he was very tentative about such results because of the difficulties of controlling motivation at different ages.

Two years later, using his recently invented self-recording T-maze, Tryon (1931) corroborated Stone's earlier conclusion with the statement that "individual differences in these maze abilities are not affected by differences in the systematic factor, age, at least for the range considered here." (p. 10)

This clarity and pleasant agreement did not last out the year. Maier (1932) reopened the confusion with his studies of reasoning. Three small tables were joined together by elevated pathways that met in the center and formed equal angles to each other. After the animals had become familiar with the apparatus they were placed on one of the tables and fed; they were then immediately moved to one of the other tables. The problem was to select the table on which they had previously been fed, which involved, of course, differentiating which pathway led to which table. The results in such a problem were quite opposite to those found on the maze: older rats were far superior and showed much less variability than younger rats.

More recent findings have merely added further contradictions. Biel (1940) contradicted Stone and Tryon by finding a definite improvement in the learning of multiple T-mazes with age. Fields (1953) contradicted Stone and Yerkes by finding no age differences in the learning of simple discriminations but a significant superiority in younger animals in the learning of complex discrimination problems. Most recently, D'Amato and Jagoda (1960) practically returned us to Watson's conclusion of 1902 in reporting that young rats were significantly superior to old rats in learning a simple Y-maze. Yet none of these studies even considered the problem of equivalent motivation or reinforcement.

WHY THE CONFLICT AND CONFUSION?

There are four main reasons for the inconsistencies of these findings; all of them reflect the naïve state of psychology at the time of the research more than the carelessness of the researcher.

Uncontrolled Motivation and Reinforcement

Uncontrolled motivation and reinforcement together are, by far, the most important of the four reasons in explaining these inconsistencies (only Stone was aware of the magnitude of the problem), so much so they could almost stand alone as *the* reason. Early investigators viewed the organism simply as a bundle of stimulus-response connections, and the particular condition or state of the animal was unimportant, provided he was behaving at all. With the advent of systematic learning theory and research in the 1930's, however, it became dramatically clear that the degrees of motivation and of reinforcement are critical components of the learning process. Thus in studies of learning ability at different ages it is extremely important to specify and control as precisely as possible the drive and reinforcement conditions. From this point of view, in reading studies such as those of Liu, the modern reader can only be appalled at the lack of control. The problem of controlling reinforcement and motivation in this area, however, is a very difficult one that is discussed in a later section.

Unlearned Behavior Unknown

In studying animals of different ages, a great deal depends, especially in the early stages of learning, on the unlearned behavior that is elicited by the test apparatus. Preferences for light and dark, which are very striking in the nocturnal rat, may change with age and thereby alter the rate at which light-dark discriminations are learned. Similarly, the amount of fear and curiosity elicited by experimental environments has been found to vary markedly with the age of the animal (Candland & Campbell, 1962), and many innate behaviors have critical periods in development (Scott, 1962) and are more pronounced at one time or another. Again such differences are likely to greatly influence learning and, although they are difficult to control or modify, they should be taken into account in interpreting developmental studies of learning.

Failure to Control for the Effects of Previous Experience

The problem of concern here is whether or not the basic ability to learn and to retain learning varies with age. In order to solve this problem, the instance must be ruled out in which an older animal simply transfers previous experience to the immediate problem, thus making him able to "learn" far better than a younger animal that did not have previous pertinent experience. Similarly, various types of previous experience may make the animal more or less "emotional" in new environments, thus impeding or enhancing learning, depending on the specific experimental conditions.

Inadequate Measures

A further and more general reason for the conflict and confusion in the learning studies under discussion arises from the narrowness and paucity of the conceptual field within which most older investigators were working. The major parameters of learning had not been spelled out much before 1940. For example, resistance to extinction as a measure of original learning (an important measure of habit strength) had not yet appeared; nor had other major dimensions of learning been studied, such as the acquisition and extinction of acquired drives and rewards, effects of delay and amount of reinforcement, or experiments comparing escape and avoidance conditioning. Learning was simply the learning of a task invented by an experimenter and its measures were usually simply the trials required or errors made to reach some arbitrary criterion of mastery.

Initial attempts to solve the problem of learning in relation to age, therefore, were inadequate; intensive analysis of the learning processes began in the 1930's and is still in progress. But even then (and this is the point at which I entered the study of the problem), the way to a solution was not at all clear. In fact, the very sophistication that psychologists had obtained made them neglect many problems, because the control of one factor or another was well-nigh impossible—whether learning changes with age was one such problem.

THE SEARCH FOR EQUIVALENT MOTIVATION AND REINFORCEMENT

In the broadest possible sense, all animals' motivations and concomitant reinforcements are in some way dependent on such factors as size, weight, and neural development, and, therefore, are never invariant with age. When we consider how we can develop techniques to equate level of motivation and amount of reinforcement for animals of different ages, the problem is incredibly complex. Take hunger, for example. Young animals with larger ratios of skin surface area to body mass, and with a higher metabolic rate and activity level, are

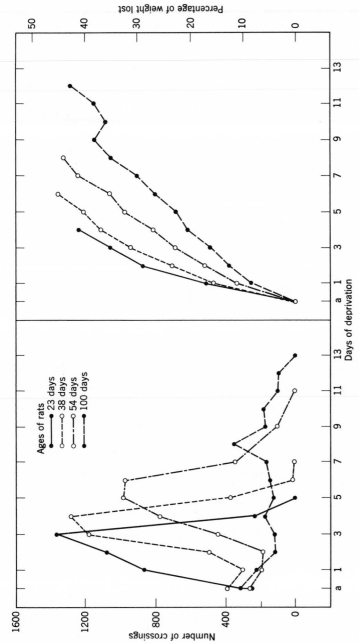

Fig. 3-1 Activity and weight-loss functions of rats of different ages during food deprivation. The left-hand panel shows number of crossings in a stabilimeter cage and the right-hand panel the percentage of weight lost during the course of deprivation (adapted from Campbell, Teghtsoonian, & Williams, 1961, p. 217).

likely to become far "hungrier" after a given period of food deprivation than adult animals deprived for the same period of time. To
illustrate the extent of the differences between young and adult rats,
Fig. 3-1 (adapted from Campbell, Teghtsoonian, & Williams, 1961)
shows the percentage of weight loss and amount of activity in stabilimeter cages during terminal food deprivation for rats aged 23, 38, 54,
and 100 days. After 24 hours of deprivation, a typical duration in
learning studies, weanling rats (23 days old) quadrupled their activity
and lost approximately 18% of their initial body weight. Adult rats
(100 days old), on the other hand, showed no increase in activity and
lost only 9% of their initial weight. By the activity measure, the
weanling rats were four times as "hungry" as the adults, and by the
weight-loss measure, twice as "hungry," confirming our supposition
that equal periods of food deprivation produce greater hunger in the
young rat than in the adult rat.

These enormous differences in the effects of deprivation on animals
of different ages generated a considerable research effort on our part
(Campbell & Cicala, 1962; Campbell, Teghtsoonian, & Williams, 1961;
Williams & Campbell, 1961) to develop ways of holding hunger (and
thirst) constant across ages. Unfortunately, we have been unsuccessful
in developing any practical way of maintaining deprivation-produced
motivations constant and equal over the periods of time necessary to
produce learning in animals of different ages.

Hunger and thirst are also inherently difficult motivating conditions
to use in developmental research because of the relatively long periods
of time necessary to produce learning. In a typical instrumental-learn-
ing paradigm animals are adapted to a deprivation schedule for
several days—if not weeks—to achieve a stable level of motivation,
and then their daily trials are held to a minimum to avoid satiation
effects. Although the time required to produce learning is not important in most research, it is a critical factor in developmental
studies on infra-primate mammals such as the rat, which reach maturity
rapidly. Only 30 to 40 days separate the weanling stage (20 to 30 days)
from sexual maturity (50 to 60 days) in the rat, and to pinpoint
developmental changes in learning ability the acquisition period must
be short in relation to this developmental period.

We therefore turned to motivation by electric shock. Could shock
provide the equal motivating conditions that we were looking for in
animals of different ages? Unfortunately, there was the same possibility
that equal intensities of shock would also produce vastly different
behavioral effects in animals at different stages of development.

Younger animals with less-developed foot pads and callouses, as well as smaller body size, might be more severely affected by shock to the feet through a grid floor than older animals. On the other hand, these same factors could alter the animal's characteristics as an electrical load and make him less sensitive to electric shock. There was thus no a priori way of knowing whether or not the motivating effects of shock varied with age or remained constant.

If, however, we were able to demonstrate the motivational equivalence of shock across ages, it would have several other advantages. First, learning with shock motivation is usually extremely rapid. Rats, for example, frequently reach an asymptote of performance within 20 to 30 trials administered in a single session lasting less than an hour. Second, shock is a well-established and widely used stimulus for producing fear. The use of shock would therefore permit us to study changes in the learning and forgetting of fear as the animal matured— a process of great importance in development. With these considerations in mind, we began a series of studies designed to measure the relative aversion of rats and guinea pigs toward shock at representative maturational stages.

Our initial work on this problem focused on the rat only, but, as a result of extensive exploratory work, we found the guinea pig also to be an excellent subject for developmental research. The guinea pig, unlike the rat, is well developed at birth. Its eyes are open and it is capable of coordinated movement. Our pilot work indicated that it would learn a variety of tasks a few hours after birth. For these reasons we included it in our recent research.

Our first step was to measure the shock aversion thresholds of young and adult rats and guinea pigs. By *aversion threshold* is meant the minimal intensity of shock that the animal will avoid in a spatial-preference situation. The apparatus was similar to that described in a previous paper (Campbell & Teghtsoonian, 1958) and consisted of a small rectangular cage (7 in. wide, 18 in. long, and 8 in. high) with a separately mounted grid floor that pivoted slightly on a central axle and thereby recorded when the animal crossed the cage and the time he spent on each side. The shock source was a 60-cps "matched impedance" source consisting of a variable step-up transformer, with a 150-Kilohm resistor in series with the animal, and a grid scrambler that changed the pattern of shock applied to the grids five times per second.

The procedure consisted of placing the animal in the apparatus with no shock present and then applying shock of a predetermined intensity to the side on which the animal was located. When the animal crossed to the other side of the cage, the shock was turned off and

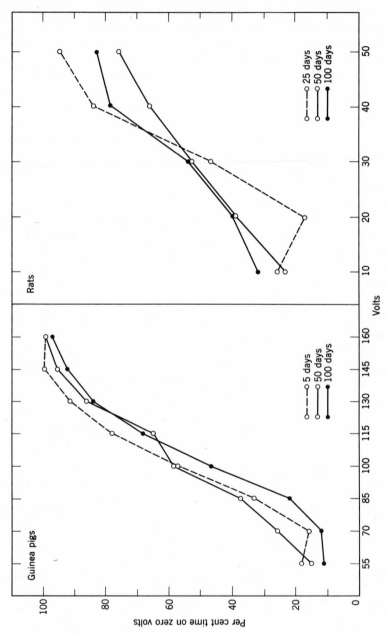

Fig. 3·2   Shock aversion threshold functions for rats and guinea pigs at different ages.

52

kept off as long as he remained on that side. If he returned to the first side of the cage, the shock was again turned on and stayed on as long as he remained there. After 15 minutes the shock level was changed to another predetermined level (see Fig. 3-2), and the S was tested for preference for the no-shock side of the cage. When shock levels were changed, shock was always delivered to the side of the cage occupied by the animal. The shock levels were presented in a random order, and each shock level was presented three times. By recording the time spent on the no-shock side of the cage, it was possible to plot the relative avoidance of the shock side of the cage as a function of shock intensity. Figure 3-2 shows the aversion functions for three age groups of rats and guinea pigs. As is clearly evident, there were no appreciable differences between the age groups for either species, although there was a considerable difference in absolute sensitivity between the rat and the guinea pig, with the guinea pig having a much higher aversion threshold. By this measure, then, there are no age-correlated differences in sensitivity to electric shock in either the rat or guinea pig.

Although the finding that there were no developmental differences in sensitivity to low intensities of electric shock stimuli was encouraging in our search for equivalent motivation across age, the absence of such a difference by no means guaranteed the absence of differences at higher shock intensities. To investigate the relative severity of shock at the higher and more commonly used intensities, we next decided to measure the amount of random bodily activity elicited as a function of shock intensity in young and adult rats and guinea pigs. The apparatus was the same as that used to determine aversion thresholds, only it was arranged so that shock was present on both sides of the cage (it was unescapable). In Fig. 3-3 there are shown the intensities of shock used and the record of the number of crossings during a 15-minute period. Each S was run only once to avoid possible adaptation to the noxious stimulus and to avoid other sequence effects.

Figure 3-3 shows the amount of activity evoked by the various intensities of shock stimuli for young and adult rats and guinea pigs. The young rats were 21 to 25 days old and the guinea pigs four to seven days old when tested; for both species the adults were 95 to 105 days of age. Eight subjects were run at each shock level for all age groups. The pattern of activity elicited was remarkably similar for the young and adult of both species, except that the young rats and guinea pigs showed an earlier and more rapid decline in activity at high-shock intensities than did the adults. The decline in activity at higher shock levels stems from the immobilization associated with

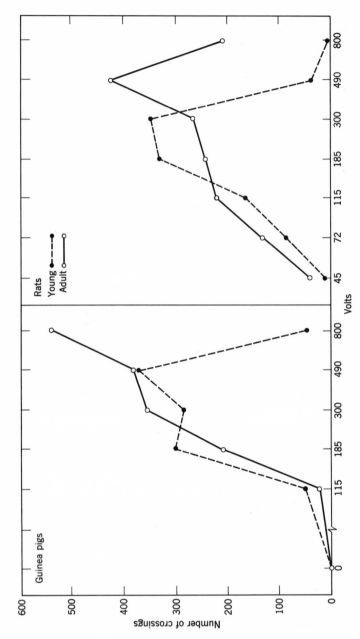

Fig. 3-3   Random activity of rats and guinea pigs of three different ages in a stabilimeter-type cage as a function of shock intensity.

54

partial or complete tetanization. It seems possible, therefore, that the weanling rat is more severely affected by very high intensities of shock than is the adult rat, but that there is little difference between the two at low and intermediate intensities.

This finding of a difference in the point at which tetanization occurs in the young rat raised the possibility that young rats were also more affected by intermediate intensities. While the gross-activity patterns did not support this conjecture, activity was a measure that could be influenced by many factors, particularly cage dimensions that were not scaled to the size of the animal. Accordingly, in a further effort to assess the relative severity of shock stimuli of intermediate intensity, we decided to determine the aversion-difference limens of weanling rats (21 to 23 days) and adult rats (95 to 105 days). By *aversion-difference limen* is meant the change in shock intensity necessary to produce avoidance or preference for a specified level of shock. The experiment utilized the same rectangular cage and a procedure similar to that used in the aversion-threshold study. In this instance, however, one of five standard voltages (45, 72, 115, 185, and 300 volts) was applied to one side of the cage, and one of a series of comparison voltages to the other. At the 185-volt standard level, for example, the comparison shock levels were 155, 165, 175, 185, 195, 205, and 215 volts. The purpose of this range of comparison stimuli was to produce preferences for the standard stimulus ranging from near zero to 100%. When the standard was 185 volts and the comparison 155 volts, preference for the standard stimulus was naturally very low, and vice versa when the comparison stimulus was 215 volts. The specific procedure used in this experiment was to preset the standard and comparison intensities, place the animal in the apparatus without the shock on, and then turn on the stimuli and record time spent on the standard and comparison sides for a 15-minute test period. Each subject was run only once to avoid adaptation and other sequence effects. Preferences for the standard shock stimuli during the last six minutes of the 15-minute test period were then converted to Z scores and plotted as a function of comparison intensity. Straight lines were fitted to the functions using a least-squares method and the level of shock producing 75% and 25% preference for the standard voltage was determined from that plot for the two age groups. Figure 3-4 shows the results of this analysis for the five standard levels. As is dramatically clear there were no age differences in the amount of shock increase or reduction required to produce avoidance of or preference for the standard stimulus.

The finding that the aversion-difference limens were invariant

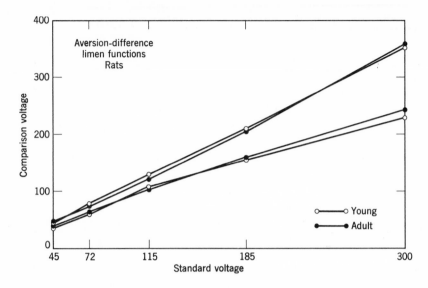

Fig. 3-4 Aversion-difference limens for weanling and adult rats as a function of shock intensity. The upper function shows the level of shock that produces 75% avoidance of the comparison voltage and the lower function the shock intensity that produces 25% avoidance of the standard level.

with age strengthened our belief and hope that there were few age-correlated differences in the degree of motivation produced by electric shock at low and moderate intensities. It was, therefore, with some confidence that we planned a series of studies on learning and retention as a function of age in the rat and guinea pig. Shock was again used as the motivating stimulus. The studies in the following section were part of the plan. In the actual execution of the research we did not follow the sequence shown; rather, we attacked the whole spectrum of problems simultaneously (including some not reported) with the result that research on some problems far along in the sequence is more complete than earlier ones.

DEVELOPMENTAL STUDIES OF LEARNING

Escape Conditioning

Having established the feasibility of using electric shock as an equivalent motivating stimulus at different ages, we were ready to

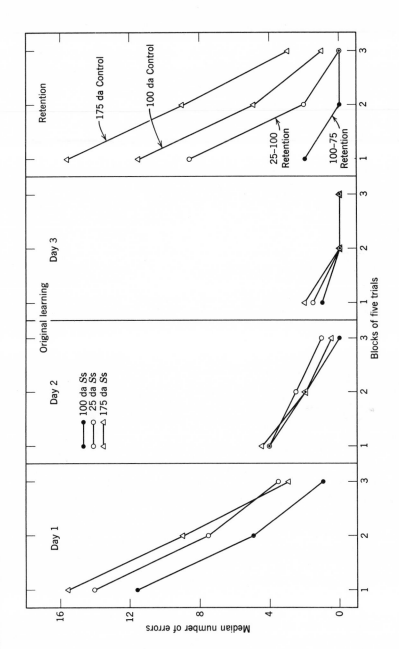

Fig. 3·5 Acquisition and retention of escape behavior in young and adult rats (adapted from Smith, 1963).

study the development of learning itself. A first step was to investigate the acquisition and retention of simple-escape learning. For this purpose we chose the T-maze or a simple variant of it, since it allowed us to measure both speed of running and errors during learning. The first study of this problem was conducted by Nelson F. Smith as part of his doctoral dissertation (Smith, 1963). The apparatus he used was actually a multiple-choice maze in which there were four possible choices, rather than the two typical of the T-maze. Without going into experimental detail, 32 young and 40 adult rats were trained—using a 185-volt electric shock as the motivating condition and shock termination as the reinforcement—in 15 trials per day for three successive days, to run to one of the four goal boxes. Following this training procedure, the animals were returned to their living cages for a 75-day retention period. At the end of the period the animals were given 15 retraining trials identical to the original learning session.

Figure 3-5 shows the errors made during the original learning period and during the retention test period. Little difference was evident between the age groups during learning. The 100-day-old rats appeared to perform somewhat better on the first day, but on subsequent days all differences disappeared. Also included was a 175-day-old group that was run as a control for animals trained at 100 days of age and tested at 175 days. The right panel shows performance of the young and adult rats after the 75-day retention period. The adult rats showed practically no forgetting; their scores were almost identical to those on the third day of original learning. The young rats, by contrast, showed considerable forgetting. Included for comparison purposes were control animals (no previous experience) run at 100 and 175 days of age respectively. In summary, this study showed that rate of original learning did not vary appreciably with age in the rat but that memory was apparently better in the adult than in the young rat.

In an effort to extend and confirm these findings, we ran a similar study with guinea pigs as subjects. In this experiment the multiple-choice maze was made into a simple T-maze by blocking off the first two alleys. The subjects were seven neonatal guinea pigs, 20 to 24 hours old at the start of the training, and seven adults, approximately 100 days old. On the first trial, the guinea pig was not rewarded in the first goal arm chosen but in the opposite goal arm. This was done so that the animal would be run away from its position preference. Learning was to a criterion of eight errorless trials in any consecutive 10. Ten original learning sessons were administered to all the subjects, each session separated by 48 hours, and the subjects were always run to the same goal arm. Original learning lasted 20 days. After the tenth original learning sesson, the guinea pigs were returned to their home cages for a 75-day retention interval. The retention task consisted of four relearning sessions spaced 48 hours apart in which the subjects were retrained to their original goal location.

Figure 3-6 shows that the performance of the young guinea pigs was significantly poorer than that of the adult guinea pigs at the end of the 75-day retention period, a finding that increases the generality of the parallel result for the rat. During original learning, however, a somewhat different pattern emerges. In the first few days of training the young guinea pig learns the T-maze more rapidly and makes considerably fewer errors. Subsequent research, however, has shown that this difference disappears when animals are run in a multiple-choice T-maze or toward their initial position preference.

Avoidance Conditioning

Avoidance is a more complex type of response than escape and is a particularly important type of learning unknown to early psychologists. Raymond H. Kirby investigated this problem as part of his doctoral dissertation (Kirby, 1963). The apparatus he used to study avoidance learning consisted of a simple 30-inch grid-floored runway with interchangeable goal and start boxes. Start-box latencies and

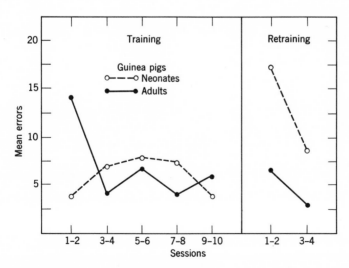

Fig. 3-6   Acquisition and retention of escape behavior in the guinea pig. Retraining took place after a 75-day retention interval.

running times were recorded by infrared photocell units that started and stopped timers as the rat interrupted the beam. The procedure was straightforward. The rat was placed in the start box at the beginning of the experiment, and the door to the start box was raised shortly thereafter. Raising the start-box door turned on a constant-frequency buzzer. Then, after five seconds, if the rat had not reached the goal box, a 300-volt shock automatically came on and remained on until the rat did reach the goal box. The buzzer, or conditioned stimulus, always remained on until the subject reached the goal box. In more descriptive terms, the rat had five seconds to reach the goal box without being shocked; if he did not run to the goal box within that period, the shock came on and stayed on until he did enter the goal box. At the completion of the trial, the goal and start boxes were interchanged and the next trial was initiated by raising the door after a 45-second intertrial interval.

The first experiment studied acquisition and extinction of avoidance responding in rats aged 25, 50, and 100 days. Figure 3-7 shows the start-box latencies and running speeds during 25 acquisition trials and during extinction to a criterion of nonresponding on four out of five trials. No significant differences were found between any age groups during either acquisition or extinction. All ages learned the response rapidly (any trial in which the combined start-box latency and running time were less than five seconds constituted an avoidance response), and there were no major systematic differences in running speed dur-

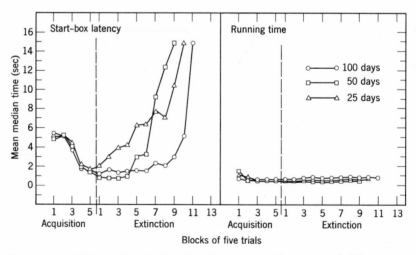

Fig. 3-7 Acquisition and extinction of avoidance responding in rats of different ages (adapted from Kirby, 1963, p. 160).

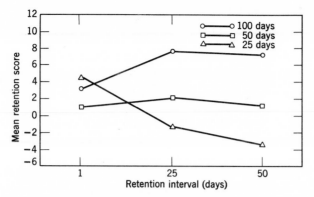

Fig. 3-8   Retention of an avoidance response in rats of different ages as a function of retention interval (adapted from Kirby, 1963, p. 161).

ing learning or extinction. The similarity in running speeds, particularly in the early stages of training, further strengthens our previous findings showing that severity of shock does not vary with age.

With this confirmation of no differences in rate of learning in animals at various maturational levels, Kirby proceeded to study retention of the avoidance response as a function of age at original learning. He trained rats at 25, 50, and 100 days of age and tested them for retention 1, 25, and 50 days later. The results of this study are shown in Fig. 3-8. The retention score shown was obtained by subtracting the number of avoidances made during a 30-trial reconditioning test from the last 30 trials of original learning. This retention score minimized individual differences by comparing the relearning scores of each animal with its original avoidance performance. The results of the study clearly show that retention of avoidance responding is poorer in the young rat.

Fear Conditioning

So far we have found that animals of all ages, once motivation is held constant, learn locomotor responses to goals at approximately the same rate. But this finding may not be applicable to the emotional responses that may be structured and learned faster in infancy. Contemporary psychologists in child development have stressed the importance of learned fears and motives acquired in childhood as major determinants of adult behavior (e.g., Whiting & Child, 1953). There is an implication here that learned motivations in infancy and childhood are more pervasive and longer lasting than those acquired in adult-hood. Thus it seemed plausible that the mammalian organism is so constructed that acquired motivations and rewards learned early in life are inherently more stable and persistent.

To see if this supposition was true, we constructed what might be described as an automated version of the Miller-Mowrer learned-drive apparatus (shown in Fig. 3-9). It consisted of a cage with one white compartment and one black. The floor on one side was shock grids, and on the other was a flat piece of aluminum that was painted to

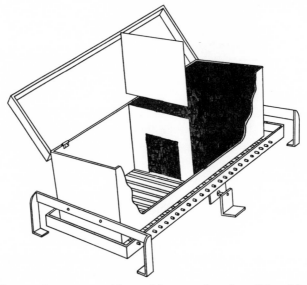

Fig. 3-9   Apparatus used for studying retention of conditioned fear.

match the walls of that compartment. The procedure for conditioning fear in this apparatus was fairly simple: The animal was placed on the shock side with the solid door in place and given a series of 15 two-second shocks on a 30-second variable-interval schedule. Then the animal was placed on the safe side of the cage and left there for an equal period of time. Half the animals were conditioned to fear the black side, and half the white side. At the end of the period, the entire procedure was repeated to complete the conditioning series. As can be seen, no instrumental response was involved during conditioning. The testing for retention of fear to the white or black side of the box took place at intervals of 0, 7, 21, and 42 days after the conditioning series. For each of these periods there were separate groups of rats at

18, 23, 38, 54, and 100 days of age. In these retention tests, the animal was placed in the apparatus with the partition removed, and the measure of learned fear was the amount of time the animal spent on the side of the apparatus in which he had been shocked. The results are shown in Fig. 3-10.

These results appear to be definitive and completely contradict the supposition that initiated the study. The results essentially demonstrated that retention of a fearful experience is dependent upon age, but in a manner opposite to all expectation. The younger the animal,

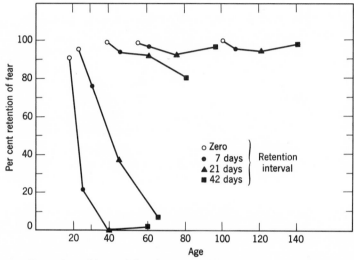

Fig. 3-10 Retention of learned fear in rats at different ages. The first point of each retention curve is the group median on the retention test immediately following training, the different groups being trained at 18, 23, 38, 54, or 100 days of age. Successive points on each curve thereafter are the retention scores for each group 7, 21, and 42 days after training (adapted from Campbell & Campbell, 1962, p. 5).

the more quickly the effects of a fearful experience dissipate. Older animals retain the effects of the experience with little or no diminution.

In other words, fear and locomotor responses are learned and retained in the same way. Extinction of these learned responses appears to be invariant with age while retention of responses acquired at different ages varies inversely with age at the time of conditioning. Thus nothing we have found offers the slightest support to the proposition that responses acquired early in life are more persistent than those acquired at a later age.

Discrimination Learning

One question naturally arises from the previous research: Are these results representative of other motivating and reinforcing conditions? Although there is little reason to suspect that basic learning and retention processes vary as a function of the type of motivation and reward used, there is always the possibility that intense aversive stimulation produces some unknown physiological disturbance that interferes with memory more in infancy than in adulthood. For comparison purposes, we decided to measure acquisition, extinction, and retention of a discriminated operant response motivated by hunger and reinforced by food. The apparatus selected was a standard operant-conditioning box with a bar 2 in. wide and 2 in. off the floor. Slight pressure (10 to 15 gm) on the bar released a pellet of food into a food cup at the left. A light was located above the bar, inset into the wall as is usual in such apparatus, and water was available at all times. The whole apparatus was enclosed in a partially soundproof chamber. Our plan was to train weanling (25 day) and adult animals on a simple discrimination, and then extinguish half of each group immediately after training and half after a 75-day retention interval. A total of 30 young and 36 adult animals were run in this experiment.

The procedure used deviated from the typical operant conditioning technique in one major way: Instead of giving the animals fixed daily sessions of an hour or some similar duration, the rats were housed continuously in the apparatus for five successive days and received all their food by pressing the bar. This technique was adopted to sidestep the issue of how to maintain "hunger" at a constant level during training. With this procedure, all the animals were presumably minimally hungry and, therefore, equally motivated—once the basic operant response had been acquired. Weanlings were reinforced with 20-mg food pellets and the adult rats received 45-mg pellets. The larger pellet was roughly in the same proportion to the average amount of food consumed by the adult rat as the 20-mg pellet was to the weanling's food consumption. (Pilot work using these pellet sizes indicated that the rate of learning a simple operant response was about the same for the two age groups, as was the total daily consumption.) The discriminative stimulus came on and went off at two-minute intervals but only during the light-off period could food be obtained. During this two-minute light-off period the bar-pressing responses were reinforced on a variable interval schedule so that a rat could receive a maximum of eight pellets during the two minutes.

Following the discrimination training, each rat was removed, weighed, and either returned to the apparatus on an extinction schedule, or returned to its home cage for a 75-day retention interval, at the end of which it was returned to the apparatus for the extinction session. Each extinction session lasted two days and was identical to training except that reinforcement was withheld.

The main results of this study are shown in Fig. 3-11 and 3-12. These data include only those rats that reached a criterion of 80% correct on the discrimination problem. This criterion was selected in order not to bias the results of the retention portion of the study by including Ss that did not acquire either the basic bar-pressing response or the discrimination. Looking at Fig. 3-11, which shows the mean number of bar-presses during successive 12-hour periods of the five-day session, it is evident that both young and adult rats showed similar patterns of acquisition of the basic bar-press response. The 23-day-old rats pressed fewer times during the first 24-hour period, but after that the total number of presses per 24-hour period was remarkably similar for the two age groups. The initial difference in the bar-pressing rate may reflect the proportionally greater effort required by the young rat to activate the lever, or a generally lower level of exploratory behavior (Candland & Campbell, 1962). Both age groups showed a distinct diurnal rhythm with the cycle somewhat more pronounced in the adult group.

Bar-pressing performance during the immediate and 75-day retention periods, shown in the right-hand portion of Fig. 3-12, produced both expected and unexpected results. First, during the 48-hour extinction test initiated immediately after the five-day training session, the young rats pressed consistently more than the adults. Assuming that the strength of the bar-pressing habit was about the same for the two groups, this greater amount of bar-pressing by the young animal was to be expected as the proportion of body-weight loss during this period was much greater in the young rats (27 versus 12%), indicating that deprivation was much more severe. The unexpected portion of these results was found at the 75-day retention interval: Here the adult rats trained at 100 days of age and tested for retention at 175 days of age showed a much greater frequency of bar-pressing than those tested immediately after training. Just why frequency of bar-pressing increased between the immediate and 75-day retention intervals is unknown and needs further investigation. The young animals showed no such reminiscencelike effect at the 75-day retention interval and, in fact, pressed significantly less often ($p < 0.01$) than the adults during the first 24 hours. This finding confirms the previous result that amount forgotten diminishes with age.

Acquisition and retention of the light-dark discrimination paralleled

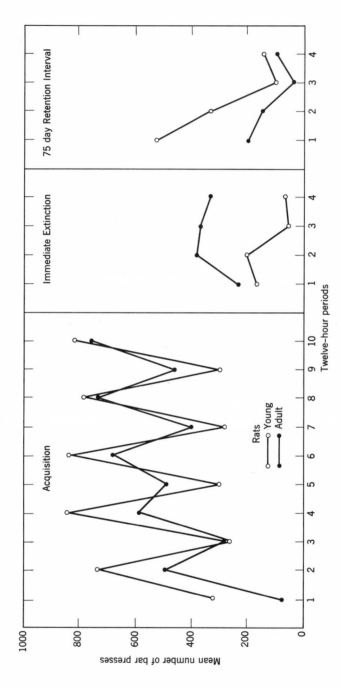

Fig. 3-11 Mean number of bar-presses made during acquisition, extinction, and retention of a light-dark discrimination.

66

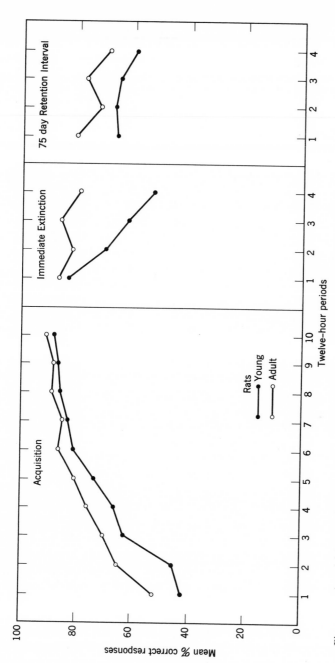

Fig. 3-12 Acquisition, extinction, and retention of a light-dark discrimination. The left, center, and right panels show respectively the percentage of responses made to the positive stimulus during acquisition, immediate extinction, and extinction after a 75-day retention period.

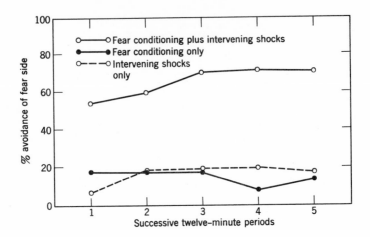

Fig. 3-13 Retention of conditioned fear in young rats 28 days after conditioning as a function of intervening experience.

the bar-pressing results, only learning was much slower (Fig. 3-12). The young animals showed an initial tendency to press more when the negative discriminative stimulus (the small pilot light over the bar) was on than did the adults. This developmental difference in initial tendency to press during the negative period apparently impeded acquisition of the discrimination, although at the end of training there was no difference between the groups ($p > 0.5$).

During the immediate retention test, the young animals showed more rapid extinction of the discrimination than did the adults (Fig. 3-13). This difference was undoubtedly a result, at least in part, of the higher rate of response by the young rats during extinction. After the 75-day retention interval, both age groups showed significant retention of the light-dark discrimination, but the amount of retention was greater for the adult animals. The young animals were significantly poorer than the adults (p's < 0.02), both in percentage of responses to the positive stimulus during the retention test and in amount of forgetting when each animal's retention performance was compared with his performance on the last day of training.

In summary, discriminations based on food reinforcement are forgotten more quickly by young than by adult rats. This finding confirms in principle the similar results obtained when learned responses were motivated by shock.

IMPLICATIONS

Let me summarize briefly our major findings. We began with an ancient problem, full of confusion and conflict, in which there were almost as many solutions as there were investigators. In reviewing the literature it became apparent that a major cause of the divergence of findings lay in the failure of early investigators to control and equate motivating and reinforcing conditions in animals of different ages.

Our first step, then, was to search for some age-equivalent motivation and reinforcement, which proved to be no easy task. After considerable research, intermediate ranges of electric shock proved to be the answer. Using this motivation, we investigated the development of learning in the rat and arrived at two major and mutually confirming conclusions. First, there is little change in simple learning ability with development, a result that agrees with Stone more than with any other previous worker. Second, memory develops with age. This conclusion has no precedent in previous work.

Does this mean that early learning experiences are not as important as adult experiences? Not at all! There are many reasons why habits acquired early in life may be more important than those acquired in adulthood even though individual responses may be forgotten more rapidly in the early period. Probably the most important one is that normal development involves the acquisition of many sequentially dependent responses. The failure of the organism to learn any particular segment prevents the acquisition of subsequent segments in the chain. For example, if the organism does not acquire affectional responses for other members of its species early in life, much adult social behavior is precluded (Harlow & Harlow, 1962).

Another way that responses acquired early in life may persist into adulthood is as a result of events occurring subsequent to the original learning. Thus a learned fear acquired in early childhood through a traumatic incident may persist into adulthood if the child is occasionally reminded of the event by an anxious parent. The following experiment illustrates this principle of occasional practice and how it may work in development. We used the conditioned-fear apparatus under the same procedures described earlier. There were three groups of 23-day-old rats (10 rats in each group). In two of the groups fear was first conditioned by pairing a 170-volt shock with either the black or white compartment, as in the earlier experiment. A third group received no early fear conditioning. Then one of the conditioned-fear groups and the group that had no previous fear training received a single 170-volt shock in the conditioned-fear apparatus each week for three weeks. The third group (which had received no early fear conditioning) was placed in the apparatus from 15 to 60 seconds each week, but did not receive shock. All three groups were then tested for retention of fear (**Fig. 3-13**). The group receiving early fear conditioning *plus* the intervening shocks showed a high degree of retention of fear, but the other two groups showed none. Thus, when fear was conditioned in weanlings without subsequent shock experience, there was no retention of fear, confirming the general principle that responses acquired early in development are forgotten rapidly. By contrast, when the original conditioning was followed by one shock per week—a procedure in itself not sufficiently strong to produce learned fear—the original fear response was maintained at a high level. It is tempting to speculate that this may be one basis for the widespread belief that early experiences are important in determining adult behavior.

An overview of these results suggests that the developmental differences in retention of learned behavior may have considerable adaptive significance. The young organism, small and helpless, is highly vulnerable to the acquisition of fears. Of course, these fears have survival value by keeping the young organism away from danger, but if they all persisted into adulthood they would be an enormous hindrance, greatly restricting the range and types of adult behavior possible. Similarly, many instrumental responses, if not forgotten or otherwise eliminated from the animal's repertoire, would impede development. Therefore, it is to the advantage of the maturing animal that early memory is weak and extends over only a short duration.

Is this the case for all animals? For all responses? Is the discovery that memory improves with age universally true? Probably not. Our work has only been concerned with a limited number of learned responses. There are probably other classes of behavior in which memory is as good at an early age as it ever will be. What I would like to prophesy, however, is that future research will extend and confirm the generalization that memory is never better at early ages, provided that the degree of original and interpolated learning is held constant.

REFERENCES

Biel, W. C. (1940) Early age differences in maze performance in the albino rat. *J. genet. Psychol.* **56**, 439–453.

Campbell, B. A., & Cicala, G. A. (1962) Studies of water deprivation in rats as a function of age. *J. comp. physiol. Psychol.* 55, 763–768.

Campbell, B. A., & Teghtsoonian, R. (1958) Electrical and behavioral effects of different types of shock stimuli on the rat. *J. comp. physiol. Psychol.* 51, 185–192.

Campbell, B. A., Teghtsoonian, R., & Williams, R. A. (1961) Activity, weight loss, and survival time of food-deprived rats as a function of age. *J. comp. physiol. Psychol.* 54, 216–219.

Candland, D. K., & Campbell, B. A. (1962) Development of fear in the rat as measured by behavior in the open field. *J. comp. physiol. Psychol.* 55, 593–596.

D'Amato, M., & Jagoda, H. (1960) Age, sex and rearing conditions as variables in simple brightness discrimination. *J. comp. physiol. Psychol.* 53, 261–263.

Fields, P. E. (1953) The age factor in multiple-discrimination learning by white rats. *J. comp. physiol. Psychol.* 46, 387–389.

Harlow, H. F., & Harlow, M. K. (1962) Social deprivation in monkeys. *Scient. Amer.* 207, 136–146.

Hubbert, H. B. (1915) The effect of age on habit formation in the albino rat. *Behav. Monog.* 2, 55.

Kirby, R. H. (1963) Acquisition, extinction and retention of an avoidance response in rats as a function of age. *J. comp. physiol. Psychol.* 56, 158–162.

Liu, S. X. (1928) The relation of age to learning ability of the white rat. *J. comp. physiol. Psychol.* 8, 75–85.

Maier, N. R. F. (1932) Age and intelligence in rats. *J. comp. physiol. Psychol.* 8, 1–6.

Paterson, D. G. (1917) The Johns Hopkins circular maze studies. *Psychol. Bull.* 14, 294–297.

Scott, J. P. (1962) Critical periods in behavioral development. *Science* 138, 949–958.

Smith, N. F. (1963) Effects of interpolated learning on retention of an escape response in rats as a function of age. Unpublished doctoral dissertation, Princeton Univer.

Stone, C. P. (1929) The age factor in animal learning. I. Rats in the problem box and the maze. *Genet. Psychol. Monog.* 5, 1–130. (a)

Stone, C. P. (1929) The age factor in animal learning. II. Rats on a multiple light discrimination box and a difficult maze. *Genet. Psychol. Monog.* 6, 125–202. (b)

Tryon, R. C. (1931) Studies in individual differences in maze ability. II. The determination of individual differences by age, weight, sex, and pigmentation. *J. comp. physiol. Psychol.* 12, 1–22.

Watson, J. B. (1903) Animal education. *Contr. Psychol. Lab. Univer. Chicago* 4, 5–122.

Watson, J. B. (1914) *Behavior: an introduction to comparative psychology.* New York: Holt.

Whiting, J. W. M., & Child, I. L. (1953) *Child training and personality: a cross cultural study.* New Haven: Yale Univer. Press.

Williams, R. A., & Campbell, B. A. (1961) Weight loss and quinine-milk ingestion as measures of "hunger" in infant and adult rats. *J. comp. physiol. Psychol.* 54, 220–222.

Yerkes, R. M. (1907) *The dancing mouse.* New York: Macmillan.

4

The Development of Handedness
in Cats and Rhesus Monkeys

J. M. Warren, Judith M. Abplanalp,[1]
and Helen B. Warren

The Pennsylvania State University

THE cerebral hemispheres in man do not function symmetrically. Lesions of the left hemisphere cause aphasia and losses in performance on tests of verbal intelligence and verbal learning, while comparable injuries to the right hemisphere do not (Milner, 1962; Penfield & Roberts, 1959; Teuber, 1962; Weinstein, 1962; Zangwill, 1960). Conversely, right-hemisphere lesions produce significantly more severe impairments of discrimination and learning tasks involving visual, auditory, or tactile stimuli devoid of verbal meaning than do left-hemisphere lesions (Milner, 1962; Teuber, 1962; Weinstein, 1962). Thus it may be said that the left hemisphere is dominant for verbal, and the right for nonverbal, behavior. Many other functional asymmetries between the right and left hemispheres have been demonstrated (see Hécaen & Ajuriaguerra, 1964, for a comprehensive review of the recent neurological literature).

The neural correlates of cerebral dominance are unknown. Anatomical differences between the hemispheres are minute and insufficient to explain the disparate functions of the right and left hemispheres (von Bonin, 1962). It seems clear, however, that cerebral dominance develops slowly in the maturing human. Severe damage to the left hemisphere in early childhood seldom retards the development of speech. The speech disorders observed in brain-injured children are more transient than those resulting from similar injuries in adults but lesions in the right hemisphere are more likely to cause speech disorders in children than in adults. Apparently, the two hemispheres are relatively equipotential in the young child and the left gradually becomes

[1] Now at Boston University.

The research reported here was supported by Grant M-04726 from the National Institute of Mental Health, U.S. Public Health Service.

73

dominant for speech over a period of several years (Zangwill, 1960).

The relation between handedness and speech dominance is also uncertain. Left-handed individuals are not "right-brained." Lesions of the left hemisphere result in aphasia more frequently than lesions in the right hemisphere in left-handed patients (Penfield & Roberts, 1959; Zangwill, 1960). This observation could mean either that handedness and dominance for speech are essentially unrelated (Penfield & Roberts, 1959), or that cerebral dominance is less well developed in left handers, who are consequently more vulnerable to lesions of either hemisphere (Zangwill, 1960).

Experiments with animals may contribute to the resolution of this problem. The view that handedness and other forms of cerebral dominance are essentially unrelated implies the possibility that nonverbal animals may have stable handedness preferences. Zangwill's (1960) position does not suggest this implication.

Current neuropsychological opinion denies the possibility of human-like handedness in animals. Jung (1962) states:

> We have no evidence whatsoever for cerebral dominance in monkeys, not to mention the carnivores . . . . Preference for one side of the body, in animals, is very different from handedness. Many experiments show this. Cole and Glees have shown that hand preference in monkeys is rather evenly distributed, in contrast to the preponderant preference for the right in man. Besides, preference for a particular hand, right or left, is much less pronounced in the monkey . . . . Paw preferences in cats, and hand preferences in monkeys, are rather plastic; the "favoring" of one upper extremity over the other increases as a function of prolonged testing and is much more easily reversed than in man.
>
> Thus I think we must distinguish between the preference for one hand in animals and the dominance of one side of the brain in man. (pp. 268–269)

Many of the data cited by Jung cannot be regarded as definitive regarding the absence of an homology between handedness in man and in infrahuman mammals. For example, Cole (1955) studied too few monkeys to estimate accurately the range of intraspecies variation in the strength and distribution of monkeys' hand preferences. Ettlinger and Moffett (1964) summarized the results obtained from 88 monkeys in three recent experiments in which 55 of 88 experimentally naïve animals showed statistically significant hand preferences. Of the 55, 69% preferred the left hand and 31% the right. A difference of 2 to 1 in the incidence of left and right handedness does not suggest an even distribution of lateral preferences in monkeys.

The argument for the lability of preferences in cats and monkeys is also inconclusive. Both the cats and monkeys studied in the experiment cited by Jung (Warren, 1958) were immature when first tested. The effects of training and maturation were confounded so that no sound conclusions regarding the influence of practice on the development of handedness were possible.

In general, previous investigations of handedness in monkeys and cats have been defective in that the number of animals studied was too small, the duration of observation was too brief, or relevant variables were inadequately controlled. Thus no unambiguous statement can be made on the presence or absence of a stable trait of handedness in mammals other than man.

The major aim of the present research, therefore, was to determine the stability of lateral preferences in cats and monkeys on a variety of manipulatory tasks over extended periods of time. The research was also designed to determine the influence of particular experimental manipulations upon lateral preferences in cats and monkeys. The specific problems investigated were (a) the effects of early practice in manipulation on the development of paw preferences by kittens; (b) the effect of forced practice with the nonpreferred paw on subsequent free-choice responding by cats; (c) the effects of maturation and practice on hand preferences in rhesus monkeys; and (d) the effects of unilateral cortical lesions on paw preferences in cats.

EARLY PRACTICE AND PAW PREFERENCE IN CATS

It has been established that cats usually use one forepaw more frequently than the other in reaching for food (Cole, 1955; Forward, Warren, & Hara, 1962; Jankowska & Gorska, 1960; Warren, 1958). Cole (1955) hypothesized that the preferential use of one paw in manipulation results from an asymmetrical distribution of pyramidal tract fibers to the two sides of the body. Relatively young cats show an increase in the strength and intertask consistency of paw preferences over 11 months of intermittent testing (Warren, 1958), but this observation is not critical of Cole's hypothesis or of other organismic explanations, because full expression of an organismically determined trait could depend upon practice, maturation, or both.

The experiment reported here was designed to test the following hypothesis: No organism has perfect bilateral symmetry so responses can be made more quickly or less effortfully with one paw than with the other. But learning is necessary for full development of a lateral preference. Only through experience will inefficient responses with the less favored paw become extinguished and more efficient responses with the preferred paw be fixated as a result of more prompt reinforcement. It is to be expected from this analysis that kittens given extensive early practice in manipulation will develop stronger paw preferences, more stable preferences, and preferences that generally are more consistent over a series of manipulatory tasks than controls that do not receive comparable early training.

Three groups of laboratory-reared kittens were studied: the experimental group ($N = 13$), the early control group ($N = 12$), and the late

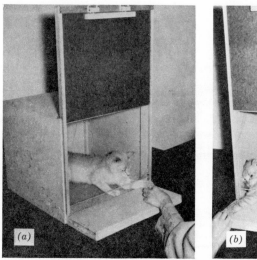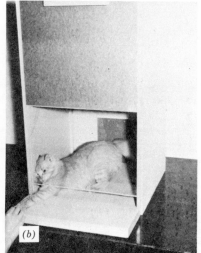

Fig. 4-1   The Handedness Box.

control group ($N = 9$). At 60 days of age the experimental and early control groups were tested in a simple "handedness" apparatus—a box with a glass front wall facing a platform outside the box on which pieces of meat were presented. The glass ended 2 in. above the floor. The kittens could reach out and obtain the food with their paws, but could not obtain it any other way. The apparatus is illustrated in Fig. 4-1. Figure 4-1*a* shows a cat reaching comfortably with his left paw for a bit of meat presented on his left. Figure 4-1*b* shows the same cat responding with the left paw again, with considerable inconvenience, to a piece of meat presented on his extreme right. (The incentive was not presented on the extreme right or left as shown in Figs. 4-1*a* and 4-1*b* during actual testing. These photographs were

made after the experiment was completed to illustrate the strength
of paw preferences in many cats.)

On the basis of the preferences manifested on 50 reaches, the kittens tested at 60 days of age were assigned to matched experimental
and control groups. The controls were not tested again until they were
180 days old. The Ss in the practice groups were given two to four 25-
trial practice sessions per week between days 62 and 180. The median
experimental cat received 1,250 trials and the range was from 1000 to
1400.

Fig. 4-2   Reach test for cats.

At 180 days the experimental and early control cats were retested
and the late control group tested for the first time, for 50 trials in the
Handedness Box. All three groups were retested in the Handedness
Box at 210 and again at 360 days of age.

Immediately after testing in the Handedness Box at 210 days, all
the cats were tested in the Wisconsin General Test Apparatus (WGTA)
for 100 trials on each of five tests that were designed to elicit different
patterns of manipulation and of postural adjustment. These tests are
illustrated in Figs. 4-2 through 4-6 and were as follows:

1. *Simple Reach.* A piece of meat (kidney) was presented in one of
two foodwells spaced 12 in. apart on a white test tray. The subject

needed only to reach out and draw into the cage the visible and readily available cube of kidney. This task differed from that in the Handedness Box only in that the cat had to reach between the vertical bars of the cage, which were 2 in. apart, to remove the food from the wells of the tray.

2. *Block Displacement.* As in the Simple Reach test, a piece of kidney was placed in one food well on a white test tray, but the well was covered with a block of wood which the cat had to push aside in order to obtain the food.

3. *Trough.* The meat was placed in one of two troughs (10 x 3 x 3 cm) with lips that prevented the cat's obtaining the food in any way other than by placing a paw into the trough behind the food and pulling it forward toward the cage.

4. *Bottle.* A piece of meat was placed in one of two glass test tubes 1⅞ in. in diameter and 7 in. long. The tubes were fixed on the white test tray with the open ends toward the cage in positions corresponding to the right and left food wells. The cat, as in the Simple Reach test, had only to reach out for the visible and available food, but somewhat more precise positioning and eye-paw coordination were required.

Fig. 4-3   Block Displacement test for cats.

Fig. 4-4   Trough test for cats.

5. *Extension*. This test was intended to force marked extension of the forepaw. A trapezoidal wooden block ($2\frac{1}{2}$ x $1\frac{5}{8}$ x 8 x 6 in.) was placed on the test tray over the central food well. The block was between wooden guides that restricted its movement so that it could only

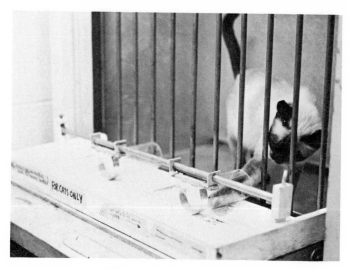

Fig. 4-5   Bottle test for cats.

Fig. 4-6   Extension test for cats.

be pushed directly back toward the rear of the tray. Attempts at forward movement toward the cage or lateral displacement failed to un-
cover the meat contained in the food well.

In all tests in the Handedness Box and in the WGTA, except for
the Extension test, the position of the food was varied from trial to
trial in a balanced irregular sequence to minimize the effects of posi-
tional biases.

The results are summarized in Figs. 4-7 and 4-8, which show the
preference scores for the individual cats on the tests administered in
the Handedness Box and the WGTA, respectively. Preference scores
represent the deviation of each subject's performance from chance
(50%) preference; the maximum possible value is 50 and indicates
that the kitten always responded with the right or left paw. In both
figures, black blocks represent experimental kittens, white blocks,
early controls, and white blocks with an X represent late controls. The
medians for the experimental group (*E*) and combined control groups
(*C*) are indicated by arrows, and a dashed vertical line separates the
scores that are significantly different from chance (50% $\pm$ 3 σ) from
those that are not. (One late control cat could not be tested in the
Handedness Box at 210 days because of illness.)

Inspection of these data reveals that in relation to the control groups
the early practice in manipulation given the experimental cats did

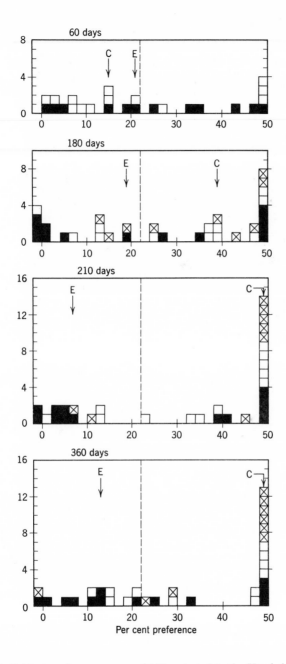

Fig. 4-7   Individual preference scorces of kittens tested in the Handedness Box at 60, 180, 210 and 360 days of age.

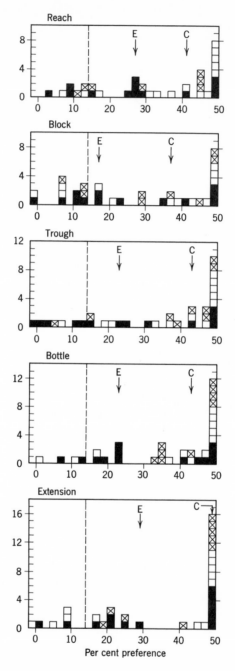

Fig. 4-8 Individual preference scores of kittens on 5 handedness tests in the WGTA.

not increase the average degree of paw preference nor the number of cases with significant paw preferences. Early practice of the sort provided in this experiment had essentially no effect on the development of lateral preferences in cats.

Because early experience had no significant effect on the indices of handedness used in this experiment, it seemed reasonable to pool the data from the experimental and control groups to obtain the best estimates of the generality of the trait of handedness in cats. Inspection of the data for individual subjects indicated that 17 of 34 cats (50%) preferred the same paw on the eight tests administered at 180 days or later (the five WGTA tests and the replications in the Handedness Box administered at 180, 210, and 360 days), and 15 of 34 (44%) had consistent and significant preferences, indicating that a substantial number of the kittens had a marked preference even by this stringent criterion. It will be recalled that the probability of eight events having the same outcome by chance is 1 in 256.

Further evidence that lateral preferences are a relatively general characteristic of the cat and are not dictated by situational factors comes from the pattern of intertest correlations obtained from the combined groups which is shown in Table 4-1. All 36 of the r's were positive;

TABLE 4-1

Intertest Correlation Coefficients: Combined Groups

Test	2	3	4	5	6	7	8	9
1. Handedness box—60	.66 **	.62 **	.59 *	.64 **	.54 *	.41	.46	.59 *
2. Handedness box—180		.98 **	.89 **	.84 **	.75 **	.78 **	.62 **	.89 **
3. Handedness box—210			.87 **	.81 **	.75 **	.70 **	.65 **	.94 **
4. Reach—WGTA				.91 **	.87 **	.81 **	.72 **	.86 **
5. Block displacement					.91 **	.80 **	.82 **	.82 **
6. Trough						.91 **	.88 **	.78 **
7. Bottle							.99 **	.75 **
8. Extension								.71 **
9. Handedness box—360								—

* $p < 0.05$.
** $p < 0.01$.

34 were significant at the 5% level of confidence and 32 at the 1% level. Note that the lowest correlations were between performance on the test at 60 days and performance on tests given after 180 days, and that all the *r*'s between performance at 180 days and performance on later tests were significant at the 1% level. The pattern indicates that scores obtained at 60 days were substantially less predictive of adult performances than were the scores obtained at 180 and 210 days. The correlation between scores at 60 and 180 days was only .66, but the correlation between scores at 180 and 360 days was .89, even though the intertest interval was 60 days longer.

The correlation data support the hypothesis that paw preference in cats is a unitary trait, and they lend some support to the hypothesis that paw preferences may be determined by organismic factors that are not fully expressed until relatively late in maturation.

THE EFFECT OF FORCED PRACTICE ON PAW PREFERENCES IN ADULT CATS

Experimentally naïve rats, like cats and monkeys, often manifest strong preferences for the use of one forepaw over the other in manipulation. Paw preferences in rats are quite labile. If rats are prevented from using the spontaneously preferred paw and are forced to manipulate with the initially nonpreferred paw, they reverse the initial preference and continue to use the nonpreferred paw on free-choice trials after forced practice is discontinued (Peterson, 1951; Peterson & Barnett, 1961; Peterson & Devine, 1963; Peterson & McGiboney, 1951). Jankowska and Gorska (1960) have induced similar reversals in paw preference in cats through forced practice with the nonpreferred paw, but did not test for the generality of the effect.

The question of the generalization of the effects of forced practice on a specific type of manipulatory task to other tasks on which forced practice was not given is critical in one respect. It would be impossible to maintain that handedness existed as a stable characteristic of the organism if forced practice on one type of manipulation resulted in a general reversal of preference on a variety of other manipulation tasks. The purpose of this experiment was to determine whether prevention of responses with the preferred paw would affect the subsequent free-choice behavior of the cats on the training task and on other manipulatory tasks.

The subjects were 23 of the cats that served in the developmental study described earlier; their median age was 15 months at the beginning of this experiment. Over a period of about one month, the experimental group ($N = 18$) was given 600 trials in the Handedness Box with the preferred paw confined in a cuffed glove. The cuff prevented the animal from extending the confined forepaw out of the box. The glove was also padded with cotton to prevent manipulation of the meat inside the box. The control group ($N = 5$) received no forced training. The experimental group was given 50 free-choice trials (without the glove) in the Handedness Box after 200, 400, and 600 forced trials, followed by 100 free-choice trials on each of the five tests in the WGTA which have already been described, and then 200 additional free-choice trials in the Handedness Box. The controls were treated identically except that they did not receive forced practice.

Eleven of the 18 experimental cats and the five controls, 16 cats in all, were retested in the Handedness Box and in the WGTA 15 months later to provide additional information on the duration of the effects of forced practice and the stability of paw preferences in cats. The results are summarized in Figs. 4-9 and 4-10. They show the percentage change in preference scores by individual experimental and control

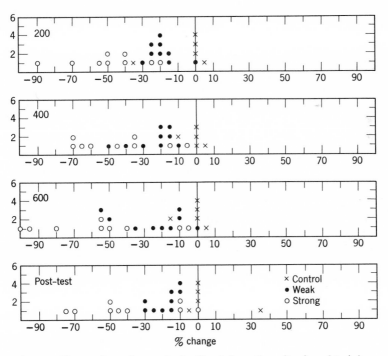

Fig. 4-9 Changes in preference in the Handedness Box after forced training.

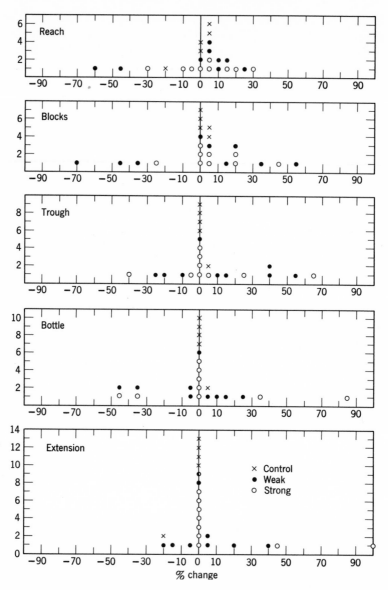

Fig. 4-10 Changes in preference of five tests in the WGTA after forced training.

cats in the Handedness Box and WGTA, respectively, after forced training. Because it was possible for a cat to switch from a 100% right preference to a 100% left preference, the maximum possible change was a 100% decrease in preference. Open and solid circles differentiate between the experimental cats that had significant (strong) or non-significant (weak) preferences before forced training.

It is clear from Fig. 4-9 that forced training strongly affected free-choice responding by the experimental cats in the Handedness Box, particularly those cats that initially had strong preferences. U-tests indicated that the magnitude of the change in the performance of the experimental group was significantly greater than that for the controls (p's were all < 0.02). The effect of forced practice was apparently permanent. On the retest after 15 months, the 11 surviving experimental cats still showed a mean reduction of 25% from their pre-forced training preference scores, whereas the five controls showed no change. The difference was significant at the 0.2% level of confidence ($U = O$). Forced practice with the nonpreferred paw thus resulted in a significant and permanent reduction in preference for the previously preferred paw on free-choice trials in the Handedness Box.

In marked contrast, Fig. 4-10 shows no evidence that forced training in the Handedness Box had any effect on the experimental cats' performance on the tests given in the WGTA.

This inference is supported in detail by the data presented in Table 4-2, which shows the retest correlations between the scores on each

TABLE 4-2

Retest Correlations for the Experimental Cat s

Test	Rho
Handedness box—after 600 forced trials	−.22
Reach	+.78 *
Block displacement	+.75 *
Trough	+.71 *
Bottle	+.61 *
Extension	+.80 *
Handedness box after WGTA	+.13

* $p < 0.01.$

test, before and after forced training, for the experimental cats. The median intertest interval was seven months. The correlations between pre- and post-forced practice scores on the tests in the WGTA were all moderately high and statistically significant. The correlations between the experimental cats' scores in the Handedness Box before and after forced training did not approach significance.

Thus it may be concluded that forced training had a significant and persistent effect on preferences in the situation in which it was given, but that this effect was not widely generalized. These findings are not consistent with the view that preferences in nonhuman animals are rather plastic and easily reversed by training, but neither are they entirely consistent with a dominance hypothesis. Almost any learning theory would predict less than perfect transfer of learned responses between two such dissimilar apparatus as the Handedness Box and the WGTA. More critical data must be obtained from experiments in which forced training and transfer testing are carried out in the same apparatus.

Since forced practice did not significantly affect the performance of the experimental group in the WGTA, we pooled the data for the experimental and control groups to ascertain the long term reliability of paw preferences in cats. Table 4-3 presents the correlations between the scores of 16 animals in the WGTA on the initial test and on the final retest given two years after the initial testing and 15 months after the forced-practice study. It is apparent that preferences in cats are consistent over long intervals.

TABLE 4-3

Reliability of 16 Cats' Paw Preferences Over Two Years

Test	Rho
Reach–WGTA	.84 *
Block displacement	.74 *
Trough	.68 *
Bottle	.74 *
Extension	.64 *

* $p < 0.01$.

MATURATION AND PRACTICE IN THE DEVELOPMENT OF HANDEDNESS IN RHESUS MONKEYS

If hand preferences in monkeys were readily influenced by either maturational or experiential variables, one would expect to find rather striking differences between groups of monkeys that vary in age and amount of previous experience in manipulation. This possibility was investigated with the cooperation of Dr. and Mrs. Robert Zimmermann. They tested 51 immature rhesus monkeys born in the Cornell Primate Laboratory and 30 trapped wild adults for 100 trials on each of the following handedness tests:

1. *Reach*. A raisin or peanut was presented in the right, left, or central sector of the test tray in the WGTA. The monkey had only to pick up the food from the surface of the tray.

2. *Trough*. A single piece of food was placed at the end of a wooden trough (4 x 4 x 10 cm). Metal lips on either side narrowed the opening on the upper surface to 1.5 cm. This apparatus was intended to force the monkeys to slide the reward the length of the trough rather than pick it up directly; this aim was frequently circumvented by those monkeys that succeeded in picking up the food with one finger.

3. *Wire*. Froot Loops (fruit flavored cereal rings) were presented on horizontal wires, 4 in. long and 4 in. above the test tray. The experimenters thought that this test would require the monkeys to slide the cereal the length of the horizontal wire, with the direction of movement varying from trial to trial. Sometimes the monkeys did so, but often they simply broke the dry cereal off the wire, frustrating the experimenters' intentions.

4. *Horizontal Bottle*. The incentive was placed about half way into one of three test tubes (1⅞ in. in diameter and 7 in. long) lying on the WGTA test tray. The monkey had to insert its hand and wrist into the tube to seize the reward. No monkey has yet discovered a successful alternative response on this test.

5. *Vertical Bottle*. This test required the monkeys to reach into one of three vertically oriented plastic glasses (3 in. high and 2 in. in diameter) to extract a raisin or peanut.

In all five tests the incentive was presented equally often in the right, left, and central thirds of the test tray in an irregular sequence to control for position biases.

The results are summarized in Table 4-4. It shows the percentage of monkeys in each age group with significant preferences on each test, the highest, lowest, and median correlation (*rho*) among the 10 intercorrelations for each group, and the mean percentage of preference for each group averaged over all tests. No consistent pattern of change in handedness with age was suggested by any of these measures of performance. The results obtained from the youngest group of baby monkeys and from the adults were quite similar, despite the fact that the infants had never previously been tested in the WGTA while most of the adults had participated in many experiments requiring manipulatory responses in this apparatus. These findings suggest that handedness appears quite early in the immature macaque and changes little as a result of further development or experience. Comparison of the intertest correlations obtained from cats and monkeys tested upon multiple manipulation tasks strongly suggest that lateral preferences are more consistent over a set of different tests in cats than in monkeys.

TABLE 4-4

The Influence of Age on Hand Preferences in Rhesus Monkeys

Age in Months

	2–3	4–8	9–12	18–23	30–32	Adult
Number of Animals	14	8	9	10	10	30
Percentage of Animals with Significant Preferences						
Reach	71	100	89	70	90	83
Trough	71	50	56	60	80	67
Wire	71	62	78	50	80	73
Horizontal Bottle	86	50	56	50	60	77
Vertical Bottle	79	87	78	70	60	93
Mean Percent Preference	33	24	28	22	28	34
Intertest *Rhos* (by age)						
Lowest	.64	.49	.38	.04	.74	.54
Median	.85	.81	.84	.78	.84	.80
Highest	.96	.95	.97	.92	.95	.93

In another study, the stability of hand preferences in monkeys was tested in a group of 14 rhesus monkeys on a series of 10 handedness tests. They were tested as naïve subjects at approximately two years of age, and then retested two years later after continuous training on discrimination-learning problems in the WGTA. The tests were the five unimanual tasks used with the Cornell monkeys, and five more complicated tests in which some monkeys used both hands. Three of these potentially bimanual tasks required the animals to displace an object or a card to obtain a food reward (these resembled the Block Displacement test for cats) or to push a block directly back toward the rear of the test tray (an adaptation of the Extension test for cats). The remaining tests required the monkeys to reach out for and draw in a wooden box with an elongated handle to obtain otherwise inaccessible food, and to draw in a chain with a piece of food impaled on its distal end.

In all the tests the incentive was placed in the right, left, and central sectors of the test tray equally often and in a balanced irregular sequence in order to control for position biases. On the tests in which it was possible that the monkeys might use both hands, both the hand used to move the manipulandum (M) and to secure the incentive (I) were recorded; at least 100 trials were given on each test in both initial testing and replication two years later.

TABLE 4-5

Reliability of 14 Monkeys' Hand Preferences Over Two Years

Test	Rho
Unimanual	
Reach	.38
Trough	.32
Wire	.74 **
Horizontal Bottle	.89 **
Vertical Bottle	.59 *
Bimanual	
Block M	.54 *
Block I	.57 *
Strings M	.30
Strings I	.30
Handle Box M	.60 *
Handle Box I	.33
Extension M	.72 **
Extension I	.64 **
Card M	.43
Card I	.84 **
All Tests	.85 **

* $p < 0.05$.
** $p < 0.01$.

The results are presented in Table 4-5 which gives the retest *rho* for each test and the retest correlation for hand preferences summed over all tests during the first and second replications. The values of *rho* for the 15 individual tests ranged from .30 to .89; and nine were significant at or beyond the 5% level of confidence. In general, the retest correlations were lower than those obtained from cats tested after a comparable interval. It is clear, however, from the number of significant individual correlations and from the correlation based upon all tests, that the hand preferences of immature rhesus monkeys are moderately stable over a period of almost daily testing on learning problems that involved manipulatory responses and provided considerable opportunities for practice effects.

The results of both studies with monkeys, then, agree in suggesting that hand preferences in this species become fairly well fixated early in life and do not change systematically with later experience in manipulation. These findings are generally more compatible with hypotheses that postulate some measure of organismic determination than with those that emphasize environmental determination of hand preferences in rhesus monkeys.

CHANGES IN PAW PREFERENCES IN CATS AFTER UNILATERAL ABLATIONS OF MOTOR AND SOMATOSENSORY CORTEX

Extensive unilateral removal of the somatic sensory and motor areas of the cortex abolishes preoperative preferences for the use of the contralateral paw in manipulation by cats (Forward, Warren, & Hara, 1962; Jankowska & Gorska, 1960). Some cats, however, resume responding with the preoperatively preferred paw within a few weeks, particularly when simple manipulations are required. The extent of recovery possible during prolonged postoperative survival periods has not been studied systematically, but even partial recovery after substantial removal of somatosensory and motor cortex suggests that the interhemispheric inequality responsible for paw preference involves more than the cortical representation of the forepaw.

The purpose of the experiment reported here was to investigate the neural basis of paw preference in cats. The experiment was designed to determine whether the functional asymmetry between the hemispheres that produces lateral preferences is focalized in the cortical representation of the forepaw or diffused more generally throughout the cortex of the dominant hemisphere. If the neural substrate for paw preference is not rather precisely focalized in the forepaw representational area, ablation of the forepaw area might be expected to produce a loss of proficiency in manipulation with the preoperatively preferred paw but not a permanent or complete reversal of preference. Whenever possible, operated cats would use the preoperatively preferred paw, and permanent reversals in preference would occur only on tasks requiring movements that the cats were incapable of executing.

Three specific predictions followed from the hypothesis that the basis of paw preferences was not focalized in the forepaw area. First, there should be a substantial return of responding with the preoperatively preferred paw during prolonged postoperative recovery from the acute postural disturbances resulting from the lesions. Second, the magnitude of the change in preference resulting from removal of the forepaw area will vary with the complexity of the manipulations required by different tasks. Performance on simpler tests should be less affected than performance on tests requiring more complicated manipulations or postural adjustments. Third, the magnitude of the change in paw preference should be greater in cats with lesions involving more of the cortex than the motor and sensory representation of the forepaw, than in cats with lesions confined to the forepaw area only.

We have previously observed (Forward, Warren, & Hara, 1962) that cats with injuries to the somatosensory and motor cortex show quite severe but transient postural disturbances during the first 7 to 10 days after surgery. The magnitude of the change in paw preference resulting from cortical insults may vary as a function of the amount of time allowed for recovery before postoperative testing is begun. This possibility was investigated by giving the first postoperative tests to half of the cats during the period of maximal postural disturbance just after surgery, and to the remaining cats only after these symptoms had disappeared.

Paw preferences were determined preoperatively in 21 cats that were then assigned to five groups. Of this number, six animals were subjected to ablation of the somatosensory and motor representation of the forepaw in the cortex of the hemisphere contralateral to the preferred paw. Postoperative testing was begun on three of the six animals after two days of recovery, and on the remaining three after 14 days of recovery. In another eight cats the contralateral representation of both the forepaw and hind leg was removed. As with the previous groups, half the subjects were retested after 2 days, and half after 14 days. The control group consisted of seven cats, six intact and one in which the forepaw representation on the hemisphere ipsilateral to the preferred paw had been removed. The boundaries of the lesions intended to destroy the representation of the forepaw and hind leg or of the forepaw only were similar to those indicated for the cat by Woolsey (1960, Fig. 4-2), with modifications based upon the results of more recent and unpublished research at the Laboratory of Neurophysiology at the University of Wisconsin.

The effects of the lesions on lateral preferences were assessed in seven manipulation tests. Five, the Reach, Bottle, Trough, Extension, and Block Displacement tests were identical in most respects with the tests described earlier. There were, in addition, two tests that had been suggested because of the difficulties in manipulation observed in other series of brain-injured cats. The Claw test, illustrated in Fig. 4-11, required the cat to pull in a piece of meat that had been placed beyond a ⅛-inch metal strip. It was added to the battery because some cats with

Fig. 4-11   Claw test.

injuries to the cortical motor areas frequently have chronically protracted claws that seriously interfere with the execution of this task.

In the Shelf test meat was presented on a small shelf 4 in. above the surface of the test tray (See Fig. 4-12). The test required a different supporting posture than the otherwise analogous Reach test.

The cats were tested five days a week, in 50 trials a day, and received 100 trials on all the manipulation tests except Block Displacement. In this test they received 200 trials to obtain more reliable data on five subtests in which objects of differing thickness were used. In the two potentially bimanual tests, Block Displacement and Extension, the paws used to move the manipulandum and to secure the reward were recorded, for the cats sometimes used different paws for the two manipulations. All the cats were observed postoperatively a second and third time on the complete battery of manipulation tasks at constant intervals of 6 and 10 weeks.

Visual placing, tactile placing, chin placing, and hopping reflexes were tested in the experimental cats at weekly intervals. Abnormalities, particularly in tactile placing, chin placing, and hopping reactions, were present in all animals, including several that were now in the seventh postoperative month. The frequency of positive responses was lower in the cats with combined fore- and hindpaw lesions than in those with lesions in the forepaw area only. The subjects with the larger lesions also had longer latencies and more grossly defective

Fig. 4-12   Shelf test.

postural reactions than those with small lesions. In general, the results of the reflex tests indicated that the lesions were accurately placed and varied in size.

Lesion size, however, did not affect the cats' performance on the manipulation tests. The differences between the large and small lesion groups were inconsistent and nonsignificant.

The results obtained in the first three postoperative replications are presented in Figs. 4-13 and 4-14; they show the mean percentage of change from preoperative preferences for the controls and experimental groups that were first tested 2 or 14 days after surgery.

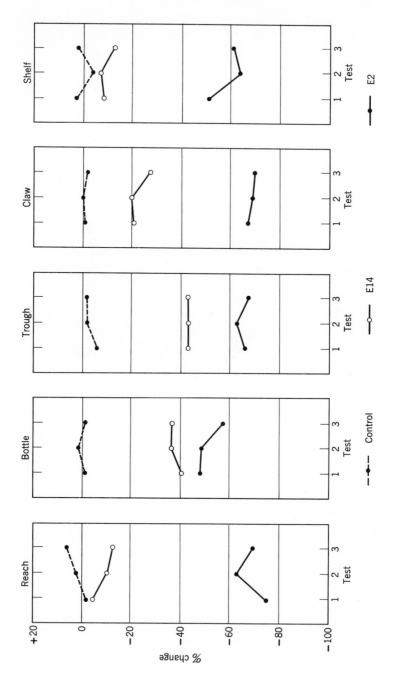

Fig. 4·13 Mean per cent change in preference on unimanual tasks by brain-injured (*E*) and control (*C*) cats.

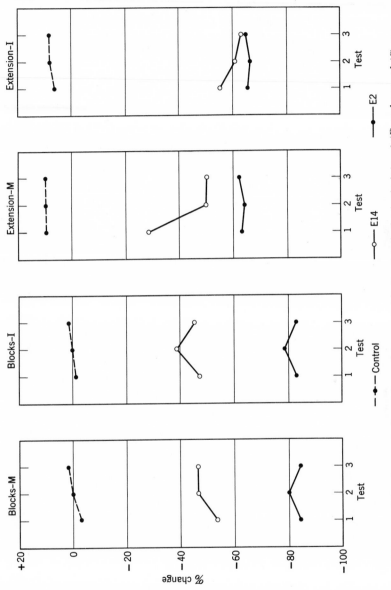

Fig. 4·14 Mean per cent change in preference on bimanual tasks by brain-injured (E) and control (C) cats.

97

The performance of the control group was relatively constant over the three replications of each task, as were the curves for the experimental groups. There was no evidence whatsoever that the magnitude of the change in preferences was attenuated with the passage of time.

The significance of the differences among the groups on the third postoperative repetition of the manipulation tasks was evaluated by U-tests to assess the chronic effects of the experimental treatments on performance of the several tasks. The experimental cats that were allowed two days' recovery differed significantly from the controls on every measure of paw preference (p's all < 0.03), and the 14-day group of experimental cats differed significantly (p's all < 0.05) from the controls on all tasks except Claw and Shelf.

Thus none of the three predictions based on the assumption that the difference between the hemispheres underlying paw preferences in cats involved cortical areas other than the representation of the fore-paw was satisfactorily confirmed. Ablation of the fore- and hindlimb areas did not cause any greater shift in preference than ablation of the forepaw region alone. Neither group of brain-damaged cats showed any convincing evidence of recovery during three postoperative months. The experimental cats that were retested beginning 14 days after ablation showed rather less drastic changes in preference on the Reach, Claw, and Shelf tasks than they did on more complicated tasks, but they showed a significantly greater change than the controls on Reach, the simplest task of all.

No general conclusions on the effects of varying the duration of recovery before the first postoperative testing are possible. On five tasks the differences between the two-day and the 14-day groups were not significant, whereas the magnitude of the change in preference by the two-day group was significantly greater than the change by the 14-day group on the following four tasks: Reach ($p < 0.001$), Block-I ($p < 0.019$), Claw ($p < 0.049$), and Shelf ($p < 0.007$).

Over-all, the results of this experiment seem most nearly compatible with the conclusion that the critical difference between the hemispheres in paw preferences is localized in the cortical representation of the forepaw on the hemisphere contralateral to the preferred paw.

SUMMARY AND CONCLUSIONS

The belief that handedness, a strong and stable preference for the use of one hand in performing manipulatory tasks, occurs only in man is generally accepted by neuropsychologists. The evidence against handedness in nonhuman animals consists primarily of observations suggesting that lateral preferences in mammals other than man are characteristically weak, labile, and easily modified by training.

A review of the evidence suggested that the available experimental data were somewhat inconclusive and that it would be premature to accept the negative conclusion that handedness is not present in cats and rhesus monkeys.

A series of experiments on lateral preferences in manipulation by cats and monkeys was therefore carried out to obtain more critical data on the possibility of handedness in nonhuman animals and to specify the neural correlates of lateral preference in cats.

1. Extensive early practice in manipulation did not significantly affect the development of paw preferences in kittens.

2. Cats frequently preferred the same forepaw in performing a variety of manipulatory tasks; 50% (17/34) of the subjects in this experiment preferred the same paw on eight tests given between 180 and 360 days of age, and 32 of 36 intertest correlations were significant at the 1% level of confidence.

3. Forcing cats to use the nonpreferred paw in manipulation (by mechanically preventing adequate manipulatory responses with the preferred paw) affected spontaneous paw preferences only in the specific situation in which forced practice was given.

4. Sixteen cats were retested on five manipulation tasks after two years. Rank order reliability coefficients ranged from $+.64$ to $+.84$. All were significant at the 1% level of confidence.

5. A sample of 81 immature and adult rhesus monkeys were tested on five tasks requiring somewhat different manipulatory responses. No evidence that hand preferences in monkeys change with age was obtained. Of this sample, 59% (48/81) preferred the same paw on all five tests; 85% (51/60) of the interest correlations were significant at the .05 level of confidence.

6. A second group of 14 rhesus monkeys was tested twice on a series of five unimanual and five potentially bimanual manipulation tasks that yielded 15 measures of lateral preference. The test-retest interval was two years. Rank-order reliability correlations for individual measures ranged from $+.30$ to $+.89$ (median $= +.57$) and nine of 16 were statistically significant. The reliability of preference scores based upon total responses, summed over all tests, on the first and second replications was $+.85$ ($p < 0.01$).

7. Unilateral ablation of the representation for the forepaw in the motor and somatic sensory cortex on the hemisphere contralateral to

the preferred paw largely abolished preoperative preferences in cats. There was no recovery of preoperative preferences during three months of postoperative observation, and destruction of the representation of both the fore- and hindlimb did not have any greater effect than removal of the forepaw area only. The results suggest that the hemispheric asymmetry responsible for handedness in the cats is restricted to the cortical representation of the forepaw in the dominant hemisphere.

It seems reasonable to conclude that cats and rhesus monkeys have lateral preferences that are relatively strong, moderately stable over many months, and rather resistant to change by training. Thus it is no longer possible to deny categorically the possibility of handedness in these species.

It remains for future research to determine the degree to which handedness in nonhuman animals is homologous to handedness in men. Quite possibly the occurrence of handedness in cats, rhesus monkeys, and humans represents the action of analogous, rather than homologous, processes. For example, we have thus far failed to detect any significant maturational changes in handedness in the rhesus monkey. In humans "hand preference shows cultural differences, it develops gradually, it fluctuates a great deal before becoming established, it differs with the task at hand, and it is remarkably susceptible to training; all of which are points favoring the view that it is learned." (Munn, 1955, p. 296)

REFERENCES

Bonin, G. v. (1962) Anatomical asymmetries of the cerebral hemispheres. In V. B. Mountcastle (Ed.), *Interhemispheric Relations and Cerebral Dominance.* Baltimore: Johns Hopkins. Pp. 1–6.

Cole, J. (1955) Paw preference in cats related to hand preference in animals and men. *J. comp. physiol. Psychol.* 48, 137–140.

Ettlinger, G., & Moffett, A. (1964) Lateral preferences in the monkey. *Nature* 204, 606.

Forward, E., Warren, J. M., & Hara, K. (1962) The effects of unilateral lesions in sensorimotor cortex on manipulation by cats. *J. comp. physiol. Psychol.* 55, 1130–1135.

Hécaen, H., & de Ajuriaguerra, J. *Left-handedness: manual superiority and cerebral dominance.* New York: Grune & Stratton. Pp. 1–162.

Jankowska, E., & Gorska, T. (1960) The effects of unilateral ablations of sensorimotor cortex on Type II conditioned reflexes in cats: I. Natural conditioned reflexes. *Acta Biol. exp.,* Warsaw 20, 193–210.

Jung, R. (1962) Summary of the conference. In V. B. Mountcastle (Ed.), *Interhemispheric relations and cerebral dominance.* Baltimore: Johns Hopkins. Pp. 264–277.

Milner, B. (1962) Laterality effects in audition. In V. B. Mountcastle (Ed.), *Interhemispheric relations and cerebral dominance*. Baltimore: Johns Hopkins. Pp. 177–195.

Munn, N. L. (1955) *The evolution and growth of human behavior*. Boston: Houghton-Mifflin.

Penfield, W., & Roberts, L. (1959) *Speech and brain mechanisms*. Princeton: Princeton Univer. Press.

Peterson, G. M. (1951) Transfers in handedness in the rat from forced practice. *J. comp. physiol. Psychol.* **44**, 184–190.

Peterson, G. M., & Barnett, P. E. (1961) The cortical destruction necessary to produce a transfer of a forced-practice function. *J. comp. physiol. Psychol.* **54**, 382–385.

Peterson, G. M., & Devine, J. V. (1963) Transfers in handedness in the rat resulting from small cortical lesions after limited forced practice. *J. comp. physiol. Psychol.* **56**, 752–756.

Peterson, G. M., & McGiboney, D. R., Jr. (1951) Reeducation of handedness in the rat following cerebral injuries. *J. comp. physiol. Psychol.* **44**, 191–196.

Teuber, H.-L. (1962) Effects of brain wounds implicating right or left hemisphere in man: Hemisphere differences and hemisphere interaction in vision, audition and somesthesis. In V. B. Mountcastle (Ed.), *Interhemispheric relations and cerebral dominance*. Baltimore: Johns Hopkins. Pp. 131–157.

Warren, J. M. (1958) The development of paw preferences in cats and monkeys. *J. genet. Psychol.* **93**, 229–236.

Weinstein, S. (1962) Differences in effects of brain wounds implicating right or left hemispheres: Differential effects on certain intellectual and complex perceptual functions. In V. B. Mountcastle (Ed.), *Interhemispheric relations and cerebral dominance*. Baltimore: Johns Hopkins. Pp. 159–176.

Woolsey, C. N. (1960) Some observations on brain fissuration in relation to cortical localization of function. In D. B. Tower & J. P. Schade (Eds.), *Structure and function of the cerebral cortex*. Amsterdam: Elsevier. Pp. 64–68.

Zangwill, O. L. (1960) Speech. In J. Field, H. W. Magoun, & V. E. Hall (Eds.), *Handbook of physiology. Section I. Neurophysiology*. Vol. 3. Washington, D.C.: American Physiological Society. Pp. 1709–1722.

5

Motivational Aspects of
Social Responsiveness in Young Chimpanzees

WILLIAM A. MASON

Delta Regional Primate Research Center
Tulane University

A few relatively stereotyped activities figure prominently in the social behavior of young chimpanzees. Play is certainly one such activity. Anyone who has spent a few hours watching young animals in a friendly, relaxed situation has probably seen social play. The pattern includes slapping, wrestling, and pushing, characteristically accompanied by half-closed eyes, a broad smile, and a panting laugh.

Grooming is also a familiar activity. In chimpanzees the pattern consists of close visual inspection of the spot being groomed, together with coordinated probing and picking movements of the fingers and lips. Vigorous mouth movements and sputtering noises are often present. Grooming is a favorite occupation of adult chimpanzees, but the pattern is also seen in animals as young as 2 years, although rarely in complete form. The biological significances of grooming is not known. Perhaps, as has been suggested, it serves a utilitarian purpose, such as ridding a companion of ectoparasites or supplying a dietary supplement in the form of minute particles of salt. There is no question, however, that it occurs when neither of these conditions can be assumed, and it is hard for most observers to escape the conviction that the primary satisfactions of grooming are found in the social act itself.

Clinging is a third common social pattern of young apes. In early infancy, of course, the response plays a vital part in maintaining contact with the mother, but clinging often occurs between young

The work on the previously unpublished experiments described in this chapter was supported by research grants (M-4100 and M-5636) from the National Institute of Mental Health, U.S. Public Health Service. I was assisted in these studies by R. Chang-Yit, F. Fitz-Gerald, B. Hare, V. Hayhurst, and N. Itoigawa. Portions of this chapter appeared in Mason (1965).

chimpanzees during much later phases of childhood, and may even be seen on occasion between fully mature animals. In adult chimpanzees (or in older children no longer closely tied to the mother) clinging has been regarded as a protective reaction, a greeting response, or an expression of affection or distress.

The clinging, grooming, and play patterns appear to be as fundamental and distinctive to the chimpanzee as the physical structure that give this species its shape. In spite of variations in the presence or form of its component responses, each pattern can usually be readily identified, even by an inexperienced observer.

These three patterns account for a surprisingly large amount of the social activities of young chimpanzees, at least in captivity. In one study, for example, we found that of all specific contacts between seven pairs of 2- to 4-year-old African-born animals, 70% was devoted to play, 5% to grooming, and 4% to clinging. Most of the remaining 21% of specific contacts consisted of simple, discrete responses such as grasping, smelling, and mouthing. Some of these behaviors were directed toward the anogenital area of the partner, but unequivocal sexual activity was infrequent, as was fighting.

Of course, these data in no way deny the possibility that occasionally a truly subtle interchange will occur, such as when an adult male carefully removed a foreign particle from the eye of his mate after she had solicited his aid (Miles, 1963). They do suggest, however, that for the immature subject, the gross features of social behavior can be described with acceptable completeness in terms of a few species-typical patterns that are identified by their form.

In our research we were interested in the role of these activities in the social development of the chimpanzee. Because suitable subjects were not available for longitudinal studies to trace behavioral changes over time, we investigated the factors that brought about short-term changes in patterns of social responsiveness, hoping that such an analysis would provide an indication of the variables that were important in the socialization process.

Our efforts to establish the role of clinging, grooming, and play in social interaction, and to assess the relevance of these activities to socialization, were directed toward the following questions:

1. Do these activities function as rewards?

2. Does their effectiveness as rewards vary with short-term motivational changes?

3. Do they show motivational consequences, that is, produce alterations in the motivational state?

4. Does their effectiveness as rewards depend on developmental status?

5. What is the role of experience in the development and expression of these behaviors?

Something is said about each of these problems in the sections that follow, although in some cases the data are meager or are derived from nonsystematic observations. A more detailed account of the experimental evidence is presented elsewhere (Mason, 1965).

Comment on the theoretical pretensions of this chapter is also appropriate here. Inasmuch as the research is presented in roughly chronological order, it is evident that there was little initial concern with theory. As the data accumulated, however, the need for conceptual guidelines, both as a means of ordering the available information and as an aid in planning research, became apparent. The arousal concept, developed by Bindra (1959), Duffy (1951), Hebb (1955), Malmo (1959), and others, was found useful and is referred to frequently in the following sections. No serious effort is made to examine the appropriateness of alternate formulations. The aim throughout is to make use of an existing theory to provide a meaningful and suggestive framework for the presentation of a collection of experimental findings that without such theory would seem heterogeneous and unwieldy.

CLINGING, GROOMING, AND PLAY AS REWARDS

It is reasonable to suppose that clinging, grooming, and play have reward value for the young chimpanzee; in fact, this has been demonstrated. McCulloch (1939) found that clasping or clinging could serve as an effective reinforcer for the solution of delayed-response and visual-discrimination problems, and Falk (1958) later showed that a similar effect could be achieved by using the opportunity to groom the experimenter as the reward.

The normative data, however, show that different social activities do not occur with equal frequency, suggesting that they may not be equivalent in their rewarding effects. Direct comparisons of different social activities support these data. Young chimpanzees were given an opportunity to play with a stimulus-person, to be groomed or petted by him, or to groom him (Mason, Hollis, & Sharpe, 1962). The animals were tested in their living cages and the principal measure of rewarding effect was the percentage of 15-second intervals spent in proximity

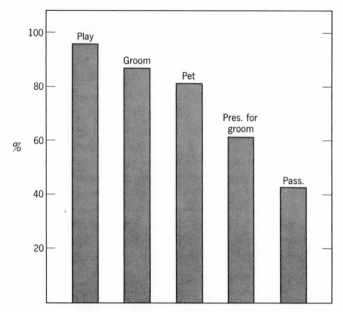

Fig. 5-1   Percentage of 15-second intervals in which the chimpanzees were in proximity to stimulus-person (from Mason et al., 1962).

to the person. Figure 5-1 shows that all activities were superior to the passive (control) condition, and that play was clearly the most effective reward. Other experiments (described later) showed that play was clearly preferred over clinging when these activities were compared directly. Play was also found to compare favorably with food as reinforcement for simple lever-pressing responses (Mason, Saxon, & Sharpe, 1963).

It is clear from these findings that clinging, grooming (both active and passive roles), and play have definite and differential rewarding effects. Knowing only this it might be possible to suggest how these activities contribute to the formation of social attachments, the development of preferences for specific companions, and the like, which are real and important phenomena in chimpanzee social life. But we would obviously be in a better position to evaluate the role of social rewards in the behavior and development of young chimpanzees if information were available on the relation of these factors to motivational variables. The experiments discussed in the next two sections were designed to clarify this question.

RELATION OF SOCIAL ACTIVITY PREFERENCES TO SHORT-TERM MOTIVATIONAL CHANGES

That young chimpanzees would rather play than be groomed or held (cling) when tested with familiar companions in situations to which they are accustomed will occasion no surprise to those who think of the resemblances between ape and child. A similar outcome would be expected with human subjects at a comparable developmental level, at least with regard to clinging and roughhouse play, which have obvious counterparts in human social behavior.

From what is known of human behavior one might also expect that an effective means of changing these preferences would be to manipulate emotional arousal. Everyone is familiar with the spectacle of the frightened or distressed child who clings tenaciously to its mother's skirts while crying to be picked up and held. Similar reactions do occur in young chimpanzees, although the form of the clinging response is more stereotyped, and clinging is probably more reliably elicited in the ape. Emotional arousal in our study was manipulated in a variety of ways: by exposing the animals to unfamiliar surroundings, noise, physical restraint, and separation from cagemates, and by treating them with drugs. An attempt to establish the generality of the effects was made by measuring responses to inanimate objects, other chimpanzees, and human beings. In addition, to provide some check on the relevance of social history, animals raised under controlled conditions in the laboratory were used in some experiments; in others the subjects were wild-caught chimpanzees about 2 to 4 years old. The findings were quite consistent. Three experiments are described to illustrate the general approach and the nature of the results.

The animals in the first experiment were five pairs of African-born chimpanzees observed in three situations that differed in degree of familiarity. Each pair was observed for three five-minute sessions in each of the three situations: in its living cage, in an identical cage placed in a different location in the colony room, and in an identical cage in an unfamiliar room. Clinging responses, expressed as a percentage of total clinging, and play responses increased progressively as a function of situational novelty. Scores in the living cage, holding cage, and novel room were 15, 23, and 51%, respectively. In the novel room, clinging decreased from 99% in the first session to 23% in the

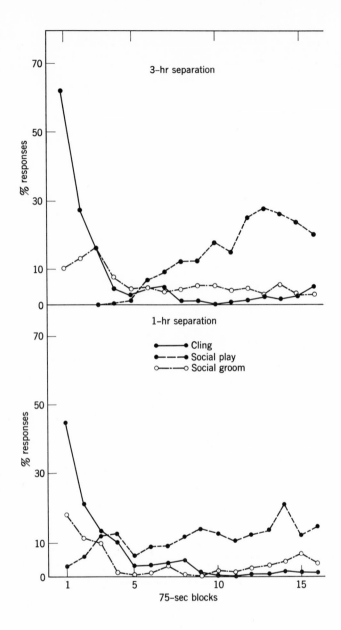

Fig. 5-2   Effects of brief periods of separation from cagemate on social responsiveness.

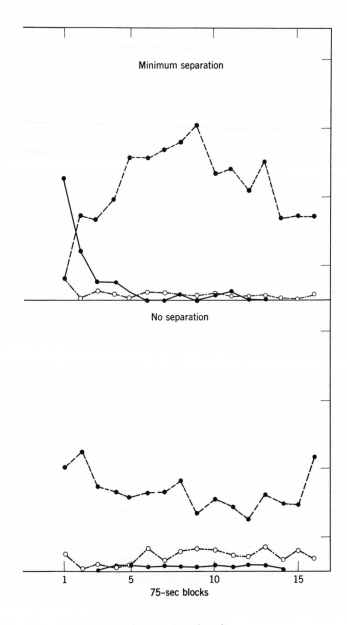

Fig. 5-2 *(continued)*

third, demonstrating that clinging may decline with repeated exposure to an unfamiliar situation.

In another experiment, the subjects were 12 African-born animals housed in pairs. It is well known that separation from cagemates is an acutely distressing experience to young chimpanzees and this information was used to manipulate arousal. Cagemates were observed for 20–minute periods following each of four conditions of separation: (a) no separation, (b) minimum separation, (c) one-hour separation, and (d) three-hour separation. Condition (a) consisted of observing interactions in the living cage in the absence of experimental manipulation. Condition (b) provided a control for the excitement induced by the act of separation itself. The animals were separated and immediately reunited. Responses were scored on a check sheet time-ruled at 15–second intervals. Figure 5-2 shows the contrasting relations between clinging, grooming, and play behavior. For the no-separation condition, play was consistently the most frequent response. For all conditions in which separation occurred, however, whether for three hours or merely for a few seconds, clinging was the most frequent ini-

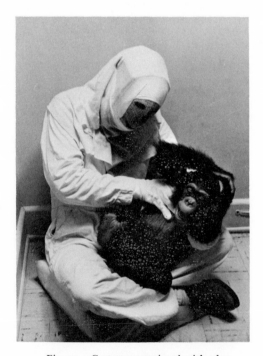

Fig. 5-3   Costume associated with play.

tial response. Moreover, it is evident that the maxima for clinging vary in orderly fashion, the highest occurring after the longest period of separation and the lowest after minimum separation. Under all separation conditions, clinging decreased rapidly, reaching levels below 10% within the first five minutes.

These experiments—and others that are not described here—showed that unfamiliar surroundings, restraint, noise, and separation from a companion produced similar effects, which suggested that the relevant motivational variable could best be described in broad terms, such as arousal. In an effort to assess this possibility more directly, the last experiment described in this section employed a stimulant drug that had been used by other investigators to manipulate arousal level.

Fig. 5-4   Costume associated with clinging.

The subjects were 12 African-born chimpanzees tested with two distinctively costumed stimulus-persons in a room to which the animals were well habituated. In earlier experiments the chimpanzees had learned that one costume represented play (the person responded by tickling and roughhousing with the animal whenever it approached, see Fig. 5-3), and the other costume represented clinging (when in proximity the animal was drawn to the person and placed in a ventro-ventral contact, see Fig. 5-4). With either stimulus-person, of course, the animal was free to initiate or break contact at any time during the test period. The chimpanzees were tested for five minutes at 15–

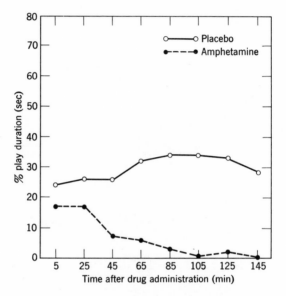

Fig. 5-5   Effects of amphetamine on play.

minute intervals over a 145–minute period, following oral administration of 1 mg/kg of amphetamine. The primary measure of activity preference was the time in contact with each stimulus-person. Figure 5-5 shows that play dropped off sharply within less than one hour after the drug was given; and Fig. 5-6 shows a steady increase in the amount of clinging accompanying this change. Comparison of these curves with performance for the placebo condition shows that in the absence of the drug, play is consistently preferred over clinging.

It has been relatively easy in our research to depress play and augment clinging. Any procedure that seems to cause a gross increment in arousal has this consequence, but to increase play over the baseline is more difficult, probably because only moderate increments in arousal produce such an effect.

Perhaps the clearest suggestion of the importance of small increments of arousal in the elicitation of play is provided by Menzel's studies with laboratory-born chimpanzees raised in enclosed cubicles (Menzel, 1964). He found, in these animals, that play did not appear on initial tests with novel objects. On the contrary, the subjects gave every indication of timidity or active distress, and it was only after repeated exposures to the same objects that play emerged. This much would be expected on the basis of information already considered. However, Menzel

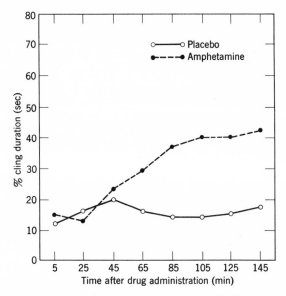

Fig. 5-6   Effects of amphetamine on clinging.

was also able to show that after the animals encountered many different objects of the same general class, novel stimuli were preferred over more familiar ones and immediately elicited approach and vigorous play.

Similar results have been obtained with social stimuli. Initial exposure to a costumed stimulus-person often produced fear, but this was eventually overcome and the animal played freely and vigorously. When this point was reached, if the chimpanzee was given the opportunity to choose between two passive stimulus-persons, one clad in the familiar play costume and the other in a novel costume, the stranger was generally preferred. The preference persisted even when both stimuli responded to approach by initiating mild play. If the stimulus-persons systematically increased the vigor of their play, however, the chimpanzee tended to play less and to shift its play responses from the novel playmate to the familiar one. One interpretation of these data is that play behavior is facilitated by the moderate increment in arousal produced by visual novelty or by the combined effects of visual novelty and the mild play stimulation provided by the person. Larger increments, which result from increasing the vigor of play, bring the total intensity of stimulation close to aversive levels, and the animal modulates this effect by playing less and by directing its responses toward the more familiar, hence less stimulating, playmate.

There are other indications that small increments in stimulation facilitate play. Slight changes in physical surroundings augment play between cagemates. It will be recalled that in the separation experiment, described earlier, it was not the baseline condition, in which the animals were unmolested, but minimum separation, in which they were separated and immediately reunited (see Fig. 5-2), that produced the highest level of play.

MOTIVATIONAL CONSEQUENCES OF CLINGING, GROOMING, AND PLAY

The experiments summarized in the preceding sections show that under ordinary circumstances play is a frequent and highly preferred activity of young chimpanzees. There is also some indication that moderate increments in arousal facilitate play, whereas high arousal produces avoidance of play and strengthens the tendency to cling. An obvious place to seek an explanation for these effects was in the psychological consequences of clinging, grooming, and play.

In human behavior clinging is commonly looked on as a source of comfort or emotional security. We propose that the basis for these effects is some form of arousal reduction. Insofar as whimpering and screaming can be considered to be measures of arousal, there is convincing evidence for such an effect. In one experiment, for example, it was shown that infant chimpanzees gave substantially fewer distress vocalizations to an electric shock to the foot when they were held in the typical clinging position than when they were resting on a bare surface (Mason & Berkson, 1962). Other experiments with older African-born animals produced comparable results and, in addition, demonstrated that being groomed has similar although less powerful effects as those associated with clinging.

Sucking probably also produces tranquilizing effects. It is a common activity of young primates during emotional disturbance, and Birns (cited in Bridger, 1962) found that human neonates with a pacifier showed significantly less arousal to cold stress than babies without the pacifier. Passive movement stimulation provided by the mother may also be arousal reducing. Harlow's (1961) data showed that rhesus monkeys preferred rocking over stationary surrogates during the first few months of life, and observations by Allesch (1921) suggested that rocking pacifies the infant chimpanzee. It is also noteworthy that monkeys and apes raised apart from the mother often develop stereotyped rocking, which is especially prominent in stressful situations and may have a tranquilizing or inhibitory action.

The motivational consequences of play contrast sharply with the foregoing responses. Play characteristically is directed toward the novel, variable, or mildly stimulating features of the environment, and it probably serves to increase arousal rather than to reduce it. The rough-and-tumble character of play, associated with violent bursts of motor activity and frequent changes in patterns of stimulation through various sensory modalities, suggests this possibility, and it receives support from the experimental finding that social responsiveness is elevated following a brief period of play (Mason et al., 1962). Moreover, Berkson (1963) has shown that tickling, a highly effective stimulus for eliciting and sustaining play, does in fact produce an increment in arousal in infant chimpanzees as indicated by an increase in skin conductance.

The thesis that clinging reduces arousal and play augments it suggests a loose homeostatic relation between these social response patterns and motivational variables. Further, there is the possibility that each pattern is part of a broader class of responses possessing similar functions. Thus in spite of the differences that distinguish sucking, clinging, passive motion, and the stimulation provided by grooming, these conditions may have a common dimension—namely, the ability to decrease arousal, to exert an inhibitory or tranquilizing effect. Similarly, it might be argued that rough-and-tumble play may be grouped with exploratory or investigatory activities and motor play (swinging, jumping, climbing), which appear to augment stimulation. Together, these two broad classes of responses provide the young chimpanzee with means for maintaining arousal within an optimum range. This characteristic is probably an important source of the effectiveness of these activities as rewards and helps to explain why their reward value varies with motivational state. As Hebb (1955) suggested, at low levels an increase in arousal is probably rewarding, whereas at high levels, it is a decrease that rewards.

RELATION TO SOCIAL DEVELOPMENT

It is not surprising that those patterns that seem to have an inhibitory or arousal-reducing effect are especially characteristic of the
relationship of the infant to the mother. Chimpanzees require a long
time to mature, and the mother is the most reliable and effective agent
available to the immature organism for coping with a hostile world.
Schneirla (1959) proposed the withdrawal from intense stimulation
as a fundamental dimension of behavioral organization. For the
preambulatory infant chimpanzee, however, physical withdrawal is
not possible, and high arousal is associated with distress vocalization
and sweeping movements of the arms (Berkson, 1963), both of which
could have the obvious effect of re-establishing contact with the
mother. In the youngster moving about under its own power mere
withdrawal could be maladaptive. The evidence suggests an evolutionary modification by which clinging and other responses performed
on or by the mother have acquired the functional properties of
withdrawal; that is, they produce a reduction in stimulation. Although
seeking the mother in a disturbing situation ordinarily results in both
clinging and physical withdrawal, it is the act of clinging rather than
the increasing distance from the source of disturbance that seems to be
the critical event. Young monkeys will approach a frightening object
in order to contact an artificial mother (Harlow, 1961), and chimpanzees in a disturbing open-field test will cling to a social surrogate
that keeps them in the situation rather than enter an enclosed cage
that would permit them to withdraw from it. If the artificial mother
is not present, however, the cage is entered readily (Mason, 1965).
Even though the mother occupies a central role in the emotional life
of the growing chimpanzee for at least the first several years of life,
it is clear that clinging and similar maternally oriented behaviors are
less frequent as development proceeds. New activities emerge, among
which play is prominent. Unequivocal play responses appear near the
middle of the first year of life. Play is primarily an activity of the
young, directed toward immature companions or conspicuous features
of the physical environment. In terms of Schneirla's (1959) formulation, it may be viewed as the dominant form of approach behavior
in the young chimpanzee. Play, like clinging, becomes less frequent
in older animals, although it remains a common activity in adolescence when clinging is rarely observed. In fully mature chimpanzees
the incidence of both play and clinging is sharply reduced, even though
neither pattern disappears entirely.

We sought a motivational explanation for these trends by examining the frequency of different social responses such as clinging and play in the neonatal animal. As would be expected, the inhibitory effects of clinging were present in early infancy. The following quotation from Yerkes (1943) reflects the experience of many observers:

Something to cling to is essential to the comfort and contentment of the infant. . . . If it be like the mother's coat—soft, pliable, and warm—all the better. But in any case it must be something which can be grasped firmly and made to yield reassuring contact stimuli. A bit of cloth, animal skin, or soft paper will suffice. (p. 43)

Such observations agree with the thesis that clinging is arousal reducing. In addition, however, they clearly suggest that the infant that is not permitted to cling is actively distressed. Play likewise displays its fundamental motivational properties during the neonatal period. At this stage of development, however, contact stimuli ordinarily effective in eliciting play are aversive, rather than pleasurable as they appear to be in later childhood.

The marked contrast in the reactions of neonatal animals to forms of stimulation associated with play and with clinging is evident from the data presented in Table 5-1.

TABLE 5-1

Mean Duration of Vocalizations per Session (in seconds), and Percentage of Sessions in which Vocalization Occurred *

Treatment	Per Cent of Sessions	Mean Duration
Manipulate limbs	80.2	8.8
Tickle	67.7	6.3
Restrain head	62.5	8.8
Restrain limbs	52.1	4.7
Pressure	43.7	3.8
Stroking	38.5	3.0
Control	43.7	2.6
Cylinder	14.6	0.5

* Data are based on 24 30-second test sessions for each of four subjects.

The subjects were tested while supine on a bare table. Their distress vocalizations were measured as they responded to stimulation of the abdomen by tickling, rhythmic stroking, steady pressure, and a cloth-covered cylinder, to manipulation of the limbs, and to restriction of spontaneous movements of the head and limbs. Testing occurred three times a week from the first to the eighth week of life. Table 5-1 shows the incidence and duration of vocalization during stimulation. Manipulation of the limbs, tickling, and restricting spontaneous movements produced a substantial increase in vocal activity as compared to the control condition (supine on table, no stimulation). Continuous light pressure on the abdomen and stroking produced no appreciable change in vocalization, compared with the control condition, but placing a cloth-covered cylinder on the animal's ventral surface caused a marked decrease in vocal activity. The cylinder, of course, closely approximated the postural adjustment and stimulus conditions of clinging, whereas tickling, manipulation of limbs, and restraint of movement were forms of stimulation commonly associated with play.

The distress of the neonate that was not permitted to cling and the increased disturbance that occurred when even mild forms of play stimulation were applied suggest that the very young chimpanzee has an extremely low tolerance for intense or varied stimulation, at least in the tactile-kinesthetic mode. It is evident that this must change significantly during the first two years as social play emerges and becomes a dominant and highly preferred activity. In terms of the arousal hypothesis, it is as though the "optimum level" is low for the neonate and even the most modest increments are aversive; as development proceeds, the hypothetical optimum shifts upward until in the older child varied stimulation is not only tolerated but actively sought.

Although this speculation makes no attempt to deal with ontogenetic changes in detail, it is in accord with the major trend of behavioral development between infancy and early adolescence. However, the same theoretical considerations, if they have any real merit, ought to be equally applicable to the important changes occurring between adolescence and full maturity.

The nature of these changes has not been described in detail. Such information that is available indicates a dramatic reduction in activity among older animals. The findings were derived from a comparison of nine adult pairs with seven pairs of 2-to-4-year-old chimpanzees at the Yerkes Laboratories. Each pair was observed in a familiar outdoor cage for 20 sessions of 30 minutes and behavior was recorded by 15–second intervals on a time-ruled check list. Table 5-2 presents the mean number of intervals in which the indicated activities occurred. It is clear that the adults had substantially lower scores for total social contacts and for all specific social activities except grooming; their scores were also lower for all nonsocial categories except self-manipulation. The tendency toward reduction in gross motor activities in older animals is consistent with human data (Shock, 1951), and the magnitude of intergroup differences, combined with the relatively slight variation within groups, lends confidence that the data reflect true age differences.

These findings show that captive adult chimpanzees engage in predominantly low-amplitude motor patterns (self-manipulation, grooming), which previous evidence suggests do not elevate arousal but, on the contrary, may actually reduce it. Young animals, on the other hand, devote much time to vigorous activities (motor play, play-

TABLE 5-2

Comparison of Mean Number of Intervals in Which Activity Occurred by Young and Adult Chimpanzees

Social Responses	Young *	Adult **	p
Total social contacts	762.4	158.2	0.002
Total specific contacts	542.1	149.3	0.002
Play	378.7	2.8	0.002
Groom	28.6	127.4	NS
Cling	20.1	0.0	0.02
Nonsocial			
Motor play	302.7	8.8	0.002
Manipulation of self	1020.9	1341.4	NS
Manipulation of environment	725.6	414.2	0.05
Travel	1214.7	635.8	0.002

* N = seven pairs.
** N = nine pairs.

fighting, travel), which we have reason to suspect are arousal increasing. The activity profile of adults thus suggests a significant motivational change between adolescence and maturity, possibly because of a reduction in responsiveness or arousability (extent of reaction to a given form or magnitude of stimulation declines with age), or a shift in optimum level (arousal-increasing activities are less preferred), or a combination of these factors.

Even the scattered information now available on different age groups suggests that an adequate description of motivational trends in chimpanzee social development from infancy to adulthood in terms of an arousal theory requires that at least three parameters be considered separately: (a) the resting or base level of arousal in different age groups; (b) the effect of different forms and magnitudes of stimulus

Fig. 5-7   Clinging with rag mop (photograph V. Hayhurst).

inputs on this level; and (c) the optimum or preferred level of stimulation. The effect of particular kinds or amounts of experience on these parameters must also be taken into account. At the moment, however, little can be said about the question. The available information relates chiefly to the form of social responses and the selection of the objects upon which they are habitually performed.

ROLE OF EXPERIENCE

It is clear that the social response patterns that have been of principal concern in this chapter are relatively resistant to alterations by experience and appear in similar form under widely different conditions of rearing and testing. Clinging, for example, is easily recognized whether it is directed toward an inanimate object (Fig. 5-7), the animal's own body (Fig. 5-8), a person (Fig. 5-4), or another chimpanzee (Fig. 5-9). Although minor variations may be discerned in the details of patterning, the essential features of bimanual grasping and ventral contact are present in every case. The same claim can be supported for grooming and for play-wrestling. The play pattern is usually unmistakable, whether it occurs with companions (Fig. 5-3),

Fig. 5-8   Self-clasping, a possible variant of clinging (Yerkes Lab. Photograph).

cardboard boxes (Fig. 5-10), or, as sometimes happens, in the apparent absence of an eliciting stimulus.

These photographs show that the forms of clinging and play are relatively stereotyped, but they suggest that the objects toward which they are directed vary considerably. This is true, but all objects are

Fig. 5-9   Clinging (Yerkes Lab. Photograph).

not equivalent and experience is an important factor in object selection. The role of experience differs, however, for clinging and for play.

Apparently, clinging may become attached to (habitually directed toward) any soft, claspable object in early infancy and, according to the present thesis, the strength of this attachment depends on the level of arousal and on the effectiveness of the object in arousal reduction. The relevance of the first factor, differences in arousal level, is suggested by the finding that monkeys stimulated with an aversive air-blast by terry-cloth mothers formed a stronger attachment to the surrogate, measured by time in contact, than did monkeys raised on identical, but nonaversive, surrogates (Rosenblum & Harlow, 1963). The second factor, effectiveness of the object in arousal reduction,

Fig. 5-10   Play-fighting with box (from Bernstein, 1962).

presumably accounts for the failure of young monkeys to form strong attachments to wire-mesh cylinders, even when these are the only social substitutes provided, and for the finding that an object that permits both sucking and clinging produces a stronger early attachment than the object designed to provide an outlet for only one of these activities (Harlow, 1961).

In situations of high arousal the object sought for clinging is the one upon which the response is habitually performed. In its absence substitutes may be taken, but their acceptability depends on resemblance to the original object and on the strength of the motivation to cling. Chimpanzees raised with cloth dummies will cling to familiar inanimate objects, such as a rag mop, but may refuse to cling to people even when acutely distressed. On the other hand, wild-born chimpanzees will unhesitatingly cling to complete strangers, if sufficiently disturbed, but show almost no clinging with inanimate objects. As development continues, the range of acceptable objects appears to narrow and it becomes increasingly difficult for new attachments to be formed. In fact, the animal that has had no opportunity to cling in early infancy may fail to do so later in life, even when entirely appropriate objects are available (Menzel, 1964).

Play, as we have indicated, is usually directed toward objects that are moderately unfamiliar. Thus experience does not lead merely to the selection of a specific object toward which play responses are directed, but to the formation of a "class" of objects, of which the more novel are the preferred targets of play. Under some conditions, of course, both play and clinging may be directed toward the same object, as in the separation experiments with chimpanzees. Similarly, Harlow (1961) has reported that rhesus monkeys play on as well as cling to artificial mothers. However, if two dummies differing in degree of familiarity are available, it can be shown that clinging occurs principally with the more familiar, whereas the novel surrogate receives most of the play responses. When three chimpanzees raised with artificial mothers were allowed to choose between them and devices similar in form but differing in color, they eventually came to make more contacts with the novel objects, and play responses were directed toward them more than 5 times as often as toward the familiar surrogate. Clinging, however, was 11 times more frequent with the familiar object. In situations in which the social stimuli are approximately equal in familiarity, one would expect the partner providing an "optimum" level of stimulation, that is, neither too low nor too high, to be a preferred playmate. Presumably, some such effect underlies the preference for specific companions (Nowlis, 1941).

CONCLUSIONS

A few species-typical patterns comprise most of the social behavior of young chimpanzees. It has been shown that these patterns can serve as rewards, but that their effectiveness, or the frequency with which they are selected in preference tests, or appear in social interaction, vary with motivational factors.

Investigations of the nature of these factors suggest that the motivational state can be described in terms of a broad concept such as arousal. This concept would account for the finding that many variables—including noise level, novel surroundings, strange companions, physical restraint, separation from cagemates, and drugs—can have similar effects on social responsiveness. The concept also provides an explanation of qualitative changes in social activity patterns by relating them to quantitative changes in a central process. The evidence indicates that an orderly transition from one social pattern to another will occur as a result of habituation procedures, drug action, or changes in the level of external stimulation, all of which have been shown to affect physiological measures of arousal level.

In addition to the evidence suggesting that social responses can be distinguished on the basis of the level of arousal at which they characteristically occur, there is reason to believe that these behaviors differ in their motivational consequences. Thus social play, which is readily evoked under ordinary conditions, appears to increase arousal and is avoided when the level is high. Clinging, on the other hand, is most frequent at high levels and appears to be arousal reducing. The ability of these activities to maintain arousal within an optimum range is presumably an important source of their rewarding effects. Motor play and various exploratory or investigatory activities are probably similar to social play with respect to predisposing conditions and motivational consequences; clinging, sucking, passive motion, and being groomed appear to form another class of responses with motivational properties in common.

The finding that early social patterns differ systematically in their relation to eliciting conditions and in their motivational consequences may throw some light on the socialization process. We have suggested that the strength of filial attachment is a joint function of level of arousal and efficacy of the mother in reducing arousal. It should be possible, therefore, to manipulate the strength or duration of filial attachment by altering maternal characteristics, as Harlow has done in his studies with social surrogates, or by varying infant arousal. Although this view might help to account for individual differences in social responsiveness during infancy and early childhood, it offers no explanation for the characteristic shift in social behavior away from the mother, nor for the apparent reduction in responsiveness that occurs at full maturity. Experience, particularly in the form of habituation, is undoubtedly important in this process, but it seems likely that intrinsic changes in motivational mechanisms are involved.

REFERENCES

Allesch, G. J. von (1921) Bericht über die drei ersten Lebensomate eines Schimpansen. *Sitzber. Preuss. Akad. Wiss.*, 672–685.

Berkson, G. (1963) Stimuli affecting vocalizations and basal skin resistance of neonate chimpanzees. *Percept. mot. Skills* **17**, 871–874.

Bernstein, I. S. (1962) Response to nesting materials of wild born and captive born chimpanzees. *Anim. Behav.* **10**, 1–6.

Bindra, D. (1959) *Motivation: A systematic reinterpretation.* New York: Ronald.

Bridger, W. H. (1962) Ethological concepts and human development. *Recent Adv. Biol. Psychiat.* **4**, 95–107.

Duffy, E. (1951) The concept of energy mobilization. *Psychol. Rev.* **58**, 30–40.

Falk, J. L. (1958) The grooming behavior of the chimpanzee as a reinforcer. *J. exp. anal. Behav.* **1**, 83–85.

Harlow, H. F. (1961) The development of affectional patterns in infant monkeys. In B. M. Foss (Ed.), *Determinants of infant behaviour.* New York: Wiley. Pp. 75–97.

Hebb, D. O. (1955) Drives and the C.N.S. (conceptual nervous system). *Psychol. Rev.* **62**, 243–254.

McCulloch, T. L. (1939) The role of clasping activity in adaptive behavior of the infant chimpanzee: III. The mechanism of reinforcement. *J. Psychol.* **7**, 305–316.

Malmo, R. B. (1959) Activation: A neuropsychological dimension. *Psychol. Rev.* **66**, 367–386.

Mason, W. A. (1965) Determinants of social behavior in young chimpanzees. In A. M. Schrier, H. F. Harlow, & F. Stollnitz (Eds.), *Behavior of Nonhuman Primates,* Vol. II. New York: Academic Press. Pp. 335–364.

Mason, W. A., & Berkson, G. (1962) Conditions influencing vocal responsiveness of infant chimpanzees. *Science* **137**, 127–128.

Mason, W. A., Hollis, J. H., & Sharpe, L. G. (1962) Differential responses of chimpanzees to social stimulation. *J. comp. physiol. Psychol.* **55**, 1105–1110.

Mason, W. A., Saxon, S. V., & Sharpe, L. G. (1963) Preferential responses of young chimpanzees to food and social rewards. *Psychol. Rec.* **13**, 341–345.

Menzel, E. W., Jr. (1964) Patterns of responsiveness in chimpanzees reared through infancy under conditions of environmental restriction. *Psychol. Forsch.* **27**, 337–365.

Miles, W. R. (1963) Chimpanzee behavior: removal of foreign body from companion's eye. *Science* **140**, 383.

Nowlis, V. (1941) Companionship preference and dominance in the social interaction of young chimpanzees. *Comp. Psychol. Monogr.* **17**, 1–57.

Rosenblum, L. A., & Harlow, H. F. (1963) Approach-avoidance conflict in the mother-surrogate situation. *Psychol. Rep.* **12**, 83–85.

Schneirla, T. C. (1959) An evolutionary and developmental theory of biphasic processes underlying approach and withdrawal. In M. R. Jones (Ed.), *Nebraska symposium on motivation.* Lincoln: Univer. Nebraska Press.

Shock, N. W. (1951) Gerontology (later maturity). *Ann. Rev. Psychol.* **2**, 353–370.

Yerkes, R. M. (1943) *Chimpanzees: A laboratory colony.* New Haven: Yale.

6

Concepts of Ethology and Their Significance in the Study of Human Behavior

IRENÄUS EIBL-EIBESFELDT

Max-Planck-Institut für Verhaltensphysiologie,
Seewiesen

STUDIES in ethology have led to the important insight that phylogenetic adaptations determine to a great extent and in various ways the behavior of even the highest vertebrates. The motor aspect of these adaptations occur as innate skills. A number of movements develop in every individual of a given species in the same way, even if he is deprived of the opportunity to learn the patterns by trial and error, imitation, or other means. The movements are constant in form but show variation according to intensity; they develop by the decoding of genetically stored information: a process similar to that by which organs develop their adaptive form and function. For that reason they are called *Erbkoordinationen*. The English term "fixed action patterns" refers to the constancy in form. Furthermore, phylogenetic adaptations are found on the receptor side, first in the capacities of the sense organs and second in the animal's ability to react with specific behavior patterns to only some of the perceived stimuli. These unconditioned stimuli are often configurative and highly specific, and because they unlock a behavior pattern, so to speak, they are termed key stimuli. We have to assume specific arousal mechanisms within the animal, for animals not only react to impinging stimuli but also demonstrate spontaneous behavior. Finally, we find phylogenetic adaptations in the form of specific learning dispositions. Special mechanisms evolve to ensure that an animal will learn the right thing at the right time.

Ethologists have used deprivation experiments to distinguish phylogenetic adaptations from adaptive modifications in behavior. The value of such experiments has been much discussed. It has been argued that one can never deprive an animal of all environmental stimulation and, therefore, the animal may learn from this source. The answer to such criticism is that it is not necessary to deprive an animal of all environmental stimuli. The behavior patterns in question are adaptive; they "fit" certain environmental features; and in order for such adaptiveness to occur, information on the environmental features to which the behavior is adapted must be fed into the organism during either phylogeny or ontogeny. Whether the information was fed in during the first or latter period can be checked. We only need to deprive the animal during ontogeny of the patterned information coming from those environmental features toward which the behavior pattern in question is normally adapted. If we find later, in the critical test, that the animal gives an adaptive response when first confronted with the releasing stimulus situation, then we know that the behavior patterns are phylogenetically adapted (for detailed discussion see Lorenz, 1961; 1965, and Eibl-Eibesfeldt, 1961; 1963).

EXAMPLES OF FIXED ACTION PATTERNS

Let us consider a few examples. Red squirrels (*Sciurus vulgaris*) hide nuts with a characteristic sequence of movements: (a) They carry the nut to the ground and scratch a hole with their forepaws, (b) deposit the nut in it, and (c) tamp the nut into the ground with rapid blows of the snout; (d) then they cover the nut with earth with sweeping movements of the paws, and (e) finally they pack the earth down by alternating stamping movements of the front paws. We took 18 squirrels out of the nest shortly before they opened their eyes. We deprived them of the opportunity to handle solid particles and to dig by raising them on a liquid diet in wire-mesh cages without nesting material. They were tested with nuts at the age of 2 to $2\frac{1}{2}$ months. When five of the animals were given the opportunity to hide the nuts in earth, they performed the complete sequence of the five pattern components described above. Thirteen animals were tested in a room where they had nothing to dig in. These animals nevertheless hid the nuts with the right sequence of movements, mostly in a corner of the room. Three went through the complete sequence from (a) to (e). They climbed down to the floor and after some scratching movements in the corner deposited the nut, tamped it down, and, although nothing was dug up in this case, the animals made the movements of sweeping earth over the nonexistent hole and packing it down. In the same situation, seven animals went through the movements (a) to (c) and three animals performed only movements (b) and (c). But all the animals that did not show the complete sequence of movements when trying to hide the nuts on the solid floor performed the complete sequence at once when they were exposed to earth. The only exception was one female.

In the search for hiding places the inexperienced squirrels were attracted to the base of vertical obstacles where they tried to dig and bury. This innate tendency normally brings the squirrel in the wild to bury nuts at the bases of trees and other conspicuous landmarks, thus helping the scatter-hoarder to locate the food in winter.

The experiments clearly show that the adaptive sequence of movements must be considered as a phylogenetic adaptation. The movements are fixed action patterns. Apart from these innate skills, the animals demonstrated innate knowledge of the hiding place. A closer study revealed that orientation of the covering-over movement of the nut was improved by learning. Inexperienced animals that dug a hole often performed the covering-over in the wrong place so that the nut was not covered by earth. Then the sight of the uncovered nut released covering-over again. And if the animals were hiding on solid ground and the covering movements were performed in vain, they picked the nut up again and tried to hide it in other places. They soon learned where to hide it successfully.

A great deal more learning is involved in the squirrels' developing a splitting technique for opening nuts. Adult squirrels open hazelnuts by gnawing. Some furrow from the base to the top of the nut and some furrow on the opposite side (Fig. 6-1). These furrows follow a shallow groove on the more flattened side of the nut. If one studies the normal ontogeny of the nut-opening behavior, one observes that young squirrels gnaw furrows all over the nut until the shell breaks (Fig. 6-2).

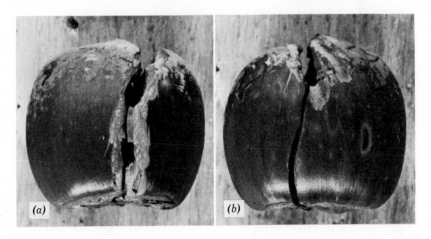

Fig. 6-1   Furrows gnawed by squirrels in hazelnuts.

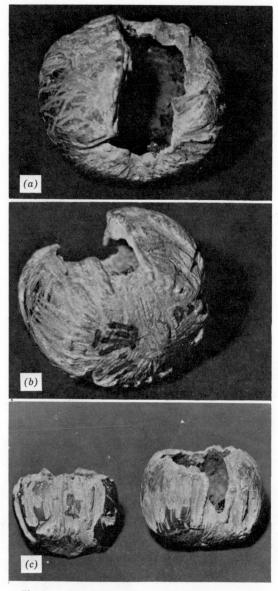

Fig. 6-2   Openings made by squirrels in hazelnuts.

In the course of ontogeny this waste of effort is reduced. The animals gnaw fewer and fewer furrows and finally concentrate for the most part on the splitting technique described earlier. This progress could be due to maturation or to learning.

To answer the question, 23 squirrels were raised under conditions of deprivation in which they had neither an opportunity to watch other squirrels opening nuts nor an opportunity to open nuts themselves. They were given their first nuts at the age of 4 to 6 months. All the animals showed a clear lack of skill in opening the nut. They were unskillful in handling them as solid objects. The nuts repeatedly slid out of their paws and fell to the ground. But all were interested in the nuts and opened them after gnawing numerous superfluous furrows. Some finally opened the nut by gnawing a hole at the top, others by gnawing at the base. Five animals discovered the splitting technique on the first trial and maintained it on subsequent trials. Most of the other animals learned the technique after they had opened seven to 20 hazelnuts. They took 15 to 20 minutes at the beginning to open a nut but took only 2 or 3 minutes once they developed the efficient splitting technique. Two animals that had gnawed a hole at the base of the nut on the first trial stuck to this technique for a longer time but gradually improved by gnawing fewer and fewer superfluous furrows. One finally developed the splitting technique, but the other animal continued to gnaw holes at the base of the nut. It did so, however, in the most efficient way by gnawing only a few short furrows approximately at right angles to each other and breaking off a piece of the shell (Figs. 6-3 and 6-4).

It is clear from these experiments that squirrels have to learn the technique for opening nuts. They are equipped with the movements of gnawing and splitting. From the very beginning they insert the lower incisors in the nut in attempts to split it, but they must discover through trial and error how to place the furrows. That most of the

Fig. 6-3   Holes gnawed by squirrels in hazelnuts.

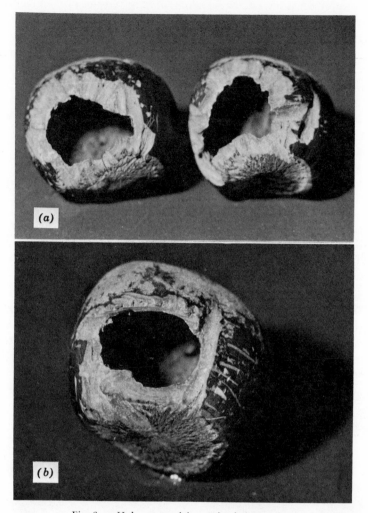

Fig. 6-4 Holes gnawed by squirrels in hazelnuts.

animals finally adopt the same technique is explained in part by the nut's structure. The fibers of the shell run parallel to each other from the base to the top of the nut. It is easier for the squirrel to gnaw in line with them. Furthermore, it is easier to gnaw on the flat side where the teeth get a good grip in the shallow groove. Thus learning is channeled in a specific direction.

The squirrel's interest in nutlike objects is inborn; gnawing and splitting are fixed action patterns that are coordinated by learning into a functional whole. One would suppose that the learning process is rewarded by the nut within the shell. But this is only part of the story. It is indeed true that the nut acts as a reward. If one presents a squirrel with both empty and full nuts he will learn to discriminate between the two and finally will reject the empty nut without opening it. If, however, one presents nuts that have been previously emptied and glued together again to animals that have never seen or opened hazelnuts before, many of the animals will gnaw them open, will continue to do so, and finally will learn an efficient cracking technique. We tested 11 squirrels with empty nuts; five learned well and opened the empty nuts, three opened only the first few nuts and later on only occasionally opened one, but they too learned the splitting technique. Three did not open the empty nuts. A closer study of the rewarding mechanism is in progress, but it seems that the performance of cracking is rewarding enough in most instances to promote the learning of the opening technique. With the additional reward of the content of the nut, however, the squirrels perform better.

We have studied the interaction between innate and acquired patterns in a number of other mammals. Exploring the ontogenesis of nest-building in rats, it was found that the species has a number of fixed action patterns but must learn their appropriate use and appropriate sequence. In polecats it was found that simple stimuli elicit hunting behavior. Polecats have fixed action patterns for hunting behavior and for hunting and killing, but must learn the orientation of the killing bite in the neck of the prey. (For further details see Eibl-Eibesfeldt, 1963.)

A large amount of information concerning the phylogenetic adaptations in behavior has been gathered by the study of the ontogenesis of bird song. (See also Chapter 1 by Klinghammer.) Sauer (1954) isolated whitethroats (*Sylvia communis*) and raised them in soundproof chambers. Nevertheless, they developed all their 25 species-specific calls and the three typical songs. Konishi (1963) deafened young chicks immediately after hatching. They, too, developed all the species-specific calls. Juncos (*Junco oregonus a. J. phaeonotus*) raised in isolation in soundproof chambers developed all the species songs, provided they were not deafened and could hear themselves (Konishi, 1964). Chaffinches raised in isolation develop a song of a certain length and with a certain number of syllables. They must learn the characteristic pattern of the three phrases in the song. They demonstrate, however, an innate knowledge of what to imitate, since they pick the species song for imitation when presented with a choice between different songs (Thorpe, 1954). The last example is of special interest since it shows that the phylogenetic adaptation is given in two ways: First, the birds are in possession of the crude song pattern, and second, they demonstrate an innate knowledge of the species song.

RELEASING STIMULI AND INNATE KNOWLEDGE

Such innate knowledge has been demonstrated in a great number of experiments. A newly metamorphosed frog or toad is equipped not only with the motor pattern of prey-catching as a ready-made tool but also with a mechanism of release that is elicited by specific stimuli to which the animal does not need to become conditioned. Any small moving object automatically releases the snapping response, even in-animate objects moved by the experimenter. After snapping, the ani-mal swallows or rejects the object (depending on the palatability); a frog soon learns to discriminate between unpalatable and palatable food, sometimes on the basis of only one or two trials.

Experiments with dummies have demonstrated that animals react to very simple configurations of stimuli with an adaptive species-specific response upon the very first confrontation. The toad is equipped with a mechanism that releases the catching response only when he sees a small moving object, such as small prey, but not when he sees pebbles, which normally do not move. Similarly, the pike responds with prey-catching behavior to moving objects that are sil-very and shining. The fisherman evokes this blind response with lures.

Lack (1943) has shown that the aggressive behavior of the male red robin is released immediately when the animal sees a red-breasted male bird. If he is presented with a stuffed male from which the red feathers have been removed, the bird does not react. If he is con-fronted with a stuffed robin with red feathers, the bird gives a full response. The red feathers are the releasing object. Similarly, the blue-throat reacts to blue feathers with aggressive behavior (Peiponen, 1960). During the mating season, the male three-spined stickleback develops a brilliant red belly that serves as a signal for other males. They attack even a very crude wax model as long as it has a red under-side (Tinbergen, 1951).

We must assume some afferent apparatus that allows the passage of the motor impulses only following the reception of specific stimuli to explain the occurrence of such specific responsiveness. This afferent mechanism is known as the "Innate Releasing Mechanism" (IRM); the stimuli to which this mechanism responds are called "sign stimuli."

A special group of sign stimuli is formed by those signals that release a social response, be it in a conspecific or a symbiont. The signaling patterns, which we call "social releasers," are special morphological structures and/or movements (expression movements). In such cases the signal-sending apparatus and IRM have developed in mutual interplay, each adapting to the other. The evolution of social releasers has been reconstructed in numerous instances by comparative studies, beginning with Lorenz' (1941) classical work on ducks. Dummy experiments revealed that the releasing stimuli often have configurative properties. Also, one reaction is often released by several different stimuli. The stimuli can substitute for each other but their releasing quality is increased if they are presented together (Seitz, 1940; Tinbergen, 1951). Furthermore, dummies can be made to function as supernormal code objects to release better responses than the natural object, which, of course, has an influence on the further evolution of signaling structures. Some birds prefer larger eggs than their own (Koehler, 1954; Koehler & Zagarus, 1937), and some butterflies give better responses to a color different from their own wing color and to a flickering frequency more rapid than the normal wing-beat (Magnus, 1954).

Often the releasing stimuli are of an unspecific nature. Young ducklings or geese show an inborn following reaction that is released by rhythmical sounds and by moving objects of a wide variety. The young duckling follows a moving box on wheels as well as its mother or a human caretaker. Once it has followed an object, however, it learns its specific properties and stays attached to it. The releasing stimulus situation thus becomes highly specific through learning. This attachment takes place only in a short sensitive period after hatching and has been proven to be irreversible. Once the duckling is fixated on an object, it prefers it in every choice situation (Hess, 1959). This special type of learning was originally discovered by Lorenz (1935) and termed "imprinting." Lorenz found that a reaction could be imprinted on an object in a critical period in which the reaction was not yet matured. Jackdaw nestlings raised in isolation by man but left with other members of the species once they were able to fly, returned to man and courted him in preference to members of their own species. Such sexual imprinting has recently been demonstrated by Schein (1963) and Schutz (1965). Imprinting must be considered as a special innate learning disposition.

SPONTANEITY

In his discussions with the reflexologist school of behaviorists, Lorenz (1937) emphasized that not all behavior is a response to impinging stimuli. There is often an observed spontaneity that can be explained only by postulating special inbuilt motivating mechanisms. Lorenz pointed out that animals actively seek releasing stimulus situations that allow certain types of behavior to be performed, a fact that has been demonstrated in the brain stimulation experiments of v. Holst and v. Saint Paul (1961). Furthermore, an animal deprived of the opportunity to perform a certain activity is more and more inclined to perform it, as shown at first by an increasing responsiveness to external stimuli and then by a reacting to less and less specific and intense stimuli so that finally the behavior pattern can even run off "in vacuum." Lorenz's starling, which was well fed but had no opportunity to catch insects, from time to time went through the complete pattern of fly-catching without the presence of any visible releasing stimulus. The starling would suddenly fly up, snap at something invisible, return to the perch, perform the killing movement, and finally swallow.

On the other hand, after repeated performance the phenomena associated with fatigue can be observed. The pattern becomes more difficult to release. This difficulty is not the result of physical fatigue, however, for the animal may readily perform another activity; neither can this effect always be explained on the basis of adaptation of sense organs or of the releasing mechanism.

Ploog (1964) reported on his studies of sucking babies. Two groups of babies were fed by bottle. In one group the nipple had a large opening, in the other, a small opening. Those fed with the bottles that had a large opening finished the bottle in a very short time. Afterward they proved restless and started to cry if one withdrew the nipple. In order to satisfy them, they had to be allowed to suck the empty bottle for about 10 more minutes. The other group performed more sucking movements as they drank the same amount or even less over a longer period, and did not start to cry when the empty bottle was withdrawn; they were even "satiated" with a smaller amount of food.

Certainly appetitive behavior depends in many instances on internal stimuli, as studies of hunger and thirst have shown. Receptors in the hypothalamus respond to osmotic pressure, and receptors in the stomach respond to fullness. But even here it can be shown that performance of the drinking pattern itself has a short-term satiating effect. A dog with an esophageal fistula, through which the drinking water runs out, drinks only for a certain time and then stops (Bellows, 1939; Towbin, 1939). In a number of instances, as in the example of the fly-catching starling, the specific responsiveness cannot be explained as a result of internal stimulation. Neurophysiological evidence, especially the studies of v. Holst (1935; 1936) and Roeder (1955; 1963), show that behavior is based on spontaneous activity of the central nervous system. Impulses are created within the nervous system for a number of activities. Continuous peripheral discharge is prevented by a special mechanism that controls the discharge to the musculature. This seems to lead to a damming up of energy. The phenomenon of spinal contrast is proof of such events, although the nature of this process has not yet been explored.

Spontaneous activity of the central nervous system is at least in some cases responsible for the spontaneity of a fixed action pattern. This was nicely demonstrated by v. Holst who found that a completely deafferentiated spinal preparation of an eel performed well-coordinated swimming movements that, when uninhibited, continued until the death of the preparation. A chain-reflex theory of locomotion cannot explain such a finding. Other examples clearly demonstrate that a coordinated movement pattern may be both centrally coordinated and spontaneous. One example is the phenomenon of damming up that is demonstrated in a spinal sea horse. The intact animal normally sits between seaweed, anchored by its tail with its dorsal fin completely folded. When the animal swims, it releases the grip of its tail and proceeds by undulating movements of its dorsal fin. A spinal preparation keeps the dorsal fin half erect. If this preparation is pressed with two fingers in the region of the gills, the fin folds completely. Released, however, the fin becomes, for a short time, more erect than before. If the preparation is held longer, the fin, after release of the grip, becomes completely erect and starts to beat in undulating motion. To explain this observation we assume that central nervous system production of excitation activates the fin movement. The excitation, however, is not strong enough to let the movement occur uninhibited, as is the case in a spinal preparation of an eel or most other fish. The constant excitation results in only a half-erection of the fin. In the intact animal, this constant outflow is inhibited when the animal rests, and a similar reflexive inhibition occurs when one presses the spinal preparation. During the time of reflexive inhibition, excitation is dammed up; on release, the swimming pattern occurs.

PLAY

Comparative studies have shown that behavior is organized along the same lines in all vertebrate groups. There are some significant differences, however. In lower vertebrates long chains of fixed action patterns often can be observed that result in comparatively little freedom for adaptive modification. In mammals only relatively small units of behavior occur as fixed action patterns and, through learning, become integrated into new functional patterns. Greater individual adaptability is the result. In ascending the ladder of evolution we observe a clear tendency for the fixed action patterns to be broken down to smaller and smaller units of behavior. Learning plays an increasingly important role and, as a consequence, mammals have developed a special type of behavior known as play behavior.

It has been repeatedly argued that play is just immature behavior that occurs during the process of maturation. Indeed, we do observe immature behavior patterns in play, but this is not its characteristic feature. In spite of the great diversity found in the expression of play behavior, there are some common characteristics. Let us first consider the phenomenology of play. Several categories can be observed: for example, hunting play in carnivorous animals, fighting play, flight play in which all sorts of locomotion are tried out and repeated (including invented patterns), and finally playful experimenting in which objects are investigated and handled without any recognizable purpose. What have all these categories of play in common?

In observing play-fighting in dogs and comparing such behavior with actual fighting we see one important difference immediately that is an aspect of play. The playing animals, although performing fixed action patterns that occur in actual fighting, demonstrate a different motivational background. The playing dogs show a strong inhibition to bite each other and their tails waggle, which is a gesture of the friendly readiness for contact. The animals may chase each other, but again it is not serious, for the pursuer and the pursued change roles frequently. Then, too, in the middle of a play-fight one animal may turn to a completely different sort of play when something else arouses its interest. Furthermore, play may even combine behavior patterns of functional cycles that normally operate in mutual exclusion; for example, hunting, fighting, and sexual behavior. Also, the phenomenon of specific fatigue does not occur in play. The same behavior pattern can be repeated over and over again, until bodily fatigue sets in. Play is free of the emotional tension that is normally shown by an animal striving toward a goal. This observation permits the interpretation that in play the behavior patterns are not activated by those arousal mechanisms that normally motivate them. The possible argument that play might simply be immature behavior does not hold, at least when adult animals play. Here the differences, for example, between play-fighting and serious fighting can be observed in the same animal in a most dramatic way. We could postulate that differences between play and nonplay are simply differences in intensity and that both are motivated from the same source. Observations show, however, that play-fighting can occur with great intensity and still show all the friendly attributes, such as tail-waggling and biting inhibition; a serious encounter, even on the lowest intensity, looks completely different.

Detachment of the normal arousing mechanisms permits fixed action patterns (e.g., fighting) to be used by the animal for experimentation; the trying out of new combinations allows it to learn the measure of its own abilities. Play is activated by strong motor drives and exploratory drives (curiosity). The existence of an exploratory drive has been experimentally demonstrated (e.g., Butler, 1953). During play an animal may even invent new motor patterns. The author's tame badger accidentally learned to somersault so well that it finally rolled down slopes for no other obvious reason than that of an exploratory drive. It also learned to skid on a sloping icy road. The ability to invent new motor patterns was for a long time supposed to be a gift of man. In children we regularly observe this form of play (walking on the heels, somersaults, etc.), but the same phenomenon can be seen in other higher mammals.

All the described play behavior involves experimentation with the organisms's own body and abilities, or experimental interaction with another species member. In principle, such play is not different from experimental play with objects, and we may consider play as an experimental dialogue with the environment, motivated by curiosity and a strong motor drive. It is a peculiarity of the higher mammals that fixed action patterns are made available to the animal to allow for this interaction. A special mechanism allows for their activation independent of the system that normally activates them. This detachment constitutes the situation that Bally (1945) calls *entspanntes Feld* (tensionless field) and he points to the fact that such a situation is a prerequisite to the occurrence of higher types of learning. In addition, special inhibitory mechanisms have developed for social play (biting inhibition) and sometimes even special expressive movements act as an invitation for play—in short, playing rules. On the basis of these mechanisms some species can indulge in social play even as adults; others only as juveniles. An example of the latter is the European squirrel, which as an adult no longer wrestles with other squirrels but still plays with cones, sticks, and other inanimate matter.

The adaptive value of play behavior as a special training mechanism seems plausible, but what is the basis from which we draw this conclusion? Somersaults and skidding in the badger are, after all, not of much use in adult life.

In a series of experiments polecats were raised in isolation from an early age. Others lived for two months with litter mates and were isolated afterwards, that is, after they had the opportunity to play with their litter mates. Significant differences were found later in the sexual behavior of males of both groups. Both groups were interested in females in heat. Ten males that had play experience immediately grasped the female by the neck in the species-specific way and thus released her response of immobility, enabling them to copulate. Of nine early isolated animals, however, six grasped the females at the rear end, thus releasing a defensive response. All except one learned to adjust after several trials.

In observing play behavior, we find that polecats grasp each other by the neck during play fights. Whenever this occurs, the grasped playmate is immobilized. This experience is essential for the normal development of sexual behavior. It is also of use in another context. Polecats with play experience that were deprived of the experience of killing prey learned to kill much faster than polecats isolated from an early age (Eibl-Eibesfeldt, 1963).

The disturbances in sexual behavior that Harlow (1962) described for monkeys raised on dummy mothers are probably caused by the lack of some earlier play experience.

Only very few nonmammals play. I know only of one good example:

Fig. 6-5 The use of a tool by the woodpecker finch.

the use of tools for play by the woodpecker finch (*Cactospiza pallida*) of the Galapagos Islands. The animal normally uses sticks and thorns to probe out insects from their retreats (Fig. 6-5) (Eibl-Eibesfeldt & Sielmann, 1962). A pair of birds that I kept indulged in this activity playfully. After having been fed to satiation, they hid the remaining food, mealworms, in cracks and holes, and then poked them out with a stick, not to eat, but to hide them again, and so forth. Both stood opposite each other at a crack passing right through a log and poked a mealworm back and forth. Later, I obtained a young male that had been caught as a very young fledgling. This animal was interested in sticks and also poked and probed around when it was satiated. When it was hungry, however, and discovered an insect in a crack or hole, it immediately threw the stick away and tried to seize the prey directly with its beak, often without success. It finally learned during play the appropriate use of the stick as a probing tool.

Summarizing, we can state that phylogenetic adaptations control behavior in the form of fixed action patterns, innate releasing mechanisms, several types of innate learning dispositions, and in the form of internal motivating mechanisms. A clear trend toward an increasingly adaptive modifiability of the individual can be observed.

HUMAN APPLICATIONS

These discoveries are of the greatest importance for every student of human behavior. Physiologists have drawn upon all the consequences of the natural relation between animals and man, and no one worries when, for example, he uses hormones of animal origin to cure a human ailment. In the study of human behavior phylogenetic concepts are also accepted but tend to be taken as curious facts that have little meaning for the student of human behavior. Because man is able to learn so much and culture shapes his personality to such an extent, many persons are inclined to believe that the human brain is actually made for learning, a *tabula rasa* at birth, and that environment alone shapes behavior.

It is not difficult to demonstrate in principle that this viewpoint is incorrect. The newborn is equipped with fixed action patterns. Sucking is an innate response released by certain stimuli; and the presence of a spontaneous seeking mechanism has been demonstrated by Prechtl and Schleidt (1950). Crying and smiling appear to be innate behavior patterns (Freedman, 1965). The smiling response occurs first quasi-spontaneously after the baby has drunk to satiation (Koehler, 1954);

later it occurs as a response to someone bending over the baby, even to crude dummies, and it is finally given as a friendly response only to known persons (Ahrens, 1953; Spitz, 1946; Ambrose, 1960; 1961).

Clasping reflexes, as well as rudimentary swimming and climbing movements, are easily observed. The basic pattern of walking has been shown to be a fixed motor pattern (Peiper, 1953). These types of behavior are all quite easy to demonstrate, for the patterns can be released and observed in the newborn. Difficulty arises, however, when we want to ascertain which of our adult patterns are inherited and which are environmentally induced. Because we can never raise a human being in a situation of deprivation, we cannot obtain the direct experimental answer to this question. We have to rely on chance experiments and on the method of comparative observation.

We know, for example, that children born blind still show the smiling response and other basic expressive movements (Goodenough, 1932; Freedman, 1964; 1965). Children born deaf start, like normal children, to babble at a certain age. The deaf children later stop doing so, for it seems that auditory feedback is needed for further development of babbling. However, we can conclude that the drive to use the motor coordination given for speech is inborn. This is confirmed by a few chance experiments. Jesperson (1925) described the case of two highly neglected Danish children who grew up with a deaf grandmother. The children spoke with each other in a language of their own that bore not the slightest resemblance to Danish. They had invented it, probably on the basis of an inherited learning disposition and some given motor coordinations.

Lorenz (1943) described a number of human behavior patterns (e.g., the threat posture) that seem to be an old inheritance. Chimps show rather similar patterns. They fluff their fur in threat, whereas man (since he has lost his fur) exhibits only shivering that is caused by a homologous contraction of the *erectores pilorum*. Both man and chimp exhibit a similar hunching of the shoulders in rage. Darwin (1872) mentioned teeth-showing in rage as an example of an ancient inherited behavior pattern. Lorenz also drew attention to the fact that man reacts spontaneously to quite crude dummies in a way similar to that shown by animals. For example, if we examine the characteristics that make an object appear "cute," we find that they can be traced to characteristic features of a baby: short, rounded extremities, small large-eyed face with—in comparison with the adult face—a much larger frontal region dominating the face. A special signal-sending structure is the *corporum adiposum buccae*. If we look at the animals or dolls that we find cute, we realize that all these objects have at least some of the characteristics just mentioned. These characteristics are especially true of pets kept by elderly ladies. There are indications that certain facial expressions are, in a similar way, signaling structures to which an innate releasing mechanism has been adapted, since again quite crude dummies release our adequate reaction.

Furthermore, it may well be that phylogenetic adaptations in the form of special training mechanisms determine our learning quite rigidly. Psychoanalysis has brought to our attention the existence of critical phases in our development in which we learn certain behavior patterns that manifest themselves in later life and prove quite rigidly fixed. One critical phase occurs around the age of 5. At this age boys and girls learn their future sexual roles. Boys show a stronger attachment to their mothers (oedipal phase) and at the same time identify with their fathers. But if the father is not a good model and/or if the mother repulses the son's approaches, the boy may not adopt the right sexual role. The resistence of homosexuals to therapy, and the occurrence of a critical phase long before sexual maturity in which the object fixation takes place, reminds one of the phenomenon of imprinting. Similarly, other social attitudes, such as group identification, which are undoubtedly learned, become so fixed that the individual cannot easily readjust to new groups. There seems to be a critical phase around puberty in which certain social values are fixed.

Our social reactions may well be less controlled by reason than we believe. They may be more strongly determined by our phylogenetic adaptation and consequently may have emotional concommitants. How could we otherwise explain the fact that we have failed, up till now, to solve our many social problems, such as the class problem or that of how to live with a neighbor, whereas, on the other hand, we have solved the most extraordinary technical problems, including flight to the moon. Lorenz (1964) actually took this paradox as a proof that man, in his social reactions, reacts in a programmed way, whereas in his intellectual reactions he is free. Man often becomes strongly emotionally involved when he approaches social problems, and we know that problem-solving is handicapped by such strong emotions. A dog will not make a single detour around a fence if a piece of meat is presented immediately in front of him. If the meat is placed farther back, tension is reduced and the dog finds the solution. Similarly, Köhler's chimpanzee Sultan failed to discover that he could make a longer stick by putting two sticks together until he left the task. As long as the chimpanzee tried to get to the banana just out of reach, he did not find the solution. When he relaxed and started to play with the sticks, he hit upon the solution and immediately returned to the task. Strong emotional tensions govern our social relations to an increasing degree and, since we are not fully aware of the tensions and their consequences, we fail to step back and detach ourselves—a prerequisite for finding an intellectual solution. Insight into the mechanisms that govern our behavior may help. We know much too little about the extent and ways in which phylogenetic adaptations control our behavior. In gathering needed information, the ethological approach will add to the traditional methods of psychology.

REFERENCES

Ambrose, J. A. (1960) The smiling and related responses in early human infancy: an experimental and theoretical study of their cause and significance. Unpublished doctoral dissertation, Univer. London.

Ambrose, J. A. (1961) The development of the smiling response in early infancy. In B. M. Foss (Ed.), *Determinants of Infant Behaviour*. London: Methuen. Pp. 179–196.

Ahrens, R. (1953) Beitrag zur Entwicklung des Physiognomie-und Mimikerkennens. *Zeitschr. exper. angew. Psychol.* **2**, 413–454, 599–633.

Bally, G. (1945) *Vom Ursprung und von den Grenzen der Freiheiteeine Deutung des Spieles bei Tier und Mensch.* Basel: Birkhauser.

Bellows, R. T. (1939) Time factors in water drinking in dogs. *Am. J. Physiol.* **125**, 87–97.

Butler, R. A. (1953) Discrimination learning by Rhesus monkeys to visual exploration motivation. *J. comp. physiol. Psychol.* **46**, 95–98.

Darwin, C. (1872) *The expression of the emotions in man and animals.* London: John Murray.

Eibl-Eibesfeldt, I. (1957) Die Ausdrucksformen der Säugetiere. *Handbuch der zoologie* **8**, 1–26.

Eibl-Eibesfeldt, I. (1961) The interactions of an unlearned behavior pattern and learning in mammals. In J. F. Delafresnaye (Ed.), *Brain mechanisms and learning.* London: Blackwell. Pp. 53–73.

Eibl-Eibesfeldt, I. (1963) Angeborenes und Erworbenes in Verhalten einiger Säuger. *Z. Tierpsychol.* **20**, 705–754.

Eibl-Eibesfeldt, I., & Sielmann, H. (1962) Beobachtungen am Spechtfinken Cactospiza pallida (Sclater & Salvin). *J. Ornithol.* **103**, 92–101

Fabricius, E. (1951) Zur Ethologie junger Anatiden. *Acta Zool. Fennica.* **68**, 1–178.

Freedman, D. G. (1964) Smiling in blind infants and the issue of innate vs. acquired. *J. Child Psychol. Psychiatr.* **5**, 171–184.

Freedman, D. G. (1965) Hereditary control of early social behavior. In B. M. Foss (Ed.), *Determinants of Infant Behavior,* III. London: Methuen.

Goodenough, F. L. (1932) Expressions of the emotions in a blind-deaf child. *J. abnorm. soc. Psychol.* **27**, 328–333.

Harlow, H. F., & Harlow, M. K. (1962) Social deprivation in monkeys. *Scient. Amer.* **207**, 137–146.

Hediger, H. (1961) The evolution of territorial behavior. In S. L. Washburn (Ed.), *Social life of early man.* Chicago: Aldine. Pp. 34–57.

Hess, E. H. (1959) Imprinting, an effect of early experience. *Science* **130**, 133–141.

Holst, E. v. (1935) Uber den Prozess der zentralnervössen Koordination. *Pflüg. Arch. ges. Physiol.* **236**, 149–158.

Holst, E. v. (1936) Versuche zur Theorie der relativen Koordination. *Pflüg. Arch. ges. Physiol.* **237**, 93–121.

Holst, E. v., & Saint Paul, U. v. (1960) Vom Wirkungsgefuge der Triebe. *Die Naturwiss.* **18**, 409–422.

Jespersen, O. (1925) *Die Sprache.* Heidelberg.

Koehler, O. (1954) Das Lachelm al angeborene Ausdrucksbewegung. *Z. meuschl. Verebu. Konst. Lehre.* **32**, 330–334.

Koehler, O., & Zagarus, A. (1937) Beiträge zum Brutverhalten des Halsbandregeupfeifers. *Beitr. Fortpfl-Biol. Vögel* **13**, 1–9.

Konishi, M. (1963) The role of auditory feedback in the vocal behavior in the domestic fowl. *Z. Tierpsychol.* **20**, 349–367.

Konishi, M. (1964) Effects of deafening on song development in two species of Juncos. *Condor* **66**, 85–102.

Lack, D. (1953) *The Life of the Robin* (rev. ed.). London: Penquin Books.

Lorenz, K. (1935) Der Kumpan in der Umwelt des Vogels. *J. Ornith.* **83**, 289–413.

Lorenz, K. (1937) Über die Bildung des Instinktbagriffes. *Naturwiss.* **25**, 289–300.

Lorenz, K. (1941) Vergleichende Bewegungsstudien an Anatiden. *J. Ornith.* **89**, 194–294.

Lorenz, K. (1943) Die angeborenen Formen möglicher Erfahrung. *Z. Tierpsychol.* **5**, 235–409.

Lorenz, K. (1961) Phylogenetische Anpassung und adaptive modifikation des Verhaltens. *Z. Tierpsychol.* **18**, 139–187.

Lorenz, K. (1964) *Das soganannte Böse.* Wien: Borotha-Schoeler.

Lorenz, K. (1965) *Evolution and modification of behavior.* Chicago: Univer. Chicago Press.

Magnus, D. (1954) Zum Problem der "überoptimalen" Schlüsselreise. *Verh. Dtsch. Zool. ges. Tübingen,* 317–325.

Peiper, A. (1953) Schreit-und Steigbewegungen beim Neugeborenen. *Arch. Kinderh.* **147**, 135.

Peiponen, V. A. (1960) Verhaltensstudien am Blaukehlehen. *Ornis Fenn.* **37**, 69–83.

Ploog, D. (1964) Verhaltensforschung und Psychiatrie. In H. W. Gruhle & R. Jung u. Coop. (Eds.), *Psychiatrie der Gegenwart.* Berlin: Springer. Pp. 1, 1B, 291–433.

Prechtl, H. F. R., & Schleidt, W. (1950) Auslösende und steuernde Mechanismen des Saugaktes. *Z. vgl. Physiol.* **33**, 53–62.

Roeder, K. D. (1955) Spontaneous activity and behavior. *Sci. Mon. Wash.* **80**, 362–370.

Roeder, K. D. (1963) *Nerve Cells and Insect Behavior.* Cambridge: Harvard Univer. Press.

Schein, W. M. (1963) On the irreversibility of imprinting. *Z. Tierpsychol.* **20**, 462–467.

Schutz, F. (1963) Uber geschlechtliche Objekfixierung sexueller Rekationen bei Enten im Zusammenhang mit dem Prachtkleid des Mannchens. *Verh. Dtsch. Zool. ges. München* 282–287.

Schutz, F. (1965) Sexuelle Pragung bei Anatiden. *Z. Tierpsychol.* **22**, 50–103.

Seitz, A. (1940) Die Paarbildung bei einigen Zichliden, II. *Z. Tierpsychol.* **5**, 74–101.

Spitz, R. A. (1946) The smiling response: a contribution to the ontogenesis of social relations. *Genet. Psychol. Monogr.* **34**, 57–125.

Thorpe, W. H. (1954) The process of song learning in the chaffinch as studied by means of the sound spectograph. *Nature.* **173,** 465.

Tinbergen, N. (1951) *The study of instinct.* Oxford: Clarendon.

Towbin, E. J. (1949) Gastric distension as a factor in the satiation of thirst in esophagostomized dogs. *Am. J. Physiol.* **159,** 533-541.

Wichler, W. (1964) Signälfalschung, natürliche Attrappa und Mimikry. *Umschau* **64,** 581-585.

7

Sucking and Looking: Two Organized Congenital Patterns of Behavior in the Human Newborn

WILLIAM KESSEN
Yale University

THERE are many sources of the renewed interest of American psychologists in the newborn child. The continuing traditions of Pavlovian work with infants in the Soviet Union and Eastern Europe (Brackbill, 1960; Papoušek, 1966), Piaget's observations and commentary on the infant (Piaget, 1951; 1952; 1954), Peiper's monumental work on newborn neurology (Peiper, 1961), the work of the new theorists of instinct (Schiller, 1957; Hess, 1962)—all played their part in forcing the attention of American child psychologists again to the first months of life. Once begun, research on problems of infancy has flourished; there are so many questions to be asked about the infant and so little reliable information that the most industrious and skillful investigators can hardly keep pace with the ambiguities of the infant.

The theoretical reasons for studying the newborn have been hidden somewhat because there were so many facts to find out and so many difficulties in the way of finding them that the larger reasons for studying the young infant have occasionally been lost among the raw empirical and technical difficulties that consumed our interest. To be sure, it has been possible to recognize that some investigators were in the tradition of the associationists and gave special attention to conditioning, learning, and discriminative behavior. There were other

The research reported in this paper was supported in large measure by USPHS Research Grant HD-0890 (formerly MH-1787), and in part by Fluid Funds of Yale University School of Medicine, and by a grant from the Carnegie Corporation of New York. Anne-Marie Leutzendorff has been my colleague in research and my guide for more than a decade; S. J. Onesti, J. P. Williams, E. J. Williams, J. Beck, L. S. Hendry, B. J. McGrade, M. Hershenson, A. J. Sameroff, H. Munsinger, D. K. Collins, M. M. Haith, and P. Salapatek have also been influential in the conduct of the research reported here. Almost all our observations of newborn infants were made in Yale-New Haven Hospital; M. J. E. Senn and L. Gluck have made research in the hospital possible and pleasant.

students of infants who could be seen to be in the tradition of the apriorists with a particular interest in biological goals and the fixed structures of behavior. But many intellectual events of recent years have demonstrated that the division of the world of infancy studies into naturist and nurturist is at best misleading and often dogmatic and trivial. There is little doubt that the dichotomy reflects variation in training, interest, and techniques among students of infancy, but willy-nilly we have all become interactionists or eclectics or neutrals. Such theoretical generosity is a certain gain over fruitless contention —fruitless often because the contestants spoke from different positions toward different problems—but it is time to examine the variation that exists among our several interactionist theories. What does the baby come with? Responses, skills, reflexes, cognitions, schemata, . . . ? What is the world of the baby? Stimuli, impressions, objects, variability, information, . . . ? How does change take place in early infancy? Reinforcement, habituation, adaptation, differentiation, maturation, . . . ?

Although the effort is known to be premature and incorrect, let me begin my report of the research on newborn infants at Yale by listing in outline some of the presuppositions that guided our research. The notions are neither complete nor novel—the voice of Piaget is still in them—but a naked statement of them may illustrate that the Age of Uniform Eclecticism among students of infancy is of uncertain stability.

The study of the newborn infant starts with the study of organized patterns of behavior. However peculiar the posturings and movements of the young infant may be, they represent our only handle on his world. Certainly we cannot depend on the categories of adult human thought to structure our study of the newborn infant and, more damaging to a quick solution of the problems of infancy, it may be unwise for us to apply the categories of contemporary psychological analysis to the study of newborns. Because we have had available elegant and systematic descriptions of the environment—the common world of objects encased in the common language and the physicist's metrical analysis of intensity and extension—we have rarely come to grips with the question of what constitutes the effective environment of the immature organism. At the very least, it is not obvious that the newborn infant, whether human or animal, divides the manifold of experience in the way characteristic of the adult layman or the adult physicist. What then shall we take as our first definition of the infant's environment? One way out of this seeming trap may be a more intense concentration on organized congenital patterns of behavior.

"Organized congenital patterns of behavior" is a difficult notion and one uncongenial to most psychologists. "Congenital" is easy enough—the word is used to indicate that the behavior under study is present at birth without prejudging the issue of whether or not the behavior is largely under the control of genetic determinants. Far more difficulty surrounds "organized patterns of behavior." The widespread acceptance by psychologists of linear theories (chiefly S - r - s - R) left speculation about the *organization* or structure of behavior to psychologists who were outside the main course of psychological analysis in the years between Watson and Hull (e.g., Katona, 1940; Piaget, *passim;* Werner, 1948; and Wertheimer, 1945). Over the last decade professional distaste for theoretical statements about organization in human behavior has diminished somewhat, and a cluster of papers and books has appeared as commentaries on the themes of structure and organization (e.g., Garner, 1962; Mandler, 1962; Miller, 1956; Munsinger & Kessen, 1966). The revival has not produced a worked-out theory of psychology; rather it has provided a language suitable for the discussion of some very old and often neglected problems in psychology. When I use the words to talk about infants, "organized pattern of behavior" covers examples of behavior that are loosely bound together by several shared characteristics. The behavior cannot be fully understood by reference to the surround defined by adults (i.e., some share of variance in the behavior probably has to be assigned to the child), the behavior can be given some temporal or spatial placement (e.g., newborn looking and sucking can be reliably described in metrics of space and time), and the behavior appears to be important in the life of the child—in another phrase, the behavior has ecological validity. Of course, our systematic aim is to relate organized infantile behavior to changes in the environment—ultimately, to establish measures of cognitive structure—but the first step in our approach is the careful description of infantile behavior that is present at birth, somehow structured, and important.

The problem of organized patterns of behavior has also appeared in attempts to understand the starting place of systematic science. Mandler and Kessen (1959) argued that the vocabulary of science must begin with behavioral regularity—what they called "response invariance"—and their words are relevant to our understanding of the newborn.

We must start with some term; some language must be available to describe the process of response invariance. Historically, this problem has been solved by assuming some stimuli, i.e., response invariances, which then form the basis for further statements. Another possibility is to use some class of presumably invariant terms to investigate a second class, which, once established as fulfilling the invariant requirement, can then be used to test the first and other classes of statements. (p. 61ff.)

Even more dramatically than in the language of science, the language of the newborn can be related to the objects of the layman's world or to the dimensions of the physicists. But to assume that we can impose on the world of the newborn the categories that are familiar to us will be to miss the most interesting problems of early development. To be sure, we impose our prejudice when we begin with regularities in behavior—after all, they are regularities only within the definition of our culture and our current science—but the possibility of error is reduced to its lowest value.

Our concentration at Yale on organized congenital patterns of behavior, then, was derived from considerations of method and of epistemology, but not from them alone. The importance of organized patterns of behavior for an understanding of man has been recognized by psychologists for almost a century. Lotze's discussion of local signs, the motor consciousness theories of Munsterberg and Holt, the circular reaction of Baldwin, even the excesses of Watson's laryngeal theory of speech—all represent attempts to find the beginnings of man's ultimate complexity in the simplicities of his early action. More recently, the organized pattern of behavior as a prototype for psychology has been discussed in quite varying terms by Piaget (1952), Sheffield (1966), and the ethologists (e.g., Tinbergen, 1951). The research on newborn infants at Yale has clearly been influenced by these discussions. Moreover, from work in other laboratories and from our own, a set of leading ideas begins to emerge. Let me state them in a quasi-axiomatic form in order to expose both their strengths and their weaknesses.

1. *The infant constructs his environment.* Piaget has spent 40 years elaborating the constructionist theme. The adult's structure of his environment is neither the product of social reinforcement nor is it given in a priori cell-blocks that need only to mature. Rather, the growing child constructs the adult categories of knowledge (e.g., space, object, number) out of a complex (and largely unknown) exchange between what he can do at any particular moment and the problems posed by phenomena. Adult reality is the last of a long series of theories of reality that the child develops, modifies, and sometimes rejects. Piaget maintains that such epistemic change (the construction of reality) is the result of encounters between organized patterns of behavior (schemata) and events unassimilable to them. If he is on the right track in proposing that we begin our invention of the world with the primitive schemata of sucking, looking, grasping, and hearing, then the in-

vestigation of organized congenital patterns of behavior becomes far more than a taxonomic exercise. The infant's first theory of reality is contained in congenital response organization; moreover, a constructionist theory of human knowledge demands that connections be established between these first patterns and the child's later theories of reality. It is important to discover how the newborn orders environmental variability in the first place; it is no less important to discover how the initial rules of order are transformed.

An implication of the postulation of the constructive child is the postulation of the active child. Theorists of every persuasion now admit the active child (cf., Bowlby, 1958 and Gewirtz, 1961), but it was no small theoretical advance to see the child as the source of behavior as well as a reactor to stimulation.

2. *The occurrence of organized patterns of behavior is important for behavior change.* Psychologists as theoretically divergent as Piaget (1952), Premack (1965), and Sheffield (1966) have argued for the importance in learning of the occurrence of a highly organized response. In prototypical statement, the event that ends a behavioral sequence and fixes (reinforces) it is a highly organized consummatory act. Thus an animal is said to learn something about the events that lead toward food not because of the reinforcing quality of food but because the food provokes the consummatory act of chewing and swallowing, a highly organized pattern of behavior. We can be confident that such a principle will not serve to comprehend all instances of behavior change, but it makes admirable sense in helping us to understand the rapidity and regularity of early change of behavior in infants.

3. *The occurrence of organized patterns of behavior will inhibit infant distress and the interruption of organized patterns of behavior will produce a state of arousal and emotion.* Mandler and I discussed the first part of this proposition some years ago in a treatment of anxiety (Kessen & Mandler, 1961), and Mandler has recently made an extended statement on the consequences of the interruption of organized behavior (Mandler, 1965). Even on superficial examination, it is clear that the occurrence of certain congenitally organized patterns of behavior (chiefly sucking) will quiet the distressed infant; it is also apparent that the interruption of an ongoing organized pattern of behavior will produce observable signs of emotional arousal in older infants. It remains to be seen whether these common observations provide a key to a better understanding of the development of human emotion.

These, then, are the leading ideas that have guided our research on organized congenital patterns of behavior in the human infant. You will see shortly that the presuppositions far outrun the data. The great bulk of our research on newborn infants over the last several years has been devoted to the examination of two response systems—sucking and looking. Further, the center of the research has been the detailed *description* of sucking and looking; the study of the later forms of these response systems in perception and knowledge, as well as the investigation of the role of organized infantile responses in behavior change, have been postponed by the problems of developing adequate measures and occasions for sensitive observation. We are in effect just at the edge of understanding the place of sucking and looking in the infant's construction of reality.

PROCEDURE AND MEASUREMENT

Typically, our observations of infants in their first several days of life were conducted under one of four procedures. The babies were seen in a small room in the Maternity Service of Yale-New Haven Hospital during the hour before feeding. Thus our subjects were normally alert and awake. A floor nurse brought the infant, dressed in diaper and shirt, to our observation room where he was observed under one of the four procedures. Our observations varied in total duration, but, by and large, the child was not seen for periods longer than one half-hour at a time. At the end of an observation, the floor nurse returned the baby to his nursery crib. Although we observed some babies being cared for exclusively by their mothers in a "rooming-in" plan, the vast majority of our subjects were babies on a somewhat less flexible (10-2-6) schedule of feeding. The subjects were from $1\frac{1}{2}$ hours to 12 days of age, but the vast majority of our observations in the hospital were made on children between 24 and 96 hours of age.

Let me describe briefly the four procedures we used in observing infants and then go on to discuss a few problems of measurement.

1. *The relation of sucking and movement.* Babies were placed on their backs on a foam-rubber mat; no restriction was imposed on their movement. They were photographed, usually at the rate of one frame per second, by a 35-mm motion-picture camera directly overhead. During observations of sucking, the babies were given a blind hospital nipple that either rides on the observer's finger or is attached by polyethylene tubing to a strain-gauge and then on to 1 channel of a Grass polygraph. On occasion, records of heart rate were made during the

studies of sucking and movement through another channel of the polygraph.

2. *Suctioning and expression.* For a more detailed study of the components of the sucking response (Sameroff, 1965) the baby was observed wrapped lightly in his blanket and, to date, not photographed. A specially designed nipple was used to monitor components of sucking and to regulate the delivery of milk to the baby.

3. *Visual preference.* Under this procedure, described in some detail by Hershenson (1964), the baby, wrapped rather tightly in his blanket and with his head and hips held steady by padded supports, was presented with two panels perpendicular to his line of sight and placed approximately 20 degrees of visual angle apart. Infrared marker lights were placed on these panels and the reflection of the lights in the infant's eyes were photographed by a 35-mm camera placed optically between the two panels.

4. *Ocular orientation.* In more detailed studies of the infant's ocular orientation, he was wrapped in his blanket, placed in the padded cradle used by Hershenson, and his head placed so that a picture filling a 35-mm motion-picture frame could be made of a single eye. The stimulus used in studies of detailed ocular orientation was a black triangle on a white field; the camera that photographed the infant's eyes

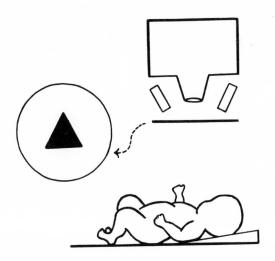

Fig. 7-1 Schematic representation of the apparatus used in determining ocular orientation.

while he looked at the triangle was placed directly behind the triangle. Figure 7-1 presents a schematic drawing of this observational setting.

As every student of the newborn infant knows, the most taxing problem of research in this area is adequate measurement. Because it will be a long time before standard measurements of the infant's behavior are established, diversity will continue to exist from one laboratory to another. Concentration at Yale has been on the measurement of the displacement of arms and legs (i.e., an index of movement), ocular orientation, and the components of sucking. Our measures of visual preference are adapted from those devised by Fantz (1963); over-all measures of sucking and measures of heart rate have been derived from the readouts of a Grass Model 5 polygraph. Reports of the measurement devices and scoring techniques peculiar to Yale have recently been described (Haith, 1966). A brief sketch is given here to define the notions of infant movement, ocular orientation, and components of sucking that are used in the discussion of results from our laboratory.

1. *The measure of movement.* Determination of the infant's movement is based on photography of his position as it changes from one moment to another. In most cases we have measured the displacement that takes place in one plane of the infant's hands and feet over an interval of five seconds. At first, the film was scored by making hand tracings of the projected film image and measuring by ruler the displacements that occur from one film frame to another (Kessen, Hendry, & Leutzendorff, 1961). Two far more efficient procedures are currently used to score film: A Vanguard Motion Analyzer permits the setting of crosshairs and the visual readoff of horizontal and vertical coordinates for any position of the baby's limbs. These coordinates are punched onto IBM cards and put through a simple computer program to determine the hypotenuse that represents the shift of position of limbs from one film frame to another. A more nearly automatic device has recently been invented by Haith (1966) in which the film is projected against a matrix of wires representing 14,400 coordinate positions. The scorer of film need only touch the wires that lie on the part of the projected film image he wishes to measure; electronic circuitry then automatically punches up cards representing the coordinate position touched. These cards are put through the simple computer program required to read out displacements of position over time. The metric we have used for movement is centimeters per limb per five-second interval.

There are several characteristics of the measure that deserve attention. Its chief limitation is the fact that it represents movement only in the plane parallel to the plane of the film; we have fantasies of a stereoscopic device or a multicamera arrangement that will permit us to get more information about the child's motility. In pursuit of optimal precision, however, we have found the present measure sensitive enough and the needed alterations complex enough to keep our fantasies as such. There are three advantages to the method. The measure of movement is a parametric one and can be used in different laboratories without special equipment. The measure also permits as refined an analysis of movement over time as one may demand. We have found intervals of 5 seconds between measured film frames to be adequate for most of our research needs, but there have been occasions when measures of film frames separated only by one second provided further information about the phenomena under study. Of course, one may make measurements over as brief an interval as the highest speed of the camera used will permit. A last advantage of this procedure prized by us is that it preserves an analogue record of the child. The more automatic we can get in our processing of data from infants, the better; but in the present exploratory nature of the field, we find it valuable to be able to go back to the original record and see not merely wiggles or numbers but the photographs of the baby. For example, we are now making a frame-to-frame analysis of the baby's response to the approach and departure of the nipple, a *post hoc* study that can be made only be examining the analogue record of the baby.

2. *Measures of ocular orientation.* Measurement of where the baby looks is made in fundamentally the same way as the measurement of his limb position. Photographs of his eye are projected either in the Vanguard Motion Analyzer or against the Haith matrix. Measurements are made of infrared corneal reflections that mark the positions of a stimulus figure. The distances of these marker reflections from the center of the infant's pupil are the raw data of our studies of ocular orientation.

3. *Measures of the components of sucking.* Sameroff (1965) has made use of the fact that the baby both laps a nipple (the expression component) and creates negative pressure in his mouth by increasing the size of the buccal cavity (the suction component) to devise a nipple that permits independent measurement of these two components of sucking. Figure 7-2 presents a schematic drawing of this nipple. Not only are expression and suctioning measured separately but it is possible to link the baby's response to a milk-delivery apparatus so

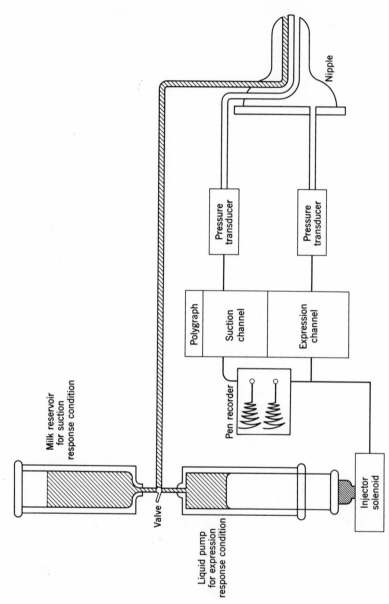

Fig. 7-2 Experimental nipple and nutrient delivery system.

that the delivery of milk can be made contingent on which component of the sucking response the baby makes and on the intensity of the response. Frequency and amplitude of the components of sucking are measured from the Grass polygraphic readout.

OBSERVATIONS ON SUCKING

There can be no doubt that the tendency of the child to suck when presented with a suckable object is present at birth. Man would not survive as a species for a single generation if we had to teach our children to suck. In the light of the earlier discussion of sucking as an inhibitor of distress with its implications for mechanisms of behavior change, we were concerned with studying the behavioral effects of sucking and the development of the relation between sucking and other behavior. Specifically, we investigated in some detail the relation between sucking and movement. The results of correlated studies of the relations among movement, sucking, and heart rate are not reported here.

It is easy enough to show that the moderately active 3- or 4-day-old infant will quiet when sucking (Kessen & Leutzendorff, 1963). It is more interesting to ask whether or not such a fixed relation between movement and sucking exists before postnatal feeding, to ask how the ingestion of food affects the relation between movement and sucking, and to study the development of this behavioral linkage over the first days of life. We expected that the relation between movement and sucking would be shown to be present at birth or shortly thereafter. Further, we expected to show that the effects of the nipple were, in part at least, independent of the state of privation. That is, even if the general level of activity was lowered by feeding, we hoped to find that the nipple would still exert a quieting effect on the fed baby, acting somewhat like a constant multiplier on initial level of activity. We made no specific prediction about the quieting effects of the first feeding, but we were attentive to this issue because of our interest in knowing how sensitive the child is to variations in privation.

Infants were seen on the first, second, and third days of life (Kessen, Leutzendorff, & Stoutsenberger, in press). The observations were made on the first day of life prior to the child's first postnatal feeding and typically occurred at about 12 hours of age. Immediately after feeding on all three days the child was brought back to the laboratory for further observations. Children were stimulated, in a counterbalanced fashion, by both a blind nipple placed in the infant's mouth

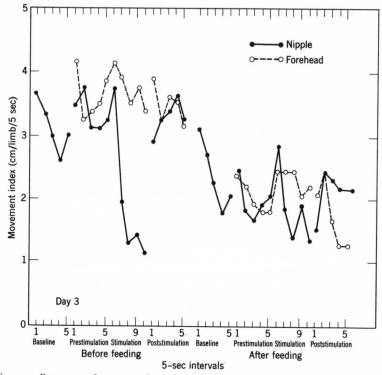

Fig. 7-3 Response of 30 normal newborn infants to nipple and forehead stimulation in the third day of life.

and by light stroking of the forehead. Figure 7-3 shows the effect on movement of these stimulations both before and after feeding on the third day of life for 30 infants. These results replicated our earlier findings and represent rather well the behavior of infants on the second and fourth day of life when presented with a nipple. It should be noted that by day 3, feeding resulted in a general lowering of the infant's activity almost immediately—another reason for the survival of man. Disappointing to us was the finding that sucking does not seem to operate as a constant multiplier on initial level of activity, reducing the low levels of postfeeding movement even further. After the fact, this disappointing outcome is less surprising. In a group of children just fed, there are some who hardly move at all. Presentation of even so benign a stimulus as the nipple will *initially* increase the child's movement. To assess the constant-multiplier hypothesis about the relation between sucking and movement, it would be necessary to segregate babies on initial level of activity before and after feeding.

It is to the data from the first day of life that we must turn for an answer to the question of the congenitality of the relation between movement and sucking. If the data from 30 babies seen before the first postnatal feeding are examined all together, a significant effect of the nipple in reducing movement can be shown. Moreover, there was a significant reduction in movement immediately after the first postnatal feeding. These combined data tend to assure us that the relation between sucking and movement is present before first feeding, to be sure, but they hide an even more interesting difference among the babies observed. Figures 7-4 and 7-5 present this divergence between good suckers and poor suckers. During the observation, and independently of the scoring of movement, a judgment was made by the observer of how effective each child was in sucking on the nipple. On the basis of these observations, the sample of 30 children was divided in half, effective suckers in one group, the poor suckers or refusers of the nipple in the other. Not surprisingly, the poor suckers showed relatively little effect of the nipple whereas the good suckers showed a dramatic reduction in activity when the nipple was inserted in their mouths. Two other characteristics of these curves are less obvious. The good suckers were more active *initially* than the poor

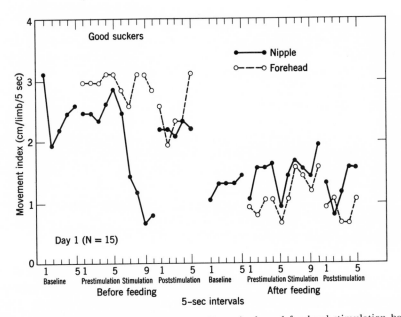

Fig. 7-4 Response of infants who suck well to nipple and forehead stimulation before and after the *first* postnatal feeding.

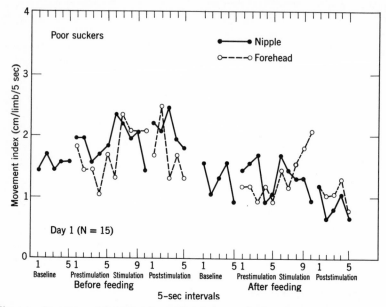

Fig. 7-5 Response of infants who suck poorly to nipple and forehead stimulation before and after the *first* postnatal feeding.

suckers and there was a greater difference between activity before feeding and activity after feeding in the group of effective suckers. These observations, taken together with the high competence of sucking, suggest that the good suckers are more mature or further developed than the poor suckers. However, the separation into levels of sucking effectiveness is not significantly related to sex, birth weight, parity, or any other simple variation from child to child that could be detected in the hospital records. It is worth noting in passing, too, that the level of movement of the good suckers while sucking was below that of the poor suckers; therefore the change in the behavior of the good suckers cannot be accounted for as a regression effect.

We concluded, then, that the relation between sucking and movement is congenital, that there is a congenital effect of feeding on activity, and that the "developmental" change in the sucking-movement relation shown over the first few days of life represents chiefly an increase in the number of children who show sudden quieting while sucking.

There are two other observations that bear on the question of the primitivity and organization of sucking in the human newborn. A

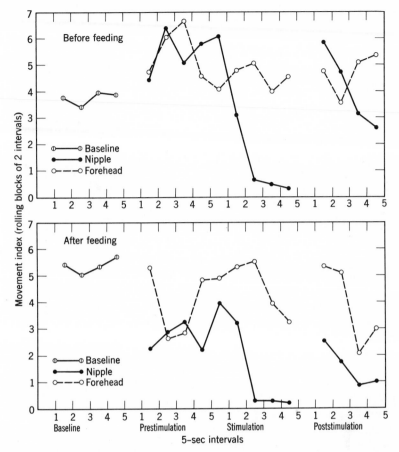

Fig. 7-6   Response of an hydrocephalous infant to nipple and forehead stimulation.

hydranencephalous child born by Caesarian section was observed in our apparatus at the age of 13 days. Transillumination of the skull of this infant indicated the presence only of brain stem. As can be seen in Fig. 7-6, his behavior under standard observation was very much like that of the normal newborn infant. Not only is the relation between sucking and movement organized congenitally; it may be organized at subcortical levels.

The regularity of the sucking-movement relation is also seen in a study of interruption. It was expected that the newborn infant would show differential frustration or arousal (and, incidentally, give us some leads on his management of time) if we interrupted his feeding

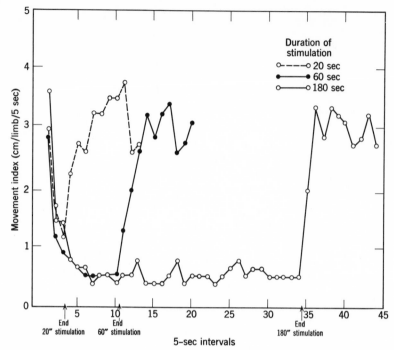

Fig. 7-7 The movement of 24 newborn infants during and after sucking of three durations.

after different durations of access to the nipple. We permitted newborn infants to suck for 20, 60, and 180 seconds before removing the nipple from their mouths. It was expected that the level of movement would be higher after interruption of long sucking than after interruption of short sucking; this "bounce-back" effect was our intended measure of differential frustration. Figure 7-7 shows the results of a within-subjects study of 24 newborn infants. The expectation of differential post-interruption levels of movement was not confirmed. There seemed to be some tendency for the infants to return to baseline levels of movement faster after interruption of long sucking than after interruption of short sucking; we are currently making a second-by-second analysis of the child's behavior immediately after the nipple was removed in order to assess the significance of this differential rate of change. Quite apart from the failure of our hopes of showing a frustration effect, these curves are interesting in demonstrating in yet another way the remarkable regularity of the effect of sucking on newborn movement. It is hardly an exaggeration to say that the infants have an on-level of movement—when the nipple is present—and an off-level of movement—when it is not. It will be interesting to see whether these characteristic levels of movement hold for single children from occasion to occasion and whether such individual variation has implication for other aspects of the child's behavior.

The work recorded in the foregoing paragraphs suggests that the sucking response of the human infant is indeed a highly stable pattern of behavior. Our interest recently has been drawn to what may be called the decomposition of the sucking response into its component patterns. As was noted earlier, sucking can be analyzed experimentally into two components: expression and suctioning. Sameroff (1965) arranged his omnibus nipple so that the child is provided with milk if he suctions, but no specific contingency is arranged for expression. Correspondingly, he arranged the nipple so that delivery of milk is contingent on expression, but no contingency exists for suctioning. Moreover, Sameroff also studied the behavior of infants when two different levels of expression pressure were required (i.e., when varying thresholds for delivery of milk were set) and when two different levels of suctioning pressure were required. He made observations on two successive feeding periods for each child, typically in the third or fourth day of life.

If no contingency is imposed on the child's feeding, there is typically

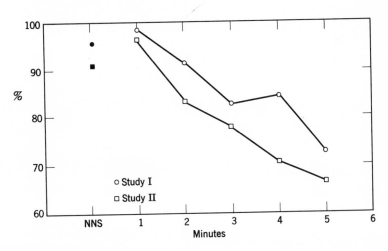

Fig. 7-8 The ratio of the suction component to the expression component over time in the expression-response condition for Study I and Study II. NNS: non-nutritive minute.

one expression movement for each suction movement; there seems to be, in the ordinary course of matters, no senior partner in this combine. This observation bears on the contention that either expression or suctioning is the more fundamental component of sucking. When a feeding contingency is introduced, however, the one-to-one relation between suctioning and expression changes. If the baby is given milk each time he expresses, in a few minutes some suctioning begins to drop out so that the ratio between suction and expression decreases over a feeding. Figure 7-8 shows the change in the suction-expression ratio over five-minute feeding periods for two studies. (There were 10 newborn infants in each study.) On the other hand, if the babies are fed each time they make a suction response, the relation between expression and suction does not break down; that is, the child given milk for suctioning does not drop the expression component of the act. This is not to say that the expression component of the sucking response is inflexible. On the contrary, measurements of expression amplitude indicate that the child is responsive to different settings of threshold of expression pressure required to obtain milk. Such responsiveness has been shown in several ways but most clearly in a condition in which the child was required to work at two different

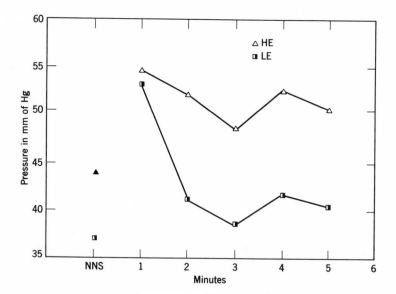

Fig. 7-9   The expression amplitude of sucking responses during an observation of feeding for infants in the high expression condition (HE) and the low expression condition (LE). NNS: nonnutritive minute.

levels of expression pressure in order to obtain milk. Figure 7-9 shows the results of a study of the child's response to two levels of required expression pressure. Within two minutes the child had adapted the amplitude of his expression response to conform to the pressure demanded by the milk-delivery system. You will remember that the children were seen twice—at a 2 A.M. feeding and the following 6 A.M. feeding. The design of the threshold study was a within-subject's balanced crossover so that all children were seen under both conditions. A detailed analysis showed that there was no interaction between threshold condition, minutes, and first or second feeding; that is, there was no carryover from the first feeding to the second. The children behaved in response to threshold at the second feeding almost exactly as they did in response to threshold at the first feeding. Thus, within the limitations of Sameroff's study, there is strong evidence of adaptation or habituation of a component of a sucking response but no evidence of persistent changes in behavior. Sameroff (1965) recently found quite parallel results when the baby was asked to respond to two thresholds of suctioning pressure. There was adaptation to the demands of the current sucking situation but no carryover from one feeding to another.

This ready adaptation of the human newborn has obvious biological utility, and again we may be happy in the name of mothers. With these data in hand, one may propose a series of questions about expression and suctioning. What do these components look like before the first feeding? How does the relation between the components change over the first days of life, particularly in children who are fed exclusively by breast or by bottle? How many "trials" of expression-contingent milk delivery or of suction-contingent milk delivery are required to produce persistent changes in the baby's behavior? Are there stable individual differences in suctioning and expression, and are these differences related to other aspects of the child's development? The decomposition of newborn sucking into two of its components has complicated our task of understanding this pattern of behavior but, perhaps paradoxically, the components appear to be more docile to experimental manipulation than does the sucking-quieting relation. The implication of the two-component analysis of sucking for some of the guiding ideas is clear. If one of the components can be organized well by control of feeding contingencies while the other remains unmodified (even though it may be generally effective in obtaining milk), we would predict greater effectiveness of the experientially organized response in inhibiting distress and in functioning as a "reinforcer" than of the less well-organized response. In order to carry out studies of this sort, it will be necessary to have available a group of infants who can be studied for the first weeks or even the first months of life.

OBSERVATIONS ON LOOKING

We have begun to see the way in which the world is constructed by the infant's sucking. We are closer to firm knowledge about the ways of construction in studies of the infant's looking, in large measure because of the provocation of Fantz's observations and because of concurrent developments in perceptual theory and in perceptual research with adults and animal subjects. As a matter of fact we now have enough studies of visual preference in the young infant for the original simplicities to be lost and for us to be faced with contradictions that require a deeper look at our preconceptions and a more precise experimental procedure. Using Hershenson's photographic modifications of Fantz's procedure for studying visual preferences in infants (Hershenson, 1964), researchers at Yale found three dimensions on which there is significant systematic variation in the direction of newborn regard. Hershenson found a transitive relation among three

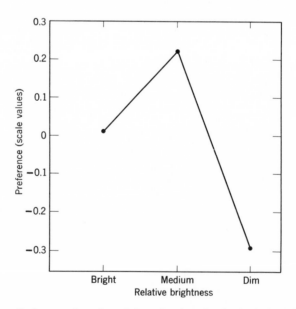

Fig. 7-10   Preference of newborn infants for three levels of relative brightness.

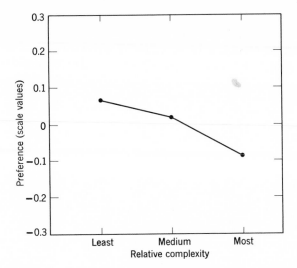

Fig. 7-11   Preference of newborn infants for three levels of relative complexity (checkerboards).

levels of brightness; a panel of intermediate brightness was preferred to a panel of high brightness which, in turn, was preferred to a panel of relatively low brightness. Weaker and therefore more ambiguous relations were found by Hershenson in what he called "complexity" with a simple checkerboard eliciting more visual regard in newborns

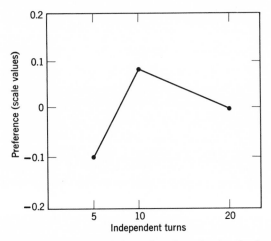

Fig. 7-12   Preference of newborn infants for three levels of stimulus variability (random shapes).

than a complex checkerboard, and by Hershenson, Munsinger and Kessen (1965) with random shapes of 10 independent turns drawing more visual regard than random shapes of five and 20 turns. These results are shown in Fig. 7-10, 7-11, and 7-12. They are not fully congruent with the findings of other investigators, and I want to discuss them only in prologue to a more recent study and to illustrate two rather general points about the study of infant orientation.

The first point, of lesser consequence, is that it is not wise to read too much into the use of the term "preference" in studies of infant orientation. Although the motivational implications of the term are almost irresistible, the word and the associated techniques of analysis are borrowed from psychophysics, and "preference" entails no more than the systematic expression of a behavioral difference. The second and more consequential point has been made earlier and is closely related to the use of the behavioral regularity of the infant as a definer of his environment (Kessen & Hershenson, 1963): We must be very careful indeed that we do not assume that the infant is responding to the dimensions that are responded to by an adult merely because those are the ones that we present to him. It is necessary, at the very least, that we demonstrate an ordered transitive relation among several stimuli through a presumed dimension and, even then, the infant may be orienting toward an aspect of the stimulus that we have not detected or varied systematically. This problem is in principle no different from that of assessing the perceptual field of animals but, by and large, studies of infant perception have not been as carefully controlled as the best studies of animal perception.

Our new ability to make somewhat precise statements about the visual world of the newborn infant brings with it the desire to make yet more precise statements about his world. We will probably be able to untangle conflicting statements in the literature only by knowing not only the general direction of the infant's ocular orientation but also specifically how he responds to a single figure. For example, it may be that newborn infants orient toward a black-white contour of a particular length and particular contrast, or that they orient toward figures that provide a fixed number of contour interruptions per unit time, or that they do in fact orient toward a preferred figure as a whole, as some theories and some theorists maintain. We began our more detailed studies of ocular orientation in an attempt to resolve some of these discrepancies and also to mount an empirical analysis of the constructionist position. Does the child show systematic change over the first days of life in the way in which he orients toward a plane geometrical figure, and can these changes, if found, be understood as the progressive organization of the child's looking behavior? Do not be surprised to learn that we have not answered this question, but we believe that we have developed a procedure that permits a continuation of the interrogation.

Under the procedure for studying ocular orientation described earlier, 10 newborn infants were presented with a large black triangle on a white field (Salapatek & Kessen, 1966). The triangle was 8 in. on each side and approximately 9 inches away from the child's eyes. Both eyes were open, but only one was photographed. Infrared marker lights placed behind the triangle permitted the determination of the precise orientation of the center of the infant's pupil. Each subject saw the triangle in two orientations, base down and base up, for a period of time that permitted 100 frames of film to be taken with the infant's photographed eye open. Figure 7-14 presents the results from these 10 infants. In order to be certain that the infrared marker lights, though invisible to adults, did not exert some attractive influence on children, 10 more subjects were run with the infrared lights in essentially the same positions in the field (i.e., forming a triangle) but without any visible triangle in the infant's field of view. The infants were presented with a homogeneous black field. Figure 7-13 presents records of ocular orientation for 10 infants in which no true triangle was presented but in which the infrared lights formed a hypothetical triangle the same size as the true one presented to the experimental group. An examination and comparison of Fig. 7-13 and 7-14 will indicate what a more detailed statistical analysis shows. The experimental subjects—those presented with a triangle—showed more concentrated orientation. The variance among positions of ocular orientation in the experimental group was very much less than the variance of positions of ocular orientation in the control group. Moreover, the direction of ocular orientation in the experimental group was clearly toward the vertices of the triangle. In a comparative analysis of ocular orientation toward vertices and toward sides of the triangle, it was found that the vertices captured significantly more ocular orientation in the experimental group than in the control group but that no significant difference existed between experimental and control subjects for orientations toward linear components of the triangle. These findings, of course, give great comfort to constructionists; they even suggest that Hebb's speculations (Hebb, 1949) may not be far off the mark. What remains to be done, and we are busily at it, is to study the development of ocular orientation toward a triangle over the first few days of life with the appropriate control observations to separate out the effects of maturation (typical experience) and the

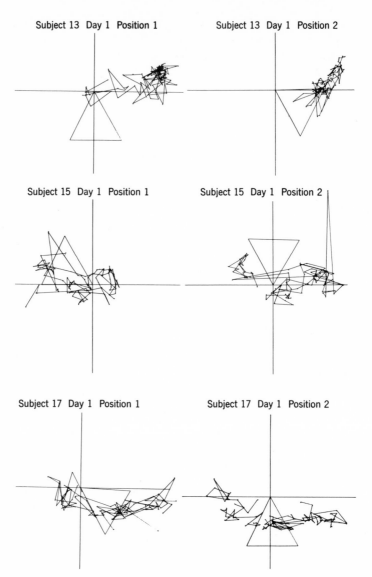

Fig. 7-13 Records of ocular orientation for *Ss* in the control group. The triangle on each record is a *hypothetical* one metrically equivalent (eight in. on each side) to the triangle presented to the experimental *Ss*. See text for full explanation.

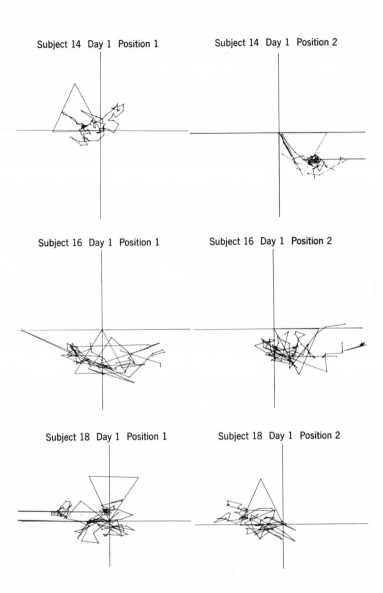

Subject 14 Day 1 Position 1

Subject 14 Day 1 Position 2

Subject 16 Day 1 Position 1

Subject 16 Day 1 Position 2

Subject 18 Day 1 Position 1

Subject 18 Day 1 Position 2

Fig. 7–13 (*continued*)

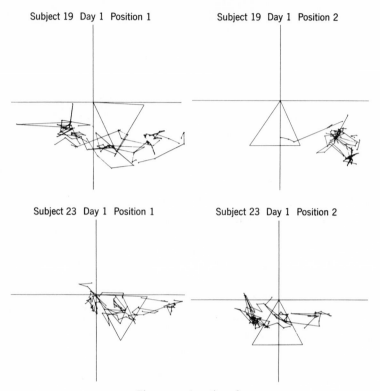

Subject 19 Day 1 Position 1   Subject 19 Day 1 Position 2

Subject 23 Day 1 Position 1   Subject 23 Day 1 Position 2

Fig. 7-13   (*continued*)

effects of specific experience. It is our conviction, however, that the triangle is far too complicated a figure for analysis of detailed ocular orientation. The children may be orienting toward an optimal number of contours, they may be orienting toward areas of optimal brightness, or they may be orienting specifically toward angles. The next order of business is to examine the looking of newborn infants when presented with a simple single contour in the field. In this way we will learn something about preference for the dark or light side of contours, something about the ability of children to maintain a contour orientation, and, by sudden displacement of the contour from one part of the field to another, we will learn more about the child's behavior of search and scanning.

As in the case of the sucking pattern of behavior, the weakest conclusion that we may draw is that looking is organized at birth. It

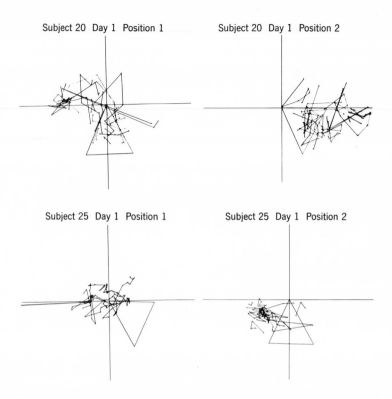

Subject 20 Day 1 Position 1

Subject 20 Day 1 Position 2

Subject 25 Day 1 Position 1

Subject 25 Day 1 Position 2

Fig. 7-13   (*continued*)

is now time to turn to a more detailed analysis of how this pattern of behavior changes with aging and specific experience of the environment. The data are certainly not inconsistent with the leading idea that the child organizes his environment through organized patterns of behavior.

It is worth saying once again that the view of the child as actively constructing his environment out of the encounters of organized responses with stimulus variability is not seen as complete or as excluding other mechanisms for influencing the behavior of the infant. However, it is our hope to develop from our observations of sucking and looking a model for development that does not depend exclusively for mechanisms of change on the repair of physiological deficit and its secondary overlay or on the good will of others that we call "social reinforcement."

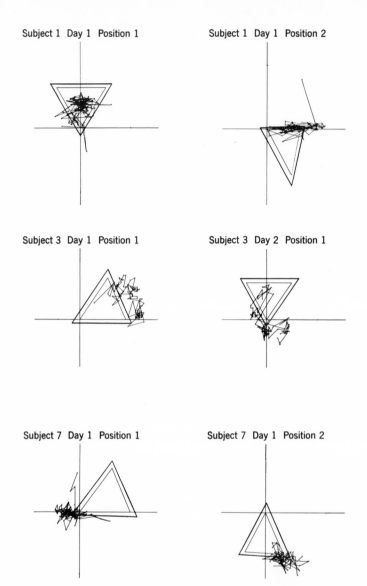

Fig. 7-14   Records of ocular orientation for Ss in the experimental group. The outer triangle on each record represents the outline of the solid, black, equilateral triangle, eight in. to a side, presented to the experimental Ss. See text for full explanation.

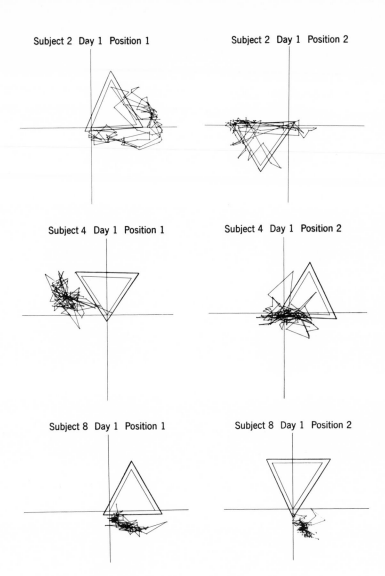

Fig. 7-14   *(continued)*

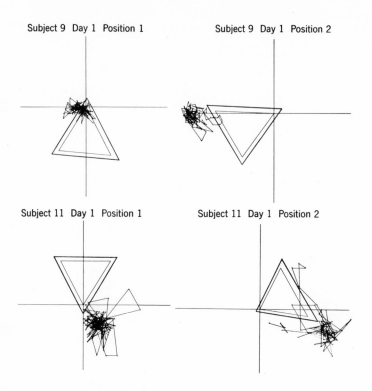

Subject 9 Day 1 Position 1

Subject 9 Day 1 Position 2

Subject 11 Day 1 Position 1

Subject 11 Day 1 Position 2

Fig. 7–14   (continued)

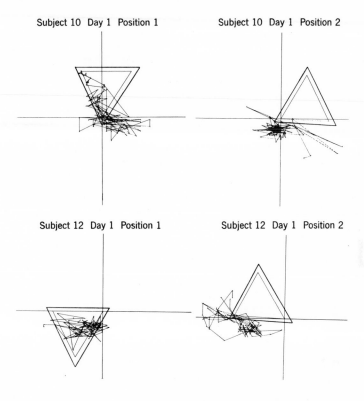

Subject 10 Day 1 Position 1

Subject 10 Day 1 Position 2

Subject 12 Day 1 Position 1

Subject 12 Day 1 Position 2

Fig. 7–14   (continued)

REFERENCES

Bowlby, J. (1958) The nature of the child's tie to his mother. *Int. J. Psychoanal.* **39,** 350–373.

Brackbill, Y. (1960) Experimental research with children in the Soviet Union: report of a visit. *Amer. Psychologist,* **15,** 226–233.

Fantz, R. L. (1963) Pattern vision in newborn infants. *Science* **140,** 296–297.

Garner, W. R. (1962) *Uncertainty and structure as psychological concepts.* New York: Wiley.

Gewirtz, J. L. (1961) A learning analysis of the effects of normal stimulation, privation and deprivation on the acquisition of social motivation and attachment. In B. M. Foss (Ed.), *Determinants of infant behavior.* New York: Wiley. Pp. 213–289.

Haith, M. M. (1966) A semi-automatic procedure for measuring changes in position. *J. exp. Child Psychol.,* **3,** 289–295.

Hebb, D. O. (1949) *The organization of behavior.* New York: Wiley.

Hershenson, M. (1964) Visual discrimination in the human newborn. *J. comp. physiol. Psychol.* **58,** 270–276.

Hershenson, M., Munsinger, H., & Kessen, W. (1965) Preference for shapes of intermediate variability in the newborn human. *Science* **147,** 630–631.

Hess, E. H. (1962) Ethology: An approach toward the complete analysis of behavior. In R. Brown, E. Galanter, E. H. Hess, & G. Mandler (Eds.), *New directions in psychology.* New York: Holt, Rinehart and Winston. Pp. 157–266.

Katona, G. (1940) *Organizing and memorizing: Studies in the psychology of learning and teaching.* New York: Columbia Univer. Press.

Kessen, W., Hendry, L. S., & Leutzendorff, A. M. (1961) Measurement of movement in the human newborn: a new technique. *Child Developm.* **32,** 95–105.

Kessen, W., & Hershenson, M. (1963) Ocular orientation in human newborn infants. Paper read at Amer. Psychol. Ass., Philadelphia.

Kessen, W., & Leutzendorff, A. M. (1963) The effect of nonnutritive sucking on movement in the human newborn. *J. comp. physiol. Psychol.* **56,** 69–72.

Kessen, W., Leutzendorff, A. M., & Stoutsenberger, K. (In press) Age, food privation, nonnutritive sucking, and movement in the human newborn. *J. comp. physiol. Psychol.*

Kessen, W., & Mandler, G. (1961) Anxiety, pain, and the inhibition of distress. *Psychol. Rev.* **68,** 396–404.

Mandler, G. (1962) From association to structure. *Psychol. Rev.* **69,** 415–427.

Mandler, G. (1965) The interruption of behavior. In Levine, D. (Ed.), *Nebraska symposium on motivation: 1964.* Lincoln: Univer. Nebraska Press.

Mandler, G., & Kessen, W. (1959) *The language of psychology.* New York: Wiley.

Miller, G. A. (1956) The magical number seven, plus or minus two: some limits on our capacity for processing information. *Psychol. Rev.* **63,** 81–97.

Munsinger, H., & Kessen, W. (1966) Stimulus variability and cognitive change. *Psychol. Rev.* **73,** 164–178.

Papoušek, H. (1966) Experimental studies of appetitional behavior in human newborns and infants. Chapter 10, 249–277.

Peiper, A. (1961) [Trans. 1963] *Cerebral function in infancy and childhood.* New York: Consultants Bureau.

Piaget, J. (1951) *Play, dreams, and imitation in childhood*. New York: Norton.

Piaget, J. (1952) *The origin of intelligence in children*. New York: Int. Univer. Press.

Piaget, J. (1954) *The construction of reality in the child*. New York: Basic Books.

Premack, D. (1965) Reinforcement theory. In Levine, D. (Ed.), *Nebraska symposium on motivation; 1965*. Lincoln: Univer. Nebraska Press.

Salapatek, P., & Kessen, W. (1966) Visual scanning of triangles in the human newborn. *J. exp. Child. Psychol.* **3**, 155–167.

Sameroff, A. J. (1965) An experimental study of the response components of sucking in the human newborn. Unpublished doctoral dissertation, Yale Univer.

Schiller, C. H. (Ed.) (1957) *Instinctive behavior*. New York: Int. Univer. Press.

Sheffield, F. D. (1966) A drive-induction theory of reinforcement. In R. N. Haber (Ed.), *Current research in motivation*. New York: Holt, Rinehart and Winston.

Tinbergen, N. (1951) *The study of instinct*. Oxford: Clarendon Press.

Werner, H. (1948) *Comparative psychology of mental development*. (2nd ed.) Chicago: Follett.

Wertheimer, M. (1945) *Productive thinking*. New York: Harper.

✑ 8 ✑

Visual Perception and Experience
in Early Infancy: A Look at the Hidden Side
of Behavior Development

ROBERT L. FANTZ

Western Reserve University

THE nativism versus empiricism controversy has had a long and eventful history. Numerous shifts have occurred from one side to the other in the prevailing thought of a time and place. Other shifts have occurred in the means used to settle the controversy. In general, the change has been from philosophy to science, from logic to data, as more and more areas of science have been opened and new techniques have been applied to the problem. Far-reaching changes came with the behavioristic revolution of the twentieth century. From this time on, the issue began to be couched in more precise terminology and attacked with more objective methods. The results have been many testable theories, numerous promising lines of inquiry, and the accumulation of a wealth of data, even though the controversy is still with us (see Fantz, 1965b; Hebb, 1949; Pratt, 1950; Taylor, 1962; Zuckerman & Rock, 1957).

A point often overlooked is that the behavioristic revolution brought to the controversy another fundamental change that extended beyond terminology and methodology. Before the twentieth century the primary issue was the *origin of knowledge* about the environment: Is this knowledge and the means for obtaining it acquired entirely through the sensory experience of the individual, or are basic kinds of knowledge built into sensory and neural structures and are thus intrinsic to perceptual processes? A secondary question was the relative

The preparation of this paper and previously unpublished studies included were supported by Public Health Service Research Grant HD-00314 from The National Institute of Child Health and Human Development, and by National Science Foundation Research Grant GB 1874.

importance of the various senses for acquiring and using knowledge. especially sight versus touch.

With the advent of behaviorism, the nativism-empiricism controversy became focused instead on the *origin of responses to the environment,* that is, on whether such responses are learned or unlearned. To an extent this change was a necessary correction to the introspective study of sensations and other mental processes apart from their behavioral context. But the tendency has been to go beyond the use of an objective response as a perceptual indicator, and to go to the study of the responses and the changes in the responses themselves, as if the perceptual events of which they are indicative have no independent reality. Thus Postman (1955) stated, "Descriptively, perceptual learning *is* the attachment of new responses, or a change in the frequency of responses, to particular configurations or sequences of stimuli." (p. 441). This tendency can affect the interpretation of studies of early development since, for example, the ability to perceive or recognize an object may develop earlier and differently than the ability to follow, grasp, or approach the object. The basing of conclusions about the development of perception entirely on the development of certain easily observable indicators of response has produced erroneous views of the perceptual capacities of the young infant, both when the missing factor was thought to be neuromotor maturation (Dennis, 1943; Gesell, 1949; McGraw, 1943) and experience and learning (e.g., Piaget, 1952; Taylor, 1962). I have argued elsewhere (Fantz, 1965b) that this confusion in the past has prevented resolution of the nativism-empiricism controversy. In this paper I will change ground somewhat and argue that this confusion has led to the perpetuation of a controversy that actually is insoluble, as usually stated, and, consequently, has obscured an important soluble issue in postnatal behavior development. Taking as the starting place whatever perceptual capacities and processes are present at birth and presumably unlearned, what is the subsequent role of learning through perceptual experience as distinct from learning through action or the consequences of action? I am proposing that the real issue is not between learned and unlearned perception, or between learned and unlearned behavior, but between two kinds of learning processes: learning as usually studied by behaviorists and learning theorists (i.e., changes in response tendencies through reinforcement or repetition); and learning as it was used by prebehavioristic empiricists and as it is still generally used outside the behavioral sciences (i.e., the acquisition of knowledge apart from specific changes in response). This issue is clarified further in the discussion.

While my understanding of this issue grew out of the research that is presented in this chapter, the research itself began as another attempt to settle the original nativism-empiricism controversy. It was based on response indicators that are present from birth and on information on perception extracted by the stimulus-preference method. This approach obviated prolonged sensory deprivation or sensory rearrangement as a means of controlling experience; it also made it unnecessary to confound the issue by using learning procedures to determine the importance of learning. The approach was inspired by the studies of ethologists and zoologists on the instinctive behavior of animals—studies that suggested considerable unlearned perceptual capacities although they were not primarily directed toward the problem of such capacities (see Chapter 6 by Eibl-Eibesfeldt; Lorenz, 1957; Thorpe, 1956; Tinbergen, 1951; Tinbergen & Perdeck, 1950). Another mainspring of the research was Hebb's (1949) theory of "primary visual learning" and the apparent support given it by studies of animals or humans reared from birth without pattern-vision experience (Beach & Jaynes, 1954; Riesen, 1961; von Senden, 1960).

FORM PERCEPTION IN NEWLY HATCHED CHICKS

Precocial birds have a high degree of motor maturity at the time of hatching and thus are good subjects in which to search for nonlearned behavior and the beginnings of learned behavior. Within several days after hatching, and independent of intervening experiences, the chick shows a wide range of relatively coordinated and adaptive responses. Prominent among them is the ability to see, peck at, and swallow small objects, which enable the chick to feed itself.

This inborn ability includes both efferent and afferent components. Motor coordination is sufficient on the day of hatching for the chick to peck close to small targets and often to hit them. Coordination improves during the following days largely without practice or visual experience (Bird, 1925; Moseley, 1925). Experiments with distorting prisms on the eyes of dark-hatched chicks proved that they could localize objects both directionally and in depth without learning (Hess, 1956).

Initial Pecking Preferences

For the pecking response to be used adaptively there must be visual discrimination and selection of those pecking targets that are likely to be edible, as well as spatial localization of those targets. The selection of relevant stimulus characteristics has in the past been stated to result entirely from trial-and-error learning, starting from random pecks (e.g., Maier & Schneirla, 1935). Such statements were based on naturalistic observation of the initial pecking at a variety of targets and the obvious effects of certain experiences on the selections (e.g., distasteful objects were soon avoided).

But in a series of stimulus preference experiments with over a thousand domestic chicks and a large variety of pecking targets, I found that initial pecking is far from random and that the preferences are adaptive relative to natural food sources. On the wall of a test box, each of several small objects encased in a plastic container was connected to the lever of a sensitive microswitch that recorded automatically the number of pecks directed toward it in a given time period. During the paired presentations of these objects there was no reward or differential experience other than the difference in form or other visual aspect of the targets themselves. The lack of reinforcement from grasping or tasting food did not prevent the chicks from pecking vigorously for hours, provided they were in the company of other chicks.

Before experience with food, chicks pecked 10 times more often at round than at angular objects. This striking preference for roundness

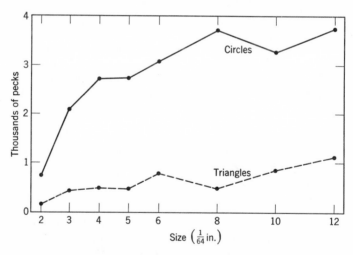

Fig. 8-1 Form and size pecking preferences of 40 2-day-old White Rock chicks with previous experience limited to one hour of vision and unrewarded pecking. Flat circles and triangles of various size, all white on black, were presented simultaneously in a large octagonal testing box; location and arrangement of the 16 stimuli varied among eight 10-minute periods (from Fantz, 1954).

was further analyzed by using chicks hatched in darkness that were tested on first visual exposure. When eight forms ranging in shape from pyramid to sphere were used, the amount of pecking increased sharply with degree of roundness, even during the the first 10 minutes of exposure (Fantz, 1957). Roundness of outline (circle over triangle) was preferred as well as roundness in curvature or depth (sphere over circle) (Fantz, 1958a). The form preference was amazingly independent of size of target, even though secondary size preferences were shown (Fig. 8-1). Round forms were preferred in experiments in which the stimulus situation differed in a number of features—color of forms or backgrounds, degree of contrast, texture, orientation of forms, and depth cues available (Fantz, 1954).

Effects of Experience

Unlearned form perception and form selectivity is clear from these studies. It is also obvious that the pecking of experienced chickens has been influenced by experience and learning, since edible objects of various forms in the farmyard are selected with few errors. The beginnings of such influence were shown by feeding one group of newly hatched chicks on round barley grains and another group on angular bits of commercial mash. Pre- and postfeeding preference tests were made with the previously described eight forms of varying roundness. After four days of the differential feeding experience, the barley group showed a heightened preference for round over pointed forms while the mash group retained only a slight preference for the round forms (Fig. 8-2). If they had been given a choice between barley and mash, each group would undoubtedly have chosen the one on which it had fed, and only effects of learning would have been evident. When the chicks were tested with abstract forms, however, a persisting influence of the unlearned selectivity was apparent and the behavior was not so easily classified as learned or unlearned.

Another effect of early experience on pecking selectivity was shown in 2-day-old chicks prior to contact with food (Fantz, 1954). Their previous visual experience had been limited to several hours in small test boxes. They were placed in a 4-foot octagonal testing box with pecking targets visible through circular openings in the walls of the box. The targets for one group of 32 chicks were flat forms—white circles or triangles on black backgrounds covered with transparent plastic. For another group of 32 chicks, the targets consisted of pink mash, also in plastic containers. After two hours in the octagonal box each group was returned to a darkroom. Both were tested the follow-

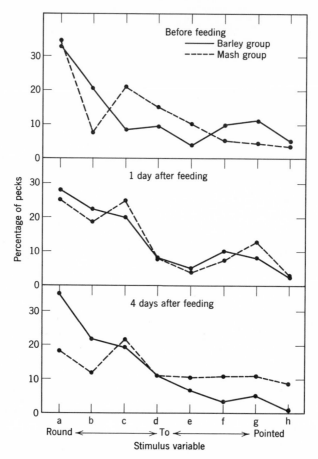

Fig. 8-2 Form pecking preferences of two groups of 28 White Leghorn chicks both before and after feeding on food of two different forms. The stimuli were eight small objects varying in both two- and three-dimensional aspects of form. The before-feeding test followed several hours visual and pecking experience (from Fantz, 1957).

ing day, two chicks at a time, in a smaller test box. When presented with forms only, the two groups showed equal preference for circles over triangles, but the total pecks for the form-experienced group was four times as high as for the mash-experienced group. The specificity of the change in pecking was brought out more clearly when a mash target was paired with a form (either a circle or a triangle); the form group pecked more at forms whereas the mash group pecked more at mash. A significant difference in the selections of the two groups was still shown 10 days later after normal visual experience and feeding on unpainted mash but with no intervening exposure to the test targets. Another experiment suggested a similar but less marked differential effect of group-pecking at circles or at triangles (Fantz, 1954).

The pecking experience was accompanied by striking changes in the chicks' social behavior, which may account for the strange learning effect. The chicks at first scattered, pecking little and "cheeping" loudly. Gradually they started following one another and then clustered in groups until all were trying to peck at one pair of targets. Then they began shifting to other targets and, after about 30 minutes, were dispersed around the box in small groups, all contentedly pecking at the targets. This change in social responsiveness in some respects resembles "imprinting" shown by chicks and other birds in other situations (see Chapter 2 by Klinghammer). Both the social and the pecking changes were rapid, without obvious reward, and long-lasting, and they involved a learned change in unlearned responses. Hess (1962) found a similar modification of pecking preferences to occur from rewarded pecking at a particular color-form; the critical age for the maximal learning effect was three days.

The pecking of chicks satisfies most criteria for instinctive behavior: It is necessary for survival; it is present in all members of the species without experience or learning; it is stereotyped on the motor side; and it is elicited by certain "sign stimuli" characteristic of the natural goal object. Without the slightest doubt, the visual elicitation and direction of pecking—as well as the motor pattern of the response—are unlearned in the newly hatched chick. And yet, two hours of pecking experience, without food reward but in the presence of other chicks, can cause a persistent and seemingly nonextinguishable change both in pecking frequency and in the preferred pecking objects. Even the fixed action pattern of pecking and its elicitation by visual stimuli in general can be severely disrupted by experiential conditions, although a radical departure from natural conditions is required, such as dark-rearing for several weeks (Padilla, 1935; Tucker, 1957). Then what is gained by classifying pecking behavior or pecking preferences as either learned or unlearned after the chick has been out of the shell long enough to be subjected to various environmental conditions or the lack of such conditions? The initial behavior of the chick has then been influenced and will thereafter continue to be influenced by experience, but it has not been and will never be replaced by behavior created out of environmental influences. More fruitful tasks are to try to isolate specific effects of specific environmental influences or the lack of such influences on the initial unlearned behavior and, at the theoretical level, to try to distinguish between fundamentally different types of learning or effects of experience.

The change in form preferences shown as a result of several days of feeding on round or angular food clearly represents an increase in the tendency to respond to a previously reinforcing stimulus. This much investigated and proven type of learning process is not so immediately evident from the experiments showing a change in pecking level and pecking preference after a period of pecking in a group situation. There was no material reward for or other differential consequence of pecking in this situation. But these results, too, can be encompassed by a broader conception of learning through reinforcement, that is, as an increase in response tendency from repeated previous elicitations under certain conditions, even though the critical reinforcing agent is not known. Social facilitation and arousal may have increased the pecking level of the chicks and heightened the effect of whatever reinforcing agent may have been present (e.g., the sound of the chick's beak against the plastic container or the slight movement of the container on the switch lever). Or, if the value of invoking the mechanism of reinforcement should be questioned, such results still fit the description of learning as a lasting change in response tendency from specific experiences.

The argument of this chapter is that even such a broad conception of learning passes over a large proportion of the effects of experience— effects that are related to, but not included within, current behavioristic conceptions of learning. This point is not easily brought out from the pecking or other consummatory behavior of birds. Other behaviors, such as exploration, migration, homing, territoriality, and social recognition, are more pertinent (e.g., Thorpe, 1951), but I do not have data on these myself. I do have relevant data from human infants to suggest an additional and quite different type of learning process. The point could be made also from numerous studies of other investigators.

DEVELOPMENT OF PERCEPTION IN HUMAN INFANTS

Human beings have a long period of development during which they are largely uncoordinated in their movements and completely dependent upon their parents for food, protection, and comfort. This motor immaturity has had profound effects on experiments and theories of early development. It has been supposed by some (perhaps from an overextended interpretation of behaviorism) that, since little behavior of an easily observable and classifiable kind is present, little of psychological importance occurs during the early weeks or months of life. They have considered the newborn infant to be essentially equivalent to a decorticate organism, incapable of sensory experience and limited to reflex reactions (e.g., Dennis, 1943; McGraw, 1943; Piaget, 1952). This viewpoint was hardly an inducement to carry out research with a subject so difficult to study in any case.

Other investigators, however, have accepted the challenge of the immature state of the young infant. They have proceeded either by adapting traditional procedures, such as conditioning, to the limited response capabilities present; or by devising new procedures that demand less in the way of overt behavior or learning from the young infant. The former approach in the past has met with little success other than to verify the inferiority of the young infant to the child or adult in learning and performance; but recent efforts have been more promising for obtaining useful information (see Chapters 9 and 10 by Lipsitt and Papoušek). The latter approach includes studies of changes in activity level and in physiological processes with sensory conditions (e.g., Eisenberg et al., 1964; Pratt et al., 1930); habituation to repeated stimulation (e.g., Bartoshuk, 1962; Bridger, 1961; Engen et al., 1963); visual fixation and pursuit (e.g., Chase, 1937; Gorman et al., 1957; Ling, 1942); visual preferences (discussed in the following section); avoidance of a "visual cliff" (Walk & Gibson, 1961); smiling to social stimuli (e.g., Ahrens, 1954; Spitz, 1946); and early unperfected reaching movements (White, Castle, & Held, 1964). From such studies information has been obtained and is being obtained at an accelerating rate on various types of interaction between the young infant and his environment. In particular, the infant has been proven to be receptive to sensory stimulation from birth, even if he rarely makes any active, coordinated response toward (or away from) objects and is with difficulty trained or conditioned to do so.

The error of assuming that infants, before development of motor coordination and tractability, are uninfluenced by environmental stimulation is most conspicuous relative to vision. That the young infant cannot see objects or patterned stimulation has been standard textbook knowledge for many years, but one has only to observe a young infant looking intently or repeatedly at himself or some other object, and to make a few repetitions with position varied, to become skeptical of this "fact." The results in the following sections are, in essence, such observations made under controlled conditions, using an objective response criterion, and aimed at determining not *whether* but *what* the young infant sees.

Pattern Preferences in Newborn Infants

The visual preferences of newborn infants were studied by placing each infant face up in a small hammock crib under a test chamber. The chamber was lined with felt to give a uniform background for the stimulus and to diffuse the illumination coming from the bottom of the chamber. A stimulus card was exposed by sliding it between a hole in the chamber ceiling and a shield above it. The eyes of the infant were observed through a ¼-inch hole to one side of the stimulus. The direction of the infant's gaze was determined from the corneal reflection of the stimulus, which was clearly visible under the conditions of the experiment. The superimposition of any part of this tiny image over the approximate center of the pupillary opening in either eye was operationally defined as fixation of the stimulus and was recorded by pressing a microswitch to operate a timer. The controversy on the age of appearance of visual fixation (Dewey, 1935; Pratt, 1954) was bypassed by using this directional response criterion and basing interpretations on relative length or frequency of response, rather than on the degree of coordination or qualitative aspects of the response. Reliability of the response measurement was shown both from photographic recordings of chimpanzee infants (Fantz, 1956; 1958b), and from simultaneous observations made by two persons on repeated tests of the same human infants (Fantz, Ordy, & Udelf, 1962).

In one experiment three black and white patterns and three plain colors, all on 6-in. circles, were exposed to the infants in random order, each for the duration of the first fixation, that is, until the infant closed his eyes or looked away. The sequence was repeated until the infant started crying or fell asleep. Of 18 infants under 5 days of age, 11 looked longest at a schematic face pattern, five at a bull's-eye pattern, and two at a section of newsprint; not one looked longest at white, fluorescent yellow, or red. An amazing degree of individual consistency in the pattern preference was shown by those subjects less than 24 hours old who could be given a long test session. One such infant looked longest at the face in seven out of eight exposures, another in three out of eight exposures, and a third looked longest at the bull's eye in three out of six exposures (Fantz, 1963).

Pattern complexity and arrangement were varied and brightness better controlled in another experiment. The six targets are shown in Fig. 8-3. The plain gray oval matched the schematic faces in over-all brightness, whereas the white oval was about equal to the "eyes" patterns. They were each exposed for 30 seconds in repeated random

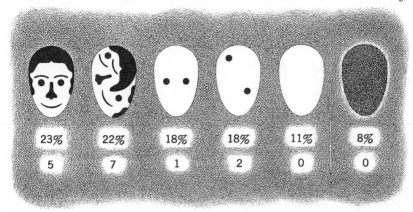

Fig. 8-3 Relative visual attention to stimulus targets with varying numbers and arrangements of schematic facial features. Figures are percentages of total fixation time, averaged for 15 infants less than one week of age; and number of infants giving longest attention to that target (from Fantz, 1965a).

sequence. There was no consistent preference between two patterns with the same number of features or between white and gray, while the differences in fixation time among the three levels of complexity were significant.

In another experiment (Fantz, 1965a), pattern organization was varied by placing black squares of the same total area in five different arrangements on a white square (Fig. 8-4). These five arrangements and a plain gray square of equal reflectance were exposed randomly and repeatedly, either for a fixed 30-second period or for the duration of the first fixation up to a maximum of 90 seconds. Results for the two procedures were similar and were combined in Fig. 8-4 for infants of increasing age levels. We will consider only the newborn infants at the moment. The two groups under 2 weeks of age, combined, showed significant differential attention among the five patterns, as well as an overwhelming preference for all patterns over gray. Most preferred was the highly linear arrangement of pattern "B," looked at longest by 16 infants, compared with 8 first choices for the random arrangement of "E," and 0 for gray.

Finally, the basic pattern vision capacity was investigated using a pattern preference acuity test similar to that used previously with older infants (Fantz et al., 1962). But instead of paired presentation of black and white striped patterns with gray of equal reflectance, gray and stripes of several widths were presented successively and repeatedly in varied sequence. Preliminary results (Fantz, in press) showed that from a distance of 9 inches, 18 of 19 newborn infants fixated longer

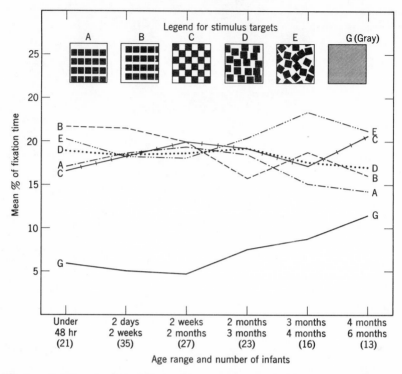

Fig. 8-4   Relative visual attention to five arrangements of ¾ in. squares, and to gray, with increasing age. Number of infants tested within each age range is given in parentheses (from Fantz, 1965a).

on ⅛-inch stripes than on gray. This is good pattern vision considering the incomplete maturation of the eye and brain and the poor oculomotor coordination. Since pattern vision requires the visual cortex, some degree of cortical functioning is indicated in the newborn infant.

These results, along with studies by other investigators (see Chapter 7 by Kessen; Hershenson, Munsinger, & Kessen, 1965; Stechler, 1964; Stirnimann, 1944), prove that the newborn infant can resolve, discriminate, and differentially attend to visual patterns. Does this indicate that all perception is unlearned in human beings? No; such a general question is unanswerable since it is just as clear from findings with older subjects that some aspects of perception or some kinds of perceptual performance are highly influenced by experience and learning. It is easy, however, to support the more limited statement that *some degree* of perception is unlearned *in the neonate,* whatever changes and improvements occur subsequently. It seems to me that this statement is debatable only if perception is arbitrarily restricted to certain types or levels of perception (e.g., depth perception, object perception, or form recognition), or if the development of perception and the development of perceptual indicators are confused by requiring certain active or learned responses for evidence of perception.

Aside from such questions of definition, the conclusion that the beginnings of perception are present from birth leaves a basic question unanswered. What is the relation, if any, between differential fixations of patterns in the neonate, and accurate and appropriate responses to minute or abstract features of the visual environment in the adult? The tendency of the chick to peck at small, solid, round objects has obvious survival value. But the tendency of the young infant to look more often and longer at certain kinds of patterns probably does not have immediate survival value; its adaptive significance must be sought in its role in the *development* of perception and behavior. The research presented in the remainder of this chapter provides several starting places for answering this question.

Early Changes in Pattern Preferences

Just as initial visual preferences reveal the unlearned beginnings of perception and visual attention, subsequent changes reveal effects of age and experience. For example, in Fig. 8-4 age changes are shown in the relative attention value of the six stimuli. After 2 weeks of age the initial preference for pattern B was gone. No consistent differential was then shown until after 3 months, when the random pattern was preferred. The longest fixated pattern was "B" for 5, "E" for 13, and "G"for 7 of the 25 infants 3 to 6 months of age. Interestingly, there was a consistent age trend toward *less* preference for patterns over gray, even though gray remained less interesting than any pattern.

The most striking age change occurred in my initial experiment with human infants. A horizontal striped pattern and a concentric circle pattern (bull's-eye), in which the two colors had the same width of line and area, were presented side by side for 30 seconds and then reversed in position. Data from the two presentations were combined to control for the position tendencies often shown by younger infants with a paired comparison procedure. Infants under 2 months preferred the stripes whereas older infants strongly preferred the bull's-eye. The shift was shown in the first test scores of infants of different ages as well as in subsequent weekly tests of the younger infants (Fantz,

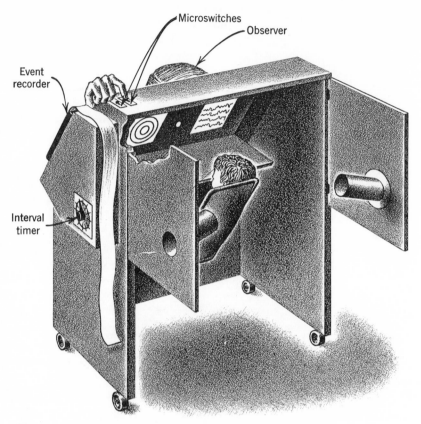

Fig. 8-5 Drawing of infant visual-preference apparatus used for paired comparison tests of infants, who were in semiupright position in a baby seat on the lap of a seated person. The view of subject was restricted by adjustable head pads to the inside of the chamber, which was lined with blue felt and illuminated by a shaded lamp on either side of the chamber, giving about 10 to 15 foot-candles of reflected light. The targets were attached to the back of a "stage"; when pivoted upward, the bottom of the stage covered the opening. Inside dimensions of chamber are 32 in. high, 28 in. across and 19 in. deep (excluding wings for lights).

1958c). The shift in preference was verified with another sample of infants of varying ages (unpublished data).

This age change was explored further in a recent study. The testing situation was modified in the attempt to keep the infants contented and testable for longer periods, and also to increase the head mobility and thus minimize the position tendencies of the younger infants (see Fig. 8-5). The infant was secured in a modified canvas baby seat and

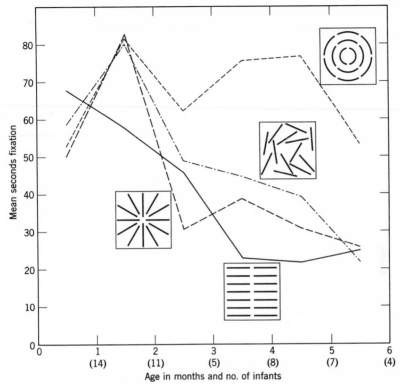

Fig. 8-6 Relative visual attention to four patterns at varying ages. Number of subjects at successive month intervals were 14, 11, 5, 8, 7, and 4. Data are mean seconds fixation time during 6 minutes testing, including six 30-second exposures of each pattern.

held on the lap of an assistant in front of and under the chamber. The patterns were exposed against a slanting surface of the chamber that could be pivoted away from the infant in a way that hid the patterns from the subject but made them available to the experimenter between exposures. The patterns were separated by 6 in. with the observation hole between them, 12 in. from the infant's eyes. Fixations were determined from corneal reflections over the pupil, and were recorded on moving tape by pressing either of two microswitches, thus activating the markers of a Rustrak event recorder.

The patterns were made by placing twelve ¼-in. black line segments in four different arrangements on 5-in. white squares (Fig. 8-6). For the bull's-eye arrangement the lines were curved but of the same number and area. These were exposed two at a time in all six combinations, with the sequence varied among the infants. Each pair was exposed for two 30-second periods with reversed right and left positions. This gave a total of 12 exposures and six minutes of testing; a particular pattern was exposed during half of this time.

Figure 8-6 shows the total duration of fixation of each pattern, averaged for the infants within age intervals of one month. All 49 subjects were from a foundling home with the exception of 3 from private homes. The striped pattern was preferred only by those under one month; it dropped markedly for older infants and overall was least preferred. The other three patterns showed an initial rise in fixation time, but only the circular pattern stayed at a high level in spite of the over-all decrease with age. In relative terms the preference for the circular pattern is still more striking. Of 24 infants over 2 months old, 22 looked more at the circular than at any other pattern whereas 16 looked less at the striped pattern than at any other (a frequency of 6 would be expected by chance in each case). The change from linear to circular preference from the first to the second month was significant according to a Mann-Whitney "U" test of ranked difference scores. These results are similar to those obtained using horizontal stripes and bull's-eye patterns in the previous studies, except that the shift occurred earlier and the striped pattern was never as consistently preferred in this study.

What characteristics of the patterns were discriminated and preferred before and after the change took place? Simple stimulus dimensions such as intensity, contrast, wavelength, area, number of elements, or length of contour were not, since these were equal in the four patterns. Novelty or familiarity were not, since they were equally novel patterns; nor was relative visibility of the patterns, since the pattern elements were large enough to be resolved by the youngest infants (Fantz et al., 1962). Several possible answers are suggested by the fact that in the three preceding experiments a highly linear organization was initially of highest attention value while after one or two months, a circular or random organization was preferred. The poor oculomotor coordination of the very young infant might explain the preference for linear patterns, since straight lines would be easier to trace with the eyes than circles or random configurations. The preference for more "complex" patterns at later ages, when incoordination is no longer a factor, might then be a result of greater stimulation of retinal receptors as the eye traverses a pattern with more frequent or less regular changes of intensity.

Recent knowledge of neural functioning also provides a possible explanation at a less peripheral level of function. Hubel and Wiesel

(1962) recorded evoked potentials from microelectrodes in the visual cortex of cats and monkeys. Single cells were maximally stimulated when a specific pattern such as an illuminated slit, a dark bar, or an edge fell on the retina in a particular place and orientation. The optimal pattern for stimulating a particular neural cell was often a linear pattern, whereas other patterns or diffused light were often ineffective. A similar degree of selective cortical responsiveness to patterns was shown in newborn kittens (Hubel & Wiesel, 1963), suggesting an unlearned mechanism underlying form perception. Assuming a similar mechanism in humans and a similar selectivity for linear patterns, it might be expected that this afferent neural selectivity would be most directly expressed in response selectivity in the newborn infant, thus giving a visual preference for linear patterns. At later ages the selectivity imposed by higher levels of neural organization might begin to influence the response selectivity, perhaps then favoring the pattern that is less redundant, contains more information, and is less quickly "taken in" and remembered, such as a random pattern.

Attention to Important Environmental Stimuli

Instead of using geometric patterns with certain stimulus dimensions equated or varied, and then speculating on the perceptual and neural mechanisms underlying the visual preferences, one may take a more functional or ecological approach by using stimulus targets that are similar to behaviorally important objects or patterns in the infant's surroundings. For example, social objects are uniquely important for the infant as well as for the adult. Visual attention to a person must precede smiling and other types of social responsiveness. Early selective attention to various characteristics of faces would thus facilitate the development of social responsiveness. This would be true whether or not the attention to faces is qualitatively or quantitatively different from the attention given to other interesting objects or patterns such as to suggest learned or unlearned "recognition" of people.

Several experiments described earlier indicated that patterns composed of schematic features of a face on a contrasting ground were of high attention value to newborn infants. A similar degree of preference for these patterns over several other patterns, as well as over plain or brightly colored stimuli, was shown by infants up to 6 months of age (Fantz, in press). Other investigators have shown a visual preference by infants 6 and 13 months of age for photographs of faces over other photographs or geometric patterns (Kagan & Lewis, 1965).

Some results (e.g., Fantz, 1961) have suggested that the correct

arrangement of features somewhat increases the attention value of schematic face drawings. Other results have failed to replicate this finding
or have found it only at certain ages. When the results of all the
studies I have carried out to date were combined, a significant preference for schematic over scrambled-face patterns, and for eye spots
over off-center spots, was shown only by infants between 2 and 3
months of age; the differential dropped off for both younger and older
subjects (Fantz, in press).

    Results obtained with a different type of representation of a face
and head were much more consistent (Fig. 8-7). A store-dummy model
of a female head, covered with nonglossy white paint, was paired with
a white plaque of the same size and shape. Infants under 2 months preferred the flat form, perhaps because it reflected more light than the
solid model with brightness gradients. Infants over 2 months, both
with the left eye covered and with both eyes open, consistently preferred the head model, either because of its similarity to a real head, or
because it was solid and contoured rather than flat.

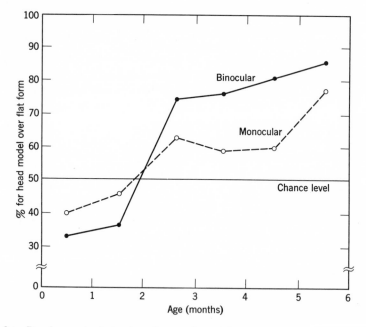

Fig. 8-7 Development of visual preference for a lifesize head model, with shadows
but without painted features, over a similar flat form. The 33 infants of varying
ages from a foundling home were given eight 25-second exposures, half with one eye
covered and half with both eyes open, with position controlled (from Fantz, in press).

The latter explanation is supported by other results with solid versus flat objects. A textured sphere was consistently preferred to a textured disc only by infants over 2 months of age, and only when the objects were illuminated by a single light source so that the solidity of the sphere was emphasized by shading; monocular or binocular viewing did not affect the results (Fantz, in press). The early development of a preference for solid objects was also shown with monkey infants and was attributable to visual experience (described in a later section).

A more recent unpublished study of human infants gives further evidence both for the developmental increase in the attention value of solidity and for the lack of a consistent developmental change in the attention value of facelike stimulus targets. Using the apparatus of Fig. 8-5, a wide variety of stimulus pairs was presented to infants of varying ages at a foundling home, preparatory to a longitudinal study now in progress. Each pair was exposed for two 30-second periods with reversed positions. The subjects were divided for analysis by age into those under 2 months (median age, 7 weeks) and those 2 to 6 months (median age, 15 weeks).

Three stimulus pairs varied in solidity or depth. Only two of 13 infants under 2 months looked more at a textured sphere than at a textured disc, whereas 12 of 13 over 2 months did so. Three of the younger group looked more at a patterned surface slanting toward the infant than at a similar flat vertical surface, while 9 of the older group did so. Both shifts to the solid object were significant according to the Mann-Whitney "U" test. However, no consistent preference was shown between a hollow box and a square, neither of which had visible surface texture.

Of six stimulus pairs containing facial representations, the infants showed a significant preference in three of the pairs for the facelike target or for the more realistic of two such targets (a solid head model with features painted black on gray over a 6-inch orange illuminated globe, the head model over an achromatic face photograph, and the photograph over a bright red square). The first-named target was fixated four times as long as the other, on the average, and was preferred by all but 4 of 28 infants. But the two age groups showed little or no difference. Two other pairs (schematic face versus scrambled pattern, eye spots versus displaced spots) yielded no consistent preference in either group. Only one pair showed a developmental increase in attention to the more realistic facelike stimulus: none of the younger group preferred a face photograph over a black-and-white schematic face pattern whereas half of the older group did so; this may have been because the younger infants were attracted to the target with the greater contrast, irrespective of the degree of facial likeness. Certainly it cannot be assumed that the schematic pattern, or any other representation of a face, was responded to as to a real face. The ability to perceive a similarity between a schematic and a real face may come at a much later age than does the ability to distinguish between such different stimuli.

Effects of Reinforcing Experiences

Some of the changes in visual preferences shown in the studies reported in the preceding two sections undoubtedly required visual experience and learning. But what kind of experience was involved, and through what process was it effective? To answer these questions it is necessary to do more than find age changes in a group of infants. And yet, experimental manipulations of the infant's experiences must be very limited to prevent degenerative effects similar to those found in animals (Beach & Jaynes, 1954). Several approaches meeting this limitation are described in this and following sections.

One way in which early experiences might be expected to influence perception is by increasing the attention value of those environmental stimuli that have been often accompanied by need reduction or reinforcement. Two such stimuli are available without any special treatment of the infants: the human face and the nursing bottle (for bottle-fed babies). The infant's fixation of the first is often followed by physical contact, feeding, or social responses from a person; fixation of the second would almost always, after the first month or so, precede nursing from the bottle and nursing would thus be contingent upon looking. The attention value of these stimuli was measured after varying amounts of reinforcing experience (i.e., infants of various ages), and with varying need conditions (i.e., before or after feeding and handling).

The "positive stimuli" were a nursing bottle (the same as that used in the reinforcing conditions and containing milk) and a solid model of a female head with achromatic but otherwise fairly realistic painted features. (Whereas the latter object only approximated certain configurational aspects of a real face and head, it avoided complicating aspects such as movement, color, and facial expression, and allowed better control of conditions of presentation.) The "negative stimuli" were ten widely different objects unfamiliar to the infants. Five of them (a ring of miniature plastic brightly colored fruit, a translucent globe containing a flickering light and covered with a colorfully patterned scarf, a wire-mesh spiral projecting from a board with holes, a textured white sphere, and a slanting board with complex, colored patterning) were presented in an apparatus similar to that shown in Fig. 8-5 together with the head model, each for two 20–second exposures with reversed positions. On alternating pairs of exposures, the bottle was paired with the other five objects (a vertically patterned board, a textured disc, four black diamonds on a white background, an ornamental nursery light-switch plaque, and random black circles drawn on white). This sequence for presenting the 10 object pairs was reversed for a second test of each infant; half of the 32 infants both under and over 2 months received the reversed sequence on either the first or second test. The two tests of each infant were given on different days and at different times of the day, either within the hour before a scheduled feeding time or within the hour after a feeding; the accompanying difference in recency of contact with persons was accentuated by several minutes of handling and play immediately before the after-feeding test. Half of the infants in each age group (and with each stimulus sequence) were tested first before feeding. The subjects were all from a foundling home, selected according to age, availability, and cooperation for two complete tests.

Taking the average results for both entire tests, the head model was fixated more than each of the five comparison objects by at least $\frac{2}{3}$ of the infants under 2 months; three of the five preferences were significant (0.05 level, sign test). For the older group, however, the head model was significantly preferred to only one of the objects (the plastic fruit); it dropped relative to the other four, and in one case the comparison object (flickering globe) was significantly chosen. In similar averages for the nursing-bottle pairings, each of the five comparison targets was significantly preferred over the bottle by both age groups; for two of the targets (diamond pattern and light-switch plaque) the bottle was looked at longer by only one of the 32 infants.

Obviously the preferences were relative to the particular comparison objects used. In selecting these objects I attempted roughly to equate them with the head model, or with the nursing bottle, in attention value. For the head model this meant selecting from the stimulus targets available from previous studies those that had elicited most visual attention and that were somewhat comparable in size, solidity, and complexity. For example, a bright red circle moving on a yellow disc was rejected for its simplicity and previous low attention value, whereas patterning was added to a plain orange flickering globe so that it would better compete with the head model. For the nursing-bottle comparisons, those smaller, simpler objects or patterns were chosen that had elicited least attention previously (excluding plain surfaces). That the head model was nevertheless preferred at all ages, and the bottle was not, suggests that intrinsic stimulus characteristics, especially configurational ones, were dominant in determining the degree of visual responsiveness.

To determine the effects of the need condition, the five object pairs containing the head model were averaged and the five bottle pairs were averaged. These results are given in the upper half of Table 8-1. The head model received slightly more visual attention during the test before feeding and handling than after. The difference was not significant for either age group but it was significant at the 0.05 level for both groups combined. The nursing bottle on the other hand received *less* attention before feeding than after. The difference was again not large, but was consistent in direction among the infants under 2 months alone, and for both groups combined. The only reliable difference between the two groups was that the head model was more highly preferred by the *younger* infants, especially when tested before feeding and handling.

Greater responsiveness to the head model before feeding and handling is the result that might be predicted for an object long associated with reinforcement when the reinforcement has not occurred for several hours or more. (Although it might also be predicted that the older infants would show this effect to a greater degree.) But the opposite to the predicted effect is present for the nursing bottle, which might be expected to be still more directly associated with reinforcement. An alternative explanation that fits both results is suggested by the fact that the percentages for both head model and bottle were closer to the 50% or chance level after feeding than before. Infants, especially very young ones, tend to be less alert and more drowsy after feeding; in this state they may be less discriminating in what they look at and show less differential responsiveness generally.

Another analysis of the data brought further complications as well as further indications that previous reinforcing experience was at best a minor influence. As a check on possible changes during the test sessions, results from the first two pairings of the head model (or the bottle) were compared with those from the last two pairings of that object. By combining for each infant the before- and after-feeding tests, in which reversed sequences of the comparison objects were used, variations in responsiveness to these objects were balanced out in the percentages for early and later exposures.

This analysis (lower half of Table 8-1) indicated that later in the test infants under 2 months looked consistently *more* at the head model while the older infants looked consistently *less*. These two effects together produced a marked developmental change in responsiveness to the head model on later exposures, whereas no difference (or even an opposite difference) was shown between the two age groups early in the test. It would seem that the age change suggested in the previous analysis resulted from different reactions by younger and older infants to a repeatedly exposed object, rather than from any difference in pre-testing experience with the object. But this interpretation received no support from the results for the nursing bottle, which showed no

TABLE 8-1

Visual Attention Given to Two Previously Reinforcing Objects by Infants in Two Age Groups and Under Different Conditions

Condition	Average Percentage of Fixation Time:					
	For Head Model Relative to Unfamiliar Objects			For Nursing Bottle Relative to Unfamiliar Objects		
	Under 2 Months	2 to 5 Months	p *	Under 2 Months	2 to 5 Months	p *
Before feeding	63%	55%	0.02	27%	29%	—
After feeding	57%	52%	—	34%	33%	—
p **	—	—		0.05	—	
Early Test Exposures	54%	58%	—	34%	32%	—
Later Test Exposures	65%	51%	0.002	30%	31%	—
p **	0.02	0.05		—	—	

* Significance of difference between two age groups determined by two-tailed Mann-Whitney "U" test of ranked percentages.

** Significance of difference between the tests at different times and different parts of the tests determined by two-tailed Wilcoxon matched-pairs signed-ranks test.

reliable difference either between early and later exposures or between the two groups of infants. And, of course, results using a head model are not necessarily the same as those that would be obtained using real persons.

Perhaps the only safe conclusion at this point is that very little is known about the effects of experience and learning on the direction of visual attention in young infants. The results also suggest that any single simple explanation of differences in the attention value of objects with age, previous experience, and need condition, such as might be provided by traditional learning principles, will prove inadequate for the task. The beginnings of an alternative approach are given in the discussion.

Effects of Repeated Exposure

Another way of studying the effects of experience and learning on visual attention in human infants is to vary the amount of exposure to specific targets by comparing the fixation of novel and repeatedly exposed patterns or objects. This comparison was incidentally made in the preceding experiment and suggested that repeated exposure can have an effect: It caused increased responsiveness to a head model for infants under 2 months of age, and decreased responsiveness for older infants. But it is not known whether these results were influenced by the use of a representation of a familiar object.

The final two studies of human infants show changes in visual preferences that can be pinned down to specific experiences during the test session. In the first study a single pattern was exposed to the infant inside the test chamber and was removed at the end of the first

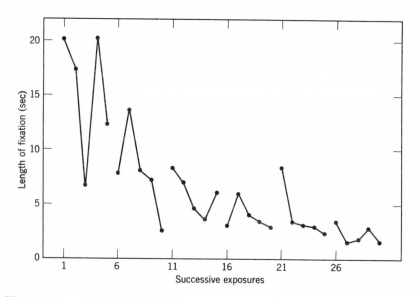

Fig. 8-8 Decreasing length of visual fixation of a pattern exposed above the infant repeatedly and removed as soon as the gaze was directed elsewhere. Times were averaged for 14 infants at a foundling home ranging from 2 to 6 months of age, half starting with two patterns; each pattern was used for five exposures (from Fantz, in press).

fixation response. Either a black-and-white bull's-eye or a section of newsprint was so presented five times; then the other pattern was presented five times; and so on for a total of 30 exposures. The average length of response for 14 infants between 2 and 6 months of age is shown in Fig. 8-8. The expected increase in response to the relatively novel pattern did not occur; fixations for the fifth exposure of a pattern were about equal to those for the next exposure of the other pattern. But there was a marked drop in response time during the entire test, suggesting decreased interest in both patterns or in the test situation, although it could also involve such factors as fatigue, sensory adaptation, and decreased arousal.

In the second study the effect of experience was specific to a particular pattern (Fantz, 1964). Pairs of complex patterns (photographs or advertisements cut from magazines) were exposed for 30-second periods and then repeated in reversed positions. One of the patterns was the same for a given infant during 10 such 1–minute exposures, while the other pattern was changed each time. For infants under 2 months the *constant* and *variable* patterns received about equal fixation throughout the test; for infants between 2 and 3 months, as well as older infants, the preference for the novel pattern increased during the

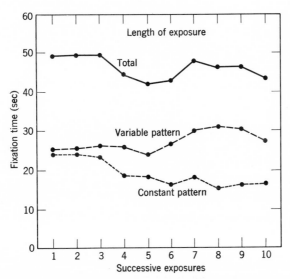

Fig. 8-9 Relative visual attention given to a complex pattern exposed repeatedly and to a comparable pattern which was novel for each successive minute of exposure. Data are from 22 infants from a foundling home between 2 and 6 months of age (from Fantz, in press).

session. This change was not accompanied by an over-all response decrement, since increased fixation of the novel pattern largely compensated for the decreased fixation of the repeatedly exposed one (Fig. 8-9), and one or the other pattern was looked at for a high proportion of the time throughout the test. Similarly, longer fixation of a simple novel stimulus over a recently exposed one was found by Saayman, Ames, and Moffett (1964) in 3-month infants.

Figures 8-8 and 8-9 bring out somewhat different effects of experience. In Fig. 8-8 an *efferent* effect is emphasized by the marked change in response level with repeated experience. Assuming that this effect was not a result of fatigue or sensory adaptation, it might be described as habituation of the looking response from repeated elicitation or, in Pavlovian terminology, extinction of the orienting reflex (Berlyne, 1960). Figure 8-9 shows a change in response to a repeatedly exposed pattern, but the constancy of the total response time emphasizes an *afferent* effect of the experience: pattern discrimination, pattern recognition, and pattern selectivity, indicating the intake of specific information during the exposures. The information input affected both the initial degree of attention to each target (all were complex and elicited considerable fixation), and the subsequent decrease of attention for the target attended to on previous exposures.

We may assume that some information intake through the senses has occurred whenever there has been a learned change in response tendency; nevertheless one is not reducible to the other and cannot always be inferred from the same kind of data. From the data of Fig. 8-8 we do not know whether the infants perceived and recognized both the patterns that were used alternately as targets, and consequently began more quickly to shift attention from each one to other unexplored parts of the test chamber, or whether the infants were attracted by the movement and sound of the target going into place overhead, and subsequently were less aroused by this stimulus change. The latter interpretation does not imply the assimilation of as much information from the environment as the former interpretation, even though based on the same change in the overt response. Most of the above visual attention results are in the form of percentages or direction of choice, rather than absolute response time, to facilitate finding out about the afferent type of experience effect.

Monkey Infants Reared in Darkness to Varying Ages

The results from human infants show few lasting changes in visual preferences clearly attributable to effects of early experience, perhaps because of the limited variations in experience. Research with animals presents opportunities for varying experience in extreme ways, such as complete visual deprivation. When intensive research using visual deprivation began some years ago, the approach appeared to hold promise of a final resolution of the nativism-empiricism controversy. Early results indicated that the decision would go to empiricism. But gradually it became evident that some, and perhaps all, of the visual deficiencies of the animal reared without pattern-vision experience resulted from lasting side effects of the deprivation, such as neural degeneration, oculomotor abnormalities, excessive arousal, or competing nonvisual habits (Beach & Jaynes, 1954; Melzack, in press; Riesen, 1961; Zuckerman & Rock, 1957). The mistake was to assume that the animal reared in darkness or diffuse light was perceptually equivalent to a newborn animal so that any deficit relative to the normally reared animal would be attributable to lack of opportunity for visual learning.

In the attempt to separate the degenerative effects of visual deprivation and the learning effects of visual experience, animals were reared in darkness to varying ages and then given equivalent visual experience instead of comparing visually deprived and visually experienced animals of the same age. The visual preference test of perception provided comparable data from subjects at all ages from birth, either with or without prolonged deprivation. By using early maturing rhesus monkey infants, other testing procedures were feasible as well; and by including unlearned as well as learned response indicators, the effects of deprivation on perception and on learning could be separated better than through discrimination training alone. Details of the research are given elsewhere (Fantz, 1965b).

The subjects were placed in a darkroom with their mothers within several days of birth. They were then taken from their mothers no later than 10 days of age and put in cages equipped with heating pads and "mother surrogates," similar to those used by Harlow and Zimmermann (1959) but lacking a head above the terrycloth-covered body. They lived in complete darkness until moved to a lighted nursery at varying ages. Visual experience during the deprivation period was limited to testing: about five minutes daily in the visual preference chamber during the final weeks of deprivation (or in some cases throughout the deprivation), and occasional other tests. At the end of the deprivation period, a variety of performance tests were begun; visual preference tests continued until the subjects were about 5 months of age.

Effects on Visual Preferences

The results from the visual preference tests are most clearcut. The testing procedure used with human and chimpanzee infants was modified for the more coordinated and active monkey infants who have a strong clinging tendency. The infant, clinging to the mother surrogate, was placed in a black cubicle where it was in position to look through a hole in a stimulus chamber at a pair of stimulus targets on the opposite wall (Fig. 8-10). Various stimulus pairs were presented randomly in the course of three test sessions; usually two entire tests were given weekly. Each pair was exposed for two 15-

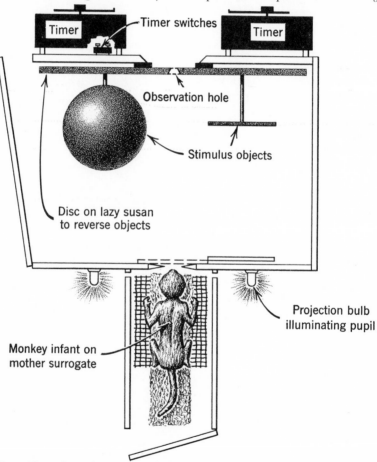

Fig. 8-10 Plan of monkey infant visual-preference apparatus, with one of the stimulus pairs (6 in. sphere and circle) in testing position (from Fantz, 1965b).

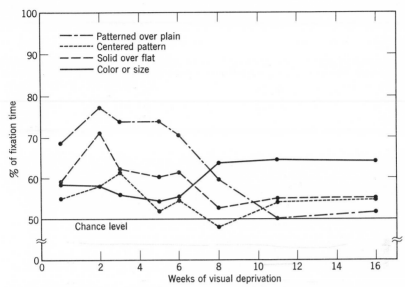

Fig. 8-11 Differences in visual preferences of monkey infants following different lengths of visual deprivation from birth. Data were averaged for each subject over all postdeprivation tests, lasting until about 5 months of age. The separate curves are averages for three or four pairs of targets.

second periods with reversed right and left positions. Fixations were observed through a center peephole with the aid of corneal reflections of the targets, and were recorded on timers.

Figure 8-11 shows the average results from all postdeprivation tests. Results were combined for two subjects with less than a week of deprivation, and for two with five weeks; otherwise, each point on the curve is from a single infant. The separate curves are for four categories of stimulus variables, with the pairs in each category averaged together. The patterned versus plain pairs were checkerboard versus square, eight-pointed star versus circle, simple black-and-white pattern versus larger red square, and square of newsprint versus larger red square. The centered versus uncentered pairs were bull's-eye pattern versus horizontal stripes, circle versus line on a square, and eye spots versus similar spots at the edge of the oval. The solid versus flat pairs were sphere versus disc, hollow box versus square, and slanting patterned surface versus a similar vertical surface. The color or size pairs were red versus yellow, black versus white, and large versus small; in this category the percentages for the preferred target of each pair, for a particular infant, were averaged together, thus showing the tendency toward differential fixations irrespective of direction of preference.

The curve for patterned over plain targets dropped sharply for the older, longer-deprived infants. This was verified by the consistency of choices on separate tests during the first 10 weeks of unrestricted experience: each infant with less than eight weeks of deprivation showed a significant preference for each of the four patterned targets, while the longer-deprived infants did not do so and even, in some cases, favored the unpatterned target. There was a similar but less marked drop in preference for the solid targets. Preferences for the centered patterns were more variable but were most consistent for three of the less-deprived infants. Results were also quite variable with the color and size category but the three longest-deprived infants generally showed stronger preferences and always in the same direction —red over yellow, black over white, and large over small. Thus, the longer-deprived animals retained the ability to attend to and discriminate nonconfigurational visual stimuli. This result is reminiscent of the accentuated attention and recognition of color relative to form by humans born with cataracts, after the cataracts have been surgically removed (von Senden, 1960). It would appear that color, brightness, and size become "primary" visual stimuli only after a long period of pattern-vision deprivation.

The over-all postdeprivation results do not show whether the effect of the deprivation was to cause deterioration of initial visual preferences or to prevent subsequent visual learning. Figure 8-12 shows changes in preferences following the deprivation period for groups of three monkeys with similar lengths of deprivation. The curves begin with tests given during the last several weeks of deprivation. The longest-deprived group failed to prefer patterned targets at any point; the other groups showed preferences throughout the postdeprivation testing, and showed perhaps some increase with experience. The two less-deprived groups showed a reliable increase in preference for solid targets with increasing experience, while the longest-deprived group never did show this preference. Responsiveness to centered patterns did not increase with experience; if anything there was a decrease in differential after the deprivation ended, especially for the longer-deprived infants. The only experiential increase evident for the longest-deprived group was relative to nonconfigurational differences. It is clear that one effect of prolonged visual deprivation was to alter the subsequent effects of visual experience.

This finding does not tell us what the initial preferences were and whether they deteriorated during the deprivation period. Of the 13

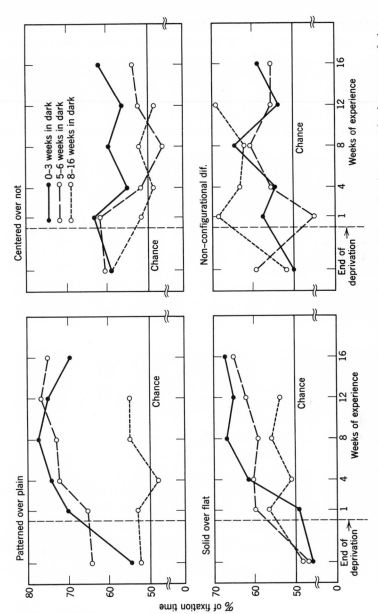

Fig. 8-12 Postdeprivation of development of visual preferences in each of four stimulus categories by groups of three monkey infants, each group having different length of deprivation preceding these tests (from Fantz, 1965b).

stimulus pairs, a consistent initial preference was shown (based on all tests given during the first two weeks to infants kept in darkness during this period) only for bull's-eye over stripes, eye spots over off-center spots, star over circle, simple pattern over red, and yellow over red. The subsequent development of configurational preferences during deprivation for those infants deprived as long as five weeks of age and tested during this time is shown in Fig. 8-13. The solid versus flat pairs continued at a chance level, again indicating the essential role of experience for attending to these variations. Preference for centered patterns was maintained although variable. The four patterned targets each increased in attention value until 3 or 4 weeks of age and then started to decline. Presumably this decline continued until in the longer-deprived monkeys the over-all response to patterns was again at the chance level (Fig. 8-12).

The relative attention value of the patterned targets varied (as shown by height of the four curves in Fig. 8-13) due to differences in the patterns and in the comparison stimuli, whereas the developmental changes were similar (as shown by the shape of the curves). This

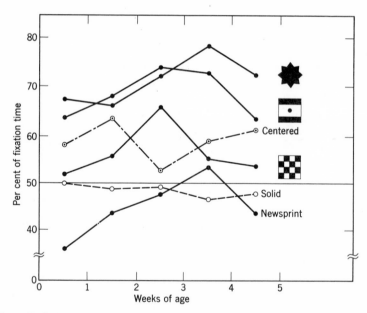

Fig. 8-13 Early development of visual preferences in infant monkeys kept in darkness except for short tests. Solid lines are for each patterned versus plain pair; dotted lines are averages for centered versus uncentered and for solid versus flat pairs. Data are averages for six animals, each tested once or twice a week (from Fantz, 1965b).

similarity, as well as the fact that marked postdeprivation preferences were shown for all four pairs by the less-deprived infants but not by the longer-deprived infants, provide a behavioral basis for putting these four into one perceptual category—"patterned versus unpatterned"—in spite of differences in physically defined stimulus dimensions. This classification is further supported by the very different results for the pairs classified as nonconfigurational differences.

Effects on Perceptual Performances

It is evident that prolonged visual deprivation interfered with the monkeys' unlearned selective attention to patterns as well as preventing experience from bringing about other preferences among configurational stimuli. Two further questions arise from this conclusion: First, why did the deprivation have these effects? And second, how did the altered visual selectivity affect the adaptive behavior of the animal? Answers to the first are suggested by knowledge of the various deteriorating effects of visual deprivation—jerky, rhythmic eye movements and poor binocular coordination; anatomical deterioration of visual structures; disappearance of the pattern-selective responses of cells in the visual cortex; and excessive arousal. Any one of these could contribute to a disturbance of the selective attention to patterned stimulation (see Fantz, 1965b).

Answers to the second question are suggested by the results of visual performance tests given daily, starting just before removal from the darkroom and continuing until each was "passed" by the particular infant. On the "visual cliff" test of depth perception (Walk & Gibson, 1961), infants kept in darkness for less than one month consistently avoided walking on glass over an apparent 30-inch spatial drop after several days or less of unrestricted experience, whereas the longer-deprived infants required many days of experience or else never did avoid the "cliff" side of the apparatus. Longer deprivation was necessary for a consistent deficit in other performances to appear.

Good spatial orientation on an obstacle field was shown within several hours or several days by all but the two animals that had been deprived longer than three months; they required several weeks of experience. These two animals were also most retarded in learning to approach and discriminate the mother surrogate and in learning to locate and discriminate the nursing bottle. A later subject with similar deprivation was unable to recognize pieces of fruit after two months of unrestricted experience. Observation of the animals during the early hours of unrestricted experience suggested a deficit in social responsiveness as well as in spatial orientation and object recognition. The younger, less-deprived infants often looked persistently at the experimenter, while the longer-deprived animals were more likely to look at the overhead light or elsewhere. This difference was verified in systematic observations of three subjects with varying deprivation. In visual preference tests in which movement and color were eliminated in the "social stimulus," a model of a human head was preferred to an orange light globe by two infants with little deprivation, while the preference was reversed for two longer-deprived infants. Another preference test suggested the loss from prolonged deprivation of an initial tendency to look more at a swinging than at a stationary block of wood, although the preference for movement returned with experience.

A more lasting effect of visual deprivation was revealed by discrimination training. At a mean age of 15 months the subjects were given 24 discrimination problems, each for a single session of 40 trials, in a modified Wisconsin General Test Apparatus. Each of eight monkeys that had been deprived less than eight weeks made more correct responses during the last 30 trials than did any of six monkeys deprived for eight weeks or longer (the point at which visual preferences had changed markedly). On the average, the less-deprived group solved nine of the individual problems (using a criterion of eight consecutive correct choices of the last 30) while the longer-deprived group solved only five. Before the training began, the longer-deprived infants also showed fewer preferences for one or the other stimulus of a pair (with response to either stimulus rewarded). This remaining disturbance of selective attention may account for the inferiority in discrimination training, since problems were more often solved by either group when there had been a pretraining differential response, even if the negative object had been preferred initially.

The original classification of the discrimination problems indicated that form, pattern, and depth variations were solved more than twice as often as variations in color, brightness, and size, and that this greater ease of discriminating configurational differences was more marked for the less-deprived animals. But a more accurate description of the critical stimulus differences was given by an analysis based on the data rather than on the arbitrary categories set up before the experiment. Only seven of the 24 problems received as high as 20 out of 30 average correct responses over all subjects; each of these seven pairs *differed tactually as well as visually* (i.e., in form, texture, solidity, or size). Five of the seven, and only these, were solved by as many as 10 of the 14 monkeys. Nontactual pattern variations as well as color and brightness variations received close to chance scores overall. Of the 14 monkeys only 1, 0, and 3 solved the seemingly simple discriminations of checkerboard versus plain square, red versus yellow, and white versus black; whereas smooth versus finely textured blocks, and dowel rod versus segment of branch—both pairs equated for color—were discriminated by nine and seven animals, respectively. Thus, although the choices between the objects were made visually and without tactual comparison as a rule, they were highly dependent on the presence of a "real" characteristic of objects, that is, a three-dimensional variation that was verifiable by touch. Those problems containing a visual-tactual form difference were solved to criterion in a single test session nine out of 10 times by those less-deprived animals that showed an initial preference for one or the other object (compared to three out of 10 by all animals for all problems).

This relation of stimulus variable, initial preferences, and early rearing experience to discrimination training performance can be interpreted in the following way: Starting with an initial visual selectivity for patterns, selectivity for subtle aspects of patterning accompanying solid objects developed through unrestricted experience given early in life. At first the effective experience was predominantly visual; but soon, visual-tactual-kinesthetic experiences from locomotion, manipulation, and play apparently entered in to produce further adaptive changes in visual selectivity and discrimination. After the infants had months of such experience in everyday contacts with their surroundings, visual variables that had proven to be consequential in their behavior (i.e., three-dimensional form differences) frequently brought out differential responses in a free-choice situation and, as a result, discrimination habits were quickly formed. As a corollary, the monkeys came to ignore differences in the pattern of painted plaques (even though initially attended to) as much as differences in color and brightness, and found these differences equally difficult to learn to discriminate. The developmental trend suggested is not that of "learning to see form" but of learning to attend to those aspects of form that are most useful (at least until the animal is placed in a discrimination training apparatus). A similar trend was suggested at an earlier age from the results on recognition of the mother surrogate (see the preceding section). After a given infant discriminated the surrogate from objects differing in many ways, it was given a choice between an object of different form but made of the same materials as the familiar surrogate and an object of the same form but made of materials of different color and patterning. The latter was chosen more often by each of eight infants so tested, however long-deprived, suggesting that this visual recognition was based on palpable form characteristics. The long-deprived infants, with disturbance of attention to configurational differences in general, were slower in recognizing the form of the surrogate and, later on, in learning visually to discriminate objects differing in palpable form.

Rearing in darkness can have a pronounced, long-lasting effect on attention, perception, and accompanying responses that is not the result simply of lack of opportunity for visual learning. The deteriorating effects prevent us from making inferences on the normal development of perception. Actually, it is not necessary to control postnatal experience in order to study the beginnings of perception. The visual preference method, for example, gives a test of form perception starting at birth. With monkey infants other discriminative responses are soon available; even form discrimination training is possible soon after birth through the use of special techniques, as shown by Zimmermann and Torrey (1965).

The developmental process cannot be stopped by experimental manipulations of conditions; but its course may be drastically changed. Unrestricted visual experience during early development accentuates initial pattern preferences, produces a preference for solid objects, results in the rapid development of spatial orientation, object recognition, and social attention, and eventually results in ease in learning discriminations based on three-dimensional object characteristics. In contrast, visual deprivation during the early critical period for perceptual development causes loss of selective attention to patterns, prevents subsequent selection of solid objects, and increases the attention to nonconfigurational stimuli; at least partly as a consequence of this disturbance of attention, deficient use of vision is shown in tasks requiring attention to patterning, such as avoidance of a visual cliff, object recognition, and discrimination of spatial differences. Which of these kinds of development should be termed "maturation"? Not the first, since experience and learning have clearly entered in. Not the second, since the development is in an abnormal direction, giving *decreased* readiness to respond and to learn with age, so that this process might better be called "backward maturation." Perhaps the concept of maturation, rather than denoting a specific developmental influence, is useful only as a synonym for development—for a growth process that may be quite different under different experiential conditions. Dark-rearing is one of the possible experiential conditions, even though an extreme one.

DISCUSSION

Why does an organism look at things and places in the environment? From a subjective viewpoint, it is partly for pleasure, excitement, diversion, etc.; objectively, visual stimulation can be shown to have arousal and reinforcing effects. But the basic biological function of visual exploration is to discover, examine, and learn about objects and places in the environment that may be relevant to the organism's health, education, and welfare. What is learned in this way may elicit and direct appropriate responses at the time, may be stored for future use, or both.

Taking a behavioristic approach to such learning, we would ask from what lasting changes in response tendencies it can be evidenced and measured and under what conditions and through what mechanisms it occurs. The most direct evidence would come from changes in visual exploratory behavior itself—such as increased fixation of certain targets—if these changes are found to be dependent on certain prior experiences.

The most marked and lasting changes in visual preferences in monkey infants occurred after several months' rearing with very little visual experience; the degenerative effects of the deprivation were not learned. Human infants showed definite changes in the relative attention value of unfamiliar geometric patterns (i.e., from linear to circular or random patterns) with increasing age and experience; it is difficult to attribute these changes to specific previous experiences or to reinforcing conditions. Monkey infants showed a marked increase in the attention value of solid objects following unrestricted experience in the early weeks of life, probably because of visual experience alone rather than visual-tactual association, since a similar change was shown in human infants before they could manipulate objects. Other than this finding, however, the learning cannot be pinned down to specific conditions or mechanisms. In tests of human infants, objects that presumably had been associated with social or food reinforcement received little or no increase in attention either after longer opportunity for learning or under greater need conditions. The only change attributable to specific previous experiences was the habituation of visual attention to a repeatedly exposed pattern.

Thus if we apply the descriptions and principles of learning of the behaviorists and learning theorists (e.g., lasting increases in response frequency or strength from repetition or reinforcement), there is little evidence that young infants learn anything from visual exploration of the environment. The obtained results might be accounted for by the unlearned and persisting attention value of intrinsic stimulus characteristics, such as figure-ground contrast, pattern complexity, solidity, and facelike configurations, plus maturational improvements in visual acuity, oculomotor coordination, depth accommodation, and neural processes, to explain such changes as the later appearance of preferences for solid objects and for circular and random patterns, plus habituation effects. This essentially nativistic interpretation (similar to Gesell et al., 1949, in the emphasis on the maturation of visual action-systems) attributes little importance to early visual experience, other than for giving oculomotor practice.

But there is another interpretation. I believe the results argue strongly for the importance of early visual experience and for what is learned from this experience. To support this position it is necessary to start with a sharp distinction between learning in the behavioristic meaning of lasting changes in response tendencies, and learning in the early empiricistic meaning of the acquisition of knowledge through the sense organs. The former requires repeated responses with accompanying reinforcement or association; the latter requires only the *capacity* to receive and discriminate stimuli, plus the *act of attending* to a stimulus. The former learning occurs through *reacting to* a stimulus; the latter from *taking in* the stimulus.

The significance of the visual preference studies is in the proof that infants from birth have the capacity to receive and discriminate patterned stimulation, that they do attend selectively to parts of the environment, and that, therefore, the *acquisition of knowledge about the environment begins at the first look.* During the early weeks or months the information acquired from a single look at a certain target may not be retained any longer than is necessary to cause the direction of attention to shift to a more interesting target, or else to be maintained on the same target. But even at this minimal level the knowledge acquired has had important consequences. It has given differential exposure to parts of the environment. For example, a tendency to look four times as long at patterns as at an unpatterned target (as in Fig. 8-4) will concentrate the infant's attention on patterned areas of his surroundings and on the configurational differences among them that contain the most information. This selective attention to patterning determines what the infant learns through visual explorations just as much as his being placed in a variegated, "rich" environment rather than in a homogeneous box or crib.

The acquisition of knowledge by the infant is influenced by factors in addition to his initial pattern preferences and the particular surroundings he is placed in. The visual world is structured in such a way that certain parts of it attract more than their share of attention. Solid objects often contrast with a more uniform, distant ground in color, brightness, and patterning, and stand out also through binocular and movement parallax. Some of these objects move, which further sets them apart from the ground and attracts attention. Some objects (e.g., human faces and the infant's own hands) are frequently close to the infant and thereby gain in retinal size, optical clarity, and visible details of patterning. Such factors would ordinarily have a beneficial effect since solid, animate, and nearby objects often deserve special attention.

The intake of information gradually becomes more efficient through past visual explorations. Just as oculomotor skill improves through practice, it is reasonable to suppose that afferent discriminative processes improve through use (e.g., Gibson, E. J., 1953), and that the improvement is dependent on the variety and subtlety of the incoming stimulation. A good analysis of this effect of experience is given in the Gibson and Gibson (1955) theory of perceptual learning that: successively finer or subtler stimulus variations are differentiated and discriminated through repeated examination. A possible mechanism for this is the progressive change in visual selectivity—attending to more complex stimuli and more subtle variations in patterning (such as the contour, texture, and gradients of solid objects).

Knowledge acquisition may at the same time be increased through better integration or organization of the stimulus input, although how this occurs is a matter for conjecture. It is often attributed to an associational process described as "primary visual learning" (Hebb, 1949), "sensory pre-linkages" (Hayek, 1952), "sensory pre-conditioning" (Brogden, 1939), or "stimulus-stimulus associations" (Riesen, 1958). Although it is now clear that such theories usually place more of a burden upon associational learning than is required—since it is not necessary to learn to see form and pattern in a basic sense—there may be a need for such processes at further levels of perceptual development. If so, the associations formed will be determined by what objects are looked at predominantly and which of their details or stimulus variables are discriminated, examined repeatedly, and associated (e.g., the various stimulus characteristics of solid objects). Alternatively, it may be better strategy to forget the venerable but threadbare concept of association and to relate the increased integration and organization resulting from the cumulative effects of experience behaviorally to the increased complexity and generality of the stimulus variables

discriminated and attended to (Gibson, J. J., 1950); or neurally to the
involvement of higher levels of the visual system and larger networks
in the brain (Hubel & Wiesel, 1962; see also Hayek, 1952).

Whether or not the preceding changes require memory and association, eventually the knowledge acquired through visual exploration is
retained beyond the momentary act of attention and has more specific
effects than to improve the effectiveness of information processing. The
infant or animal becomes familiar with his surroundings and with particular objects. Familiarization with the environment is a basic form
of learning in all organisms, occurring through visual and more active
exploration. It gives the context for all subsequent learned or instinctive behavior in that or a similar environment. For example, this
learning is part of the adaptation to the situation preceding discrimination training or conditioning.

One evidence of familiarization is the habituation of attention to
specific parts of the environment demonstrated to be present in infants
at least by two months of age. Even if the knowledge of the familiar
stimulus is retained only a short time, it has the useful effect of concentrating attention on less familiar, unexplored parts of the environment, thus accelerating the acquisition of information. In fact, all visual preferences would tend to disappear in a familiar environment if
such effects were retained indefinitely, since the original preferred targets would be looked at longer and habituated to more quickly. Probably this condition is prevented by the rapid revival of preferences
based on intrinsic stimulus characteristics and by the *opposite* effect
of longer-term familiarization under certain conditions. The latter
effect was indicated in a study by Uzgiris and Hunt (1965): two-month
infants showed longer fixation of a mobile that had hung over the home
crib for five weeks (although at 3 months an unfamiliar mobile received equal or longer fixations).

These two observable effects of familiarization—increase or decrease
in visual attention—represent only the small above-water part of the
iceberg. Knowledge may be acquired from visual examination of an
object without any subsequent change in the attention value of that
object, or in any other response indicator, although such overt change
is very helpful to the investigator when it does occur. A person may
read a book or watch a moving picture without giving any indication
of what has been learned either in immediate responses or in lasting
changes in behavior; and yet it would be rash to claim that the person has learned nothing. It is doubtful if the most thorough testing or
questioning could reveal all the information that is taken in from reading a book and that can be utilized at some future time.

The young infant does not have access to such concentrated sources of information. But there is good reason to hypothesize that his more limited information-processing capacities are being utilized throughout his waking hours and that some part of what he learns is important for the development of perception and behavior. By the time the infant is able to make use of the knowledge so acquired for directing active responses, his visual world probably contains patterns, objects, surfaces, and persons, moving or still, of various forms and colors, at various locations and distances, familiar or unfamiliar, and seen against a stable background, even if to the newborn infant this world is to a large extent the "blooming buzzing confusion" suggested by James (1890). It is not so strange that the remarkable visual system of the primate, perfected through the millennia for the function of giving immediate, accurate knowledge of the environment from a distance, begins to serve this function at birth; and that the means for further development and use of this function (i.e., visual exploration and selective attention) are incorporated within the system so that less efficient and more dangerous trial-and-error procedures are not necessary for acquiring basic knowledge of the environment.

This analysis of learning through early visual explorations can be attacked from two directions, assuming that the data themselves are accepted: The data do not indicate learning of any kind in the young infant, or else the data can be encompassed by traditional learning paradigms. The first argument is a sound one since learning is currently defined to require a *lasting change in response.* It might indeed be better to use another term such as *acquisition of knowledge* in place of *learning,* even though the two effects of experience are related. I would argue only that *length of retention* by itself is an unsatisfactory criterion for learning as well as for the acquisition of knowledge. Any specific lower limit for memory is arbitrary, whether it is one second, one hour, one week, or one year. And it does not take into account the possible effects from sequences of quickly forgotten experiences. What the infant learns from one visual fixation may last only until the next, and yet the cumulative effect may continue through hours of visual exploration.

Regarding the second argument, there is a simple interpretation of early visual preferences in terms of behavioristic learning principles. Let us say that at first the direction of gaze of the infant is random, and that various visual stimuli are reinforcers of different strengths. Then, if the gaze falls on a complex, highly reinforcing stimulus, it will tend to be maintained and to return to that stimulus frequently, except that repeated responses within a short time might reduce the drive for that particular stimulus and give decreased response strength for a repeatedly exposed stimulus. One might question whether anything is gained by thus substituting "reinforcing value" for "attention value" other than to further dilute the term "reinforcing." But the main point is that the present issue is bypassed completely by this formulation, which only deals with the strength of the response tendencies for various stimuli and how they are affected by past responses. It does not tell us what information is taken in during each response (as distinct from what reinforcement is received). It does not tell us whether this information facilitates perceptual development and familiarization with the environment. It does not tell us if looking can be educational as well as pleasurable to the infant. And it does not throw any light on the hidden side of behavior development.

REFERENCES

Ahrens, R. (1954) Beitrag zur Entwicklung des Physiognomie und Mimikerkennens. *Z. exp. angew. Psychol.* **2**, 413–454, 599–633.

Bartoshuk, A. K. (1962) Human neonatal cardiac acceleration to sound: habituation and dishabituation. *Percept. mot. Skills* **15**, 15–27.

Beach, F. A., & Jaynes, J. (1954) Effects of early experience upon the behavior of animals. *Psychol. Bull.* **51**, 239–263.

Berlyne, D. E. (1960) *Conflict, arousal, and curiosity.* New York: McGraw-Hill.

Bird, C. (1925) The relative importance of maturation and habit in the development of an instinct. *J. genet. Psychol.* **22**, 68–91.

Bridger, W. H. (1961) Sensory habituation and discrimination in the neonate. *Amer. J. Psychiat.* **117**, 991.

Brogden, W. J. (1939) Sensory pre-conditioning. *J. exp. Psychol.* **25**, 323–332.

Chase, W. P. (1937) Color vision in infants. *J. exp. Psychol.* **20**, 203–222.

Dennis, W. (1943) Is the newborn infant's repertoire learned or instinctive? *Psychol. Rev.* **50**, 330–337.

Dewey, E. (1935) *Behavior development in infants.* New York: Columbia Univer. Press.

Eisenberg, R. B., Griffin, E. J., Coursin, D. B., & Hunter, M. A. (1964) Auditory behavior in the human neonate: a preliminary report. *J. Speech and Hear. Res.* **7**, 245–269.

Engen, T., Lipsitt, L. P., & Kaye, H. (1963) Olfactory response and adaptation in the human neonate. *J. comp. physiol. Psychol.* **56**, 73–77.

Fantz, R. L. (1954) Object preferences and pattern vision in newly hatched chicks. Unpublished doctoral dissertation, Univer. of Chicago.

Fantz, R. L. (1956) A method for studying early visual development. *Percept. mot. Skills* **6**, 13–15.

Fantz, R. L. (1957) Form preferences in newly hatched chicks. *J. comp. physiol. Psychol.* **50**, 422–430.

Fantz, R. L. (1958) Depth discrimination in dark-hatched chicks. *Percept. mot. Skills* **8**, 47–50. (a)

Fantz, R. L. (1958) Visual discrimination in a neonate chimpanzee. *Percept. mot. Skills* **8**, 59–66. (b)

Fantz, R. L. (1958) Pattern vision in young infants. *Psychol. Rec.* **8**, 43–48. (c)

Fantz, R. L. (1961) The origin of form perception. *Scient. Amer.* **204** (5), 66–72.

Fantz, R. L. (1963) Pattern vision in newborn infants. *Science* **140**, 296–297.

Fantz, R. L. (1964) Visual experience in infants: decreased attention to familiar patterns relative to novel ones. *Science* **146**, 668–670.

Fantz, R. L. (1965) Visual perception from birth as shown by pattern selectivity. In H. E. Whipple (Ed.), *New issues in infant development. Ann. N. Y. Acad. Sci.* **118**, 793–814. (a)

Fantz, R. L. (1965) Ontogeny of perception. In A. M. Schrier, H. F. Harlow, & F. Stollnitz (Eds.), *Behavior of nonhuman primates.* Vol. II. New York: Academic Press. Pp. 365–403. (b)

Fantz, R. L. (In press.) Pattern discrimination and selective attention as determinants of perceptual development from birth. In A. H. Kidd, & J. L. Rivoire (Eds.), *Perceptual development in children.* New York: Int. Univer. Press.

Fantz, R. L., Ordy, J. M., & Udelf, M. S. (1962) Maturation of pattern vision in infants during the first six months. *J. comp. physiol. Psychol.* **55**, 907–917.

Gesell, A., Ilg, F. L., & Bullis, G. D. (1949) *Vision, its development in infant and child.* New York: Hoeber.

Gibson, E. J. (1953) Improvement in perceptual judgments as a function of controlled practice or training. *Psychol. Bull.* **50**, 401–431.

Gibson, J. J. (1950) *The perception of the visual world.* Boston: Houghton Mifflin.

Gibson, J. J., & Gibson, E. J. (1955) Perceptual learning: differentiation or enrichment. *Psychol. Rev.* **62**, 32–41.

Gorman, J. J., Cogan, D. G., & Gellis, S. S. (1957) An apparatus for grading the visual acuity of infants on the basis of optokinetic nystagmus. *Pediatrics* **19**, 1088–1092.

Harlow, H. F., & Zimmerman, R. R. (1959) Affectional responses in the infant monkey. *Science* **130**, 421–432.

Hayek, F. A. (1952) *The sensory order.* Chicago: Univer. Chicago Press.

Hebb, D. O. (1949) *The organization of behavior.* New York: Wiley.

Hershenson, M., Munsinger, H., & Kessen, W. (1965) Preference for shapes of intermediate variability in the newborn human. *Science* **147**, 630–631.

Hess, E. H. (1956) Space perception in the chick. *Scient. Amer.* **195** (1), 71–80.

Hess, E. H. (1962) Imprinting and the "critical period" concept. In E. L. Bliss (Ed.), *Roots of behavior.* New York: Harper. Pp. 254–263.

Hubel, D. H., & Wiesel, T. N. (1962). Receptive fields, binocular interaction and functional architecture in the cat's visual cortex. *J. Physiol.* **160**, 106–154.

Hubel, D. H., & Wiesel, T. N. (1963) Receptive fields of cells in striate cortex of very young, visually inexperienced kittens. *J. Neurophysiol.* **26**, 994–1002.

James, W. (1890) *The principles of psychology.* New York: Holt.

Kagan, J., & Lewis, M. (1965) Studies of attention in the human infant. *Merrill-Palmer Quart.* **11**, 95–127.

Ling, B. C. (1942) A genetic study of sustained visual fixation and associated behavior in the human infant, from birth to six months. *J. genet. Psychol.* **61**, 227–277.

Lorenz, K. (1957) The nature of instinct. In C. H. Schiller (Ed.), *Instinctive behavior.* New York: Int. Univer. Press. Pp. 129–175.

Maier, N. R. F., & Schneirla, T. C. (1935) *Principles of animal psychology.* New York: McGraw-Hill.

Melzack, R. (In press) Effects of early experience on behavior: experimental and conceptual considerations. In P. H. Hoch, & J. Zubin (Eds.) *Psychopathology of perception.* New York: Grune & Stratton.

McGraw, M. B. (1943) *The neuromuscular maturation of the human infant.* New York: Columbia Univer. Press.

Moseley, D. (1925) The accuracy of the pecking response in chicks. *J. comp. physiol. Psychol.* **5**, 75–97.

Padilla, S. G. (1935) Further studies on the delayed pecking of chicks. *J. comp. Psychol.* **20**, 413–443.

Piaget, J. (1952) *The origins of intelligence in children.* New York: Int. Univer. Press.

Postman, L. (1955) Association theory and perceptual learning. *Psychol. Rev.* **62**, 438–446.

Pratt, C. C. (1950) The role of past experience in visual perception. *J. Psychol.* **30**, 85–107.

Pratt, K. C. (1954) The neonate. In L. Carmichael (Ed.), *Manual of child psychology.* New York: Wiley.

Pratt, K. C., Nelson, A. K., & Sun, K. H. (1930) The behavior of the newborn infant. *Ohio State Univer. stud. contrib. psychol.,* No. 10.

Riesen, A. H. (1958) Plasticity of behavior: psychological aspects. In H. F. Harlow, & C. N. Woolsey (Eds.), *Biological and biochemical bases of behavior.* Madison: Univer. Wisconsin Press. Pp. 425–450.

Riesen, A. H. (1961) Stimulation as a requirement for growth and function in behavioral development. In D. W. Fiske, & S. R. Maddi (Eds.), *Functions of varied experience.* Homewood, Ill.: Dorsey, Pp. 57–80.

Saayman, G., Ames, E. W., & Moffet, A. (1964) Response to novelty as an indicator of visual discrimination in the human infant. *J. exp. child Psychol.* **1**, 189–198.

Spitz, R. A. (1946) The smiling response: a contribution to the ontogenesis of social relations. *Genet. Psychol. Monogr.* **34**, 57–125.

Stechler, G. (1964) The effect of medication during labor on newborn attention. *Science* **144**, 315–317.

Stirnimann, F. (1944) Über das Farbenempfinden Neugeborener. *Ann. Paediat.* **163**, 1–25.

Taylor, J. G. (1962) *The behavioral basis of perception.* New Haven: Yale Univer. Press.

Thorpe, W. H. (1951) The learning abilities of birds. *Ibis* **93**, 1–32, 252–296.

Thorpe, W. H. (1956) *Learning and instinct in animals.* London: Methuen.

Tinbergen, N. (1951) *The study of instinct.* Oxford: Clarendon Press.

Tinbergen, N., & Perdeck, A. C. (1950) On the stimulus situation releasing the begging response in the newly hatched herring gull chick (*Lazarus argentatus argentatus* Pont). *Behaviour* **3**, 1–39.

Tucker, A. F. (1957) The effect of early light and form deprivation on the visual behaviors of the chicken. Unpublished doctoral dissertation, Univer. of Chicago.

Uzgiris, I. C., & Hunt, J. McV. (1965) A longitudinal study of recognition learning. Paper read at *Soc. res. child developm.* Minneapolis, Minn., March.

Senden, M. v. (1960) *Space and sight: the perception of space and shape in congenitally blind patients before and after operation.* Glencoe, Ill.: Free Press.

Walk, R. D., & Gibson, E. J. (1961) A comparative and analytical study of visual depth perception. *Psychol. Monogr.* **75**, No. 15.

White, B. L., Castle, P., & Held, R. (1964) Observations on the development of visually directed reaching. *Child Developm.* **35**, 349–364.

Zimmerman, R. R., & Torrey, C. C. (1965) Ontogeny of learning. In A. M. Schrier, H. F. Harlow, & F. Stollnitz (Eds.), *Behavior of nonhuman primates.* Vol. II. New York: Academic Press. Pp. 405–447.

Zuckerman, C. B., & Rock, I. (1957) A reappraisal of the roles of past experience and innate organizing processes in visual perception. *Psychol. Bull.* **54**, 269–296.

ᔆ 9 ᔆ

Learning in the Human Infant

LEWIS P. LIPSITT

Brown University

$\mathbf{F}$EW persons in the field of child development ever doubted that all life processes depend on hereditary as well as experiential circumstances. It goes without saying at the present time that the behavior of humans is a product of both maturational and environmental determinants. Because controversy has persisted in different guises over the relative importance of these very general classes of variables, however, and because this report deals principally with experiential or stimulus determinants of psychological change in infants, the writer wishes to enter one disclaimer and a justification.

It is acknowledged at the outset that no learning can occur in the absence of a congenital response repertoire on which all behavior change capitalizes. Thus the attention accorded, and the emphasis placed on, experiential determinants here is no attempt to resolve the nature-nurture conflict in favor of the latter. By now the controversy, as it is usually posed, is widely recognized as substantially empty (Anastasi, 1958; Spiker, 1965). Rather, the studies reported here are the result of a simple research strategy involving the investigation of certain stimulating conditions and learning mechanisms that effect changes in children's behavior. Although justification of the strategy is not obligatory, reviews of children's learning studies (Munn, 1954; Lipsitt, 1963) do reveal that child-development researchers have, until relatively recently, sponsored very few scholarly investigations of early conditioning processes. This imbalance, paradoxical as it seems in the historical light of both Watson's and Freud's proclamations concerning the great importance of early experience in determining later be-

Much of the research reported here has been supported by USPHS Grant No. NB 04268. The writer is indebted also to the Brown University unit of the National Collaborative Study of Perinatal Factors in Child Development, and particularly to its director, Dr. Glidden L. Brooks, for facilitating this research in numerous ways over an eight-year period. Thanks are also expressed to the Providence Lying-In Hospital and its staff for their kind cooperation in the newborn research.

havior, has tended to favor morphological or constitutional interpretations of development (Carmichael, 1954; Gesell, 1954) that emphasize
time and physiological maturation as primary determinants of behavior modification. It can be hoped that the study program reported
here will help to neutralize the imbalance.

CONTEXT OF STUDIES

The setting in which the present research program is being conducted has been particularly propitious for certain kinds of learning
studies. We have had access to a population of infants who are, with
their parents, participants in a longitudinal investigation of child development (National Collaborative Study of Perinatal Factors in Child
Development). The entire project, conducted by 14 collaborating centers throughout the country and sponsored by the National Institute
of Neurological Diseases and Blindness, is collecting and processing extensive obstetrical, pediatric, and psychological data on the prenatal
circumstances, birth events, and developmental progress of about 50,-
000 children. The major focus has been on neurological aberrations,
mental retardation, and, in general, the biological and psychological
precursors of such dysfunctions.

As one of the collaborating institutions, the Brown University unit
follows an extensive protocol common to all. The infants are seen
during the first few days of life at the Providence Lying-In Hospital,
then at a follow-up center at 4, 8, and 12 months of age, and thereafter
at longer intervals. The present program of studies resulted from the
fortunate availability of a fair portion of the Brown sample at each of
these age periods for the ancillary work reported here. While a handi-
cap and a challenge were imposed by the necessarily limited amount
of time for which each infant was available (1 hour for neonates and
no longer than 20 minutes at each of the other ages), the data show
that for some learning procedures, this amount of time was sufficient.

THE NEWBORN LABORATORY

The neonate laboratory at Brown University is equipped, as shown
in Figs. 9-1 and 9-2, with a stabilimeter crib (Lipsitt & DeLucia, 1960),
a six-channel polygraph with an integrator unit, an audio-oscillator
and associated speaker, a physiological stimulator unit, interval timers for the controlled presentation of stimuli, sterilization equipment,

Fig. 9-1 View of newborn laboratory at Providence Lying-In Hospital, showing stimulating and recording equipment. Stabilimeter crib is in foreground.

and various accessories for the recording of such behavior as sucking by means of a pressure-transducer linked with tubing and ordinary bottle nipples. The stabilimeter provides continuous polygraphic recording of the infant's movement and enables the documentation and

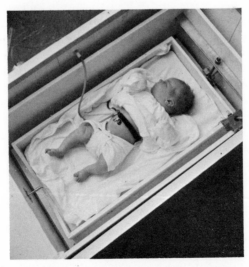

Fig. 9-2 Newborn in stabilimeter, with pneumograph attached.

measurement of startle or other activity in response to specific stimulation. Breathing activity is monitored by means of an infant pneumograph, attached firmly around the subject's abdomen and linked
with an appropriate transducer and the polygraph.

Habituation in Newborns

One of the most easily observed behavioral attributes of the human
newborn is that with repetitive stimulation by an initially effective or
unconditioned stimulus, response diminution tends to occur. This
phenomenon was described in very early literature on child development (Disher, 1934; Forbes & Forbes, 1927; Peiper, 1925) but it has
been only relatively recently that this response-decrement, extinction-
like process has been systematically studied in newborns (Bartoshuk,
1962; Bridger, 1961). The phenomenon is documented by recording
the startle response as measured by body movement, respiration, or
heart rate, and by noting the gradual lessening of reaction to the
repetitive stimulation.

Use of the habituation procedure for the assessment of perception
and stimulus discrimination of infants has been investigated by Bronshtein et al. (1958). They reported that if a tone or odor is administered to a sucking infant, the stimulus will at first disrupt the sucking pattern. With successive repetitions of that stimulus, however, the
sucking disruption will diminish and eventually cease. Recovery or
dishabituation of the response will occur after a minimal temporal interval elapses or if the stimulus is discriminably changed. Unfortunately, the promise of the Bronshtein method has not been real-
ized in at least two attempts that used the sucking response to replicate the interruptive effects of external stimulation (Kaye & Levin,
1963; Solomons, Hardy, & Melrose, 1965).

However, two studies utilizing response decrement and recovery of
body movement and respiratory measures associated with olfactory
stimulation have yielded the anticipated effect (Engen & Lipsitt, 1965;
Engen, Lipsitt, & Kaye, 1963). In these studies, infants' reactions to
olfactory stimuli were compared with responses under nonodorous
control presentations administered on alternate trials. In one study
of olfactory response and its diminution with repetitive stimulation,
subjects were presented 10 trials of each of two odorants, anise oil
and asafetida, half of the subjects receiving one of the odors first and
half the other odor first in a one-minute intertrial interval condition.
After the 20 trials, and under the same condition, the first-given odor
was reintroduced for 2 additional trials.

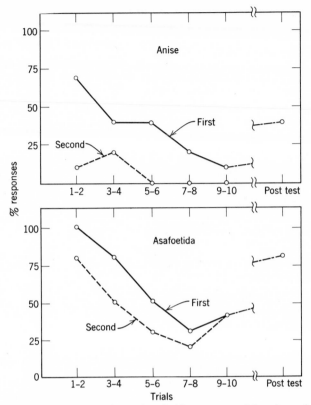

Fig. 9-3   Percent responses to anise and asafetida over ten trials, when administered first or second, and after interpolated stimulation with alternate odorant (Engen, Lipsitt, & Kaye, 1963).

Figure 9-3 shows the percentage of responses to the odors obtained across trials. From the results, it was apparent that (a) response-decrement occurred to repetitive stimulation with each odorant, (b) cross-odor habituation did occur, such that stimulation by one odor tended to decrease sensitivity to the second odor, and (c) there oc-curred recovery of response to the second stimulus following habitua-tion to the first, with recovery occurring a second time when the first stimulus was reintroduced following habituation to the second. This recovery of response to novel or unfamiliar stimulation raised the question of whether constituents or components of olfactory solutions in compounds could be discriminated by infants. Such a finding would support the assumption that olfactory habituation is a cortical or subcortical process rather than a peripheral, sensory-adaptation phenomenon.

In an experiment designed to illuminate further the olfactory habituation and dishabituation phenomena (Engen & Lipsitt, 1965) neonates
were administered an odorant mixture consisting of amyl acetate and
heptanal along with a nonodorous diluent in 20 trials. Following these
trials and with no change in intertrial interval, tests were given with one
or the other component in solution with the nonodorous diluent.
Figure 9-4 shows the response over those 10 trials for 10 subjects exposed to the mixture. Following these presentations and the occurrence of response-decrement, the amyl-acetate odorant, presented
alone, produced recovery. The level of response on these recovery
trials was not different from that of a comparable control group (represented by the open circle on the left in Fig. 9-4) that had no experience with the mixture. A similar group of subjects, shown in Fig.

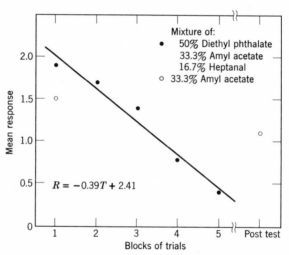

Fig. 9-4 Mean response to odorant mixture and, subsequently, to the component
amyl acetate. Response level to amyl acetate by a control group with no previous
experience with mixture is indicated by open circle at left (Engen & Lipsitt, 1965).

9-5, was administered the heptanal solution following habituation to
the mixture and yielded the expected recovery, although not to the
extent produced by the amyl acetate. It is of interest to note that this
implicit ordering of odorant similarity (mixture to heptanal to amyl
acetate) was identical to that produced by articulate adults who were
requested to make similarity judgments of the same stimuli in a
psychophysical experiment. Thus it can be concluded that the human

newborn is capable of discriminating components of odorant compounds and that higher nervous-system function is implicated in the process.

Neonate Sucking Behavior

The sucking response is present in almost all human infants at birth, and has caught the fascination of many observers of newborn behavior (McKee & Honzik, 1962). Although the complete sucking act is a complex pattern of response, it is executed by the newborn with rhythm and grace. Sucking is probably practiced by a fair proportion of infants before birth and is vital for survival under any but the most highly civilized of human conditions. The mouth area is

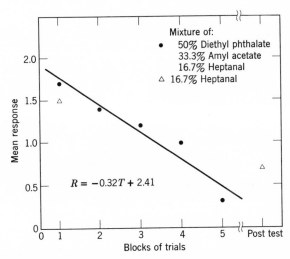

Fig. 9-5 Mean response to odorant mixture and, subsequently to the component heptanal. Response level to heptanal without previous experience shown by open triangle at left (Engen & Lipsitt, 1965).

the site of this crucial act of dependency; through Freud, orality has become the focus of one of the most widely heralded aspects of personality development and psychological aberration. It is probably precisely because of its seeming maturity at birth that the sucking response has not been subjected to frequent experimental study and particularly to manipulations that might shed more light on the role of learning in shaping and altering various characteristics of the response.

Recently, Gunther (1961) suggested that the nature of the eliciting stimulus is of enormous importance in determining the ease and intensity with which sucking behavior is obtained from newborns. She has indicated that differentially shaped nipples, both natural and manufactured, have varying capacities for evoking sucking behavior, that individual differences among infants determine in part the readiness with which they will latch on to different types of nipples, and that the behavior of the mother or caretaker can sometimes induce inhibition of response, or nipple aversion, in the neonate.

To investigate the differential cumulative effects of "optimizing" and "nonoptimizing" intra-oral stimuli, a good elicitor and a poor elicitor of sucking were used in a study by Lipsitt and Kaye (1965). The two stimuli, respectively, were an ordinary rubber bottle nipple

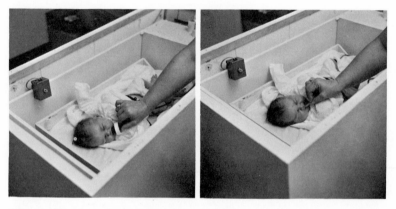

Fig. 9-6   Newborn with nipple inserted   Fig. 9-7   Newborn with tube inserted in
               in mouth.   mouth.

and a piece of straight ½-inch rubber laboratory tubing. Of 30 subjects, all between 2 and 4 days of age, 10 received stimulation with just the nipple, 10 with just the tube, and 10 with both, under a 50-trial procedure of 10 seconds' duration each and separated by approximately 30 seconds. In contrast to the tube-only and nipple-only groups, the tube-nipple group received alternating five-trial blocks in which first the tube was administered for five trials, then the nipple, and so on. Highly reliable observational counts of sucks per 10-second unit were taken. The method of stimulus presentation was such that the stimulus was touched to the infant's lips; when the mouth opened, the stimulus was inserted, the experimenter pushed a button operating a timer, and the 10-second count commenced. Figures 9-6 and 9-7 show one of the tube-nipple subjects, first with the nipple inserted, then with the tube inserted. Casual inspection and comparison of the pictures suggest that the infant finds the tube somewhat less agreeable than the nipple. Figure 9-8, which shows the results in mean numbers of sucking responses for each of the groups separately, confirms this hypothesis. It can be seen that the tube-only

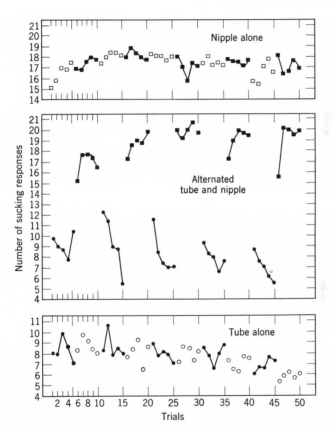

Fig. 9-8 Mean number of sucking responses produced over 50 trials by three groups of 10 subjects each (Lipsitt & Kaye, 1965).

group sucked at about half the rate of the nipple-only group, and a comparison of nipple-sucking rate with tube-sucking rate in the alternated group reveals a similar effect. More pertinent to the question of effects of experience on subsequent behavior is an examination of the rate changes within five-trial blocks for the tube-nipple group in comparison with the sucking rates on comparable trials in the nipple-only and tube-only groups. In the alternated group, there occurred a

cumulative effect of sucking on one or the other stimulus such that
response in each nipple block started low and increased, whereas response to the tube started high and decreased. This effect is seen
clearly in Fig. 9-9, which was drawn by collapsing the five-trial blocks
of sucking rates (eliminating the first block in which no such effect
should be expected) to examine the trends within blocks and compare them across groups.

Statistical analyses confirmed that for the alternated (tube-nipple)
group the upward trend within blocks for nipple sucking and the
downward trend for tube sucking were reliable, compared with comparable data from the nipple-only and tube-only groups. That sucking on one of these stimuli produced a clear effect on the sucking rate

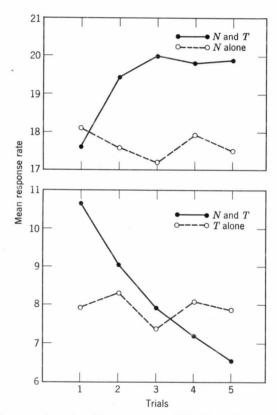

Fig. 9-9   Mean number of sucking responses within five-trial blocks for the three
groups. The within-blocks sucking rate of the nipple-only group is compared with
the nipple-sucking rate of the tube-nipple group above. Similar rates are compared
below for the tube-only group with the tube-nipple group (Lippsitt & Kaye, 1965).

to the other stimulus was demonstrated by the fact that in the alternated group, the response rate on the first trials of tube blocks was reliably greater than the response rate on comparable trials for the tube-only group. The nature of the intra-oral stimulus, then, clearly determines the frequency with which neonates will suck, and the sucking is affected by other oral stimuli with which the infant has experience.

Conditioned Sucking Using Dextrose

Since in the previous study the tube proved to be a relatively weak elicitor of sucking, this finding provided an opportunity to attempt manipulation of sucking rate to the tube through reinforcement (Lipsitt, Kaye, & Bosack, in press). Twenty neonates were administered one of two treatments: One involved six baseline trials of 15-second tube presentation, followed by a conditioning period, extinction period, then reconditioning and re-extinction periods. During conditioning and reconditioning a 5% dextrose-water solution was injected through the tube after the first 10 seconds of sucking; 1 cm^3 of the solution was given on each trial. A control group received the same treatment except that during the conditioning periods the dextrose solution was given by syringe in the intertrial intervals separating the tube presentations. To control for differential amounts of oral stimulation incurred by syringe feeding of the control group, an empty syringe was used at comparable times for the experimental subjects. Sucking was recorded for the first 10 seconds of each 15-second trial. Figure 9-10 shows the difference in response rate for the two groups throughout the experiment. The difference in rate during the first conditioning period was reliable. The difference during reconditioning fell short of significance but suggests strongly that a longer period of training would have increased the magnitude of the effect. Thus a "nonoptimizing" sucking stimulus can be transformed into a more effective elicitor of sucking through association with a suitable reinforcing agent, a phenomenon previously documented in newborn dogs by Stanley et al. (1963).

Conditioned Babkin Responding

Recently, Kaye (1965) demonstrated a conditioning phenomenon in the human newborn through the Babkin reflex by associating a kinesthetic conditioning stimulus with a hand-mouth reflex. The reflex, consisting of a wide opening of the mouth and a tendency for the head to turn toward midline from the tonic-neck-reflex position, is elicited by pressing on the neonate's palms. To use this reflex in an approximation of classical Pavlovian procedures, Kaye paired the palm-press stimulation with the initially ineffective stimulation of transporting the arms from the infant's sides to a position next to the head. The kinesthetic arm-transport stimulation was administered just before pressing the subject's palms. An experimental group received five baseline trials of arm transport alone prior to receiving

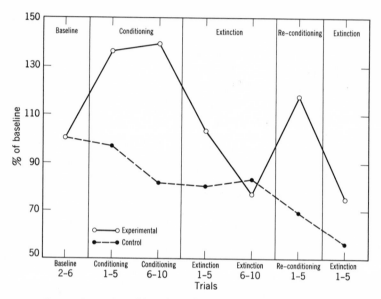

Fig. 9-10 Comparison of sucking data for experimental and control groups in sucking-conditioning experiment using dextrose reinforcement (Lippsitt, Kaye, & Bosack, in press).

35 conditioning trials, and then received 15 extinction trials. Following the five baseline trials, a control group received 35 trials of palm-press alone with the arms retained in the up posi on, and the 15 extinction trials. Baseline and extinction (test) responses by the two groups are compared in Fig. 9-11. Although the two groups did not differ during the baseline period, the experimental group gave reliably more responses to arm transport in the extinction period than did the control group. The analysis of frequency of unconditioned Babkin responding in both groups during the 35-trial "conditioning" period revealed no differences between the two groups, although an apparent (but not significant) habituation of Babkin responding occurred. It

can be added that a second control group, involving arm transport alone during the conditioning period, was checked for the possibility that the differences shown in Fig. 9-11 could be attributed to an arousal effect induced simply by the kinesthetic stimulation of the experimental group. This procedure did not result in an increase in extinction (test) responding relative to baseline responding.

Conditioned Head-turning in Newborns

Based upon earlier work of Papoušek (1959; 1960; 1961), Siqueland and Lipsitt (1965) developed procedures for studying conditioned head-

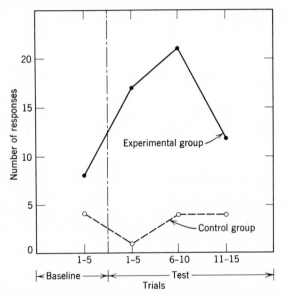

Fig. 9-11 Results of conditioning experiment involving Babkin responding: comparison of baseline and test performance for a conditioning group and a control group (Kaye, 1965).

turning behavior in neonates, utilizing both tactual stimulation and nutritive reinforcement. One procedure consisted of sounding a buzzer for a 5–second period, during the latter half of which the experimenter stroked the subject's left cheek near the mouth. If the infant responded by turning toward the tactile stimulus, or responded in the same manner to the buzzer preceding it, a bottle with dextrose solution was administered and the infant was allowed to suck for a brief period (two seconds). Half of a group of 36 infants within the second and third days of life were administered 30 trials of conditioning as described, separated by 30–second intertrial intervals, while the other half were used as matched control subjects and received dextrose presentations 8 to 10 seconds after termination of the tactile stimulus. All subjects received at least 12 but not more than 30 extinction trials following training.

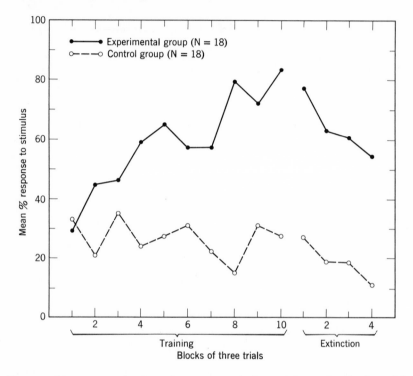

Fig. 9-12   Mean percent head-turning responses during training and extinction trials for an experimental group and a control group (Siqueland & Lipsitt, 1966).

Although the tactile stimulus was a low-level elicitor of head-turning at the start of training, response to this stimulus increased greatly as an apparent consequence of the administration of reinforcement contingent upon the occurrence of the response. This effect is seen in Fig. 9-12 by comparing the mean percentage response of the two groups over trials.

The success of the procedure just described suggested an elaboration of the technique for the study of discriminative behavior in the newborn child. Two groups of 20 infants 2 to 4 days old were subjected to procedures designed to assess the effect of pairing reinforcement differentially with two responses, left head-turning and right head-turning. The method, similar to that in the foregoing study, involved presentation of two different auditory stimuli on alternating trials: tactual stimulation on one side was paired with a "buzzer" and on the other side with a "tone." For the 20 experimental subjects, reinforcement was presented, following ipsilateral turns to the positive stimulus (R^s+), but not following turns to the negative stimulus (R^s-).

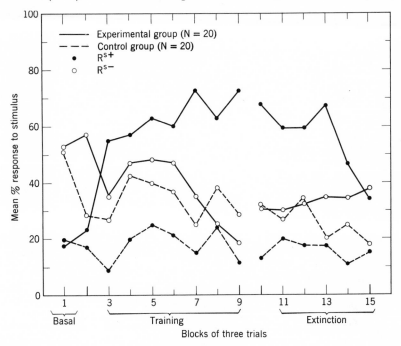

Fig. 9-13 Comparison of percentage responses to positive and negative stimuli separately in an experimental group over training and extinction trials, and responses on comparable trials for control group (Siqueland & Lipsitt, 1966).

The 20 control subjects were matched on total number of reinforcements given during training trials, but the dextrose solution presented to them 8 to 10 seconds following tactile stimulation was not contingent on head-turning.

The response measure was percentage of occurrence of ipsilateral head-turns to the positive and negative stimuli over six-trial blocks during baseline, training, and extinction. Learning was reflected by a shift in relative percentages of R^s+ and R^s- over trials. Such a shift in favor of R^s+ was expected to occur in the experimental but not in the control group. As seen in Fig. 9-13, and as was borne out by statistical treatment of both the training and extinction data, the expected effects were obtained, substantiating the occurrence of learned differentiation.

In a third experiment on neonatal head-turning, the two auditory stimuli served as positive and negative cues for reinforcement at one side only. Turns to right-sided stimulation in the presence of one auditory stimulus were reinforced, whereas right-sided turns in the presence of the other auditory stimulus were not. Following such training, reversal was instituted so that turning to the previously reinforced auditory cue was now not reinforced and vice versa. A head-turning apparatus, used by Siqueland (1964) in a study with 4-month-old subjects, provided instrumentation and automatic recording of head movements. This equipment consisted of a headpiece connecting with a potentiometer circuit via a flexible shaft, enabling the polygraphic recording and measurement of lateral head movements about the horizontal axis. Sixteen infants, aged 48 to 116 hours, were divided into two groups; for one the tone was the positive and the buzzer was the negative stimulus, and for the other the positive-negative designations were reversed. After original training, S^+ became S^-, and S^- became S^+ in each group. All subjects received 60 training trials (30 with each auditory stimulus) followed by 60 reversal trials, one trial every 30 seconds. Stimulus presentations consisted of right-sided tactile stimulation overlapping the last half of the tone or buzzer.

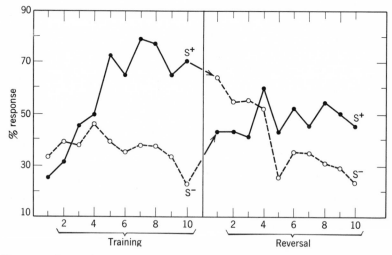

Fig. 9-14 Comparison of percentage head-turning responses to a positive and a negative stimulus during 60 trials of training and 60 trials of reversal (Siqueland & Lipsitt, 1966).

Response criterion was a minimum 10° head rotation to the right; and reinforcement was contingent upon a response of that magnitude. On the polygraphic recording, this criterion translated into a 2-mm downward deflection. An observer signaled the occurrence of such responses to the experimenter who then presented 0.2 cm³ of a dextrose solution via a 4-second nipple presentation.

The results of the study are given in Fig. 9-14. It shows the mean percentage of right turns to S+ and S− over training and reversal trials. Statistical analysis indicated that responding increased sharply to the positive stimulus during training, whereas response to the negative stimulus showed negligible change. During reversal, the major effect was a decrease in S− responding over trials, whereas S+ responding showed no significant change. At the end of reversal training, the 16 subjects were responding reliably more to the positive than the negative stimulus.

Comments on Neonatal Conditioning

These experiments show that under certain experimental conditions, environmental events can function as reinforcing stimuli to shape or selectively strengthen responses in the behavioral repertoire of the newborn. The magnitude of the effect, induced experimentally in the first few days of life and with a relatively short period of training, lends credibility to the proposition that the human neonate is not only a learning organism but may be remarkably sensitive to environmental events, perhaps particularly to those relating to oral stimulation and to food intake. It should be obvious that much research will be required to elucidate the basic parameters controlling such learned changes in behavior, to determine the long-term effects of various types of early learning opportunity, and to study the effect and import of individual differences as they affect such processes.

LABORATORY FOR OLDER INFANTS

Our subjects who were participants in the child development study were returned to a follow-up center every four months during the first year following the neonatal period. Some of the children were available for perceptual and learning studies during those visits. Two techniques developed in this setting are discussed here because of their apparent success in producing conditioned responding in a relatively short period of time, at least in some babies, and because of their seeming adaptability across a large part of the first-year period, thus enabling their use in longitudinal-study designs.

Siqueland (1964) used an operant-conditioning technique in 4-month-old infants using food reinforcement that was provided from a bottle of the baby's regular formula brought by the mother. His apparatus consisted of an infant reclining seat on which was mounted a lightweight head cradle lined with foam plastic. A potentiometer circuit polygraphically recorded changes in potential occurring with head rotations. Head-turns were defined as rotations of 45° or greater to the right or left of the central position. A white experimental chamber, open on one side, in which the infant was faced toward the back, provided the subjects with an environment devoid of distracting stimuli. The experimenter stood behind the subject and, during conditioning, presented the bottle for a 3-second period; each presentation was registered on the polygraph record by a foot-activated event marker. An eight-minute procedure consisted of one-minute baseline, three minutes of conditioning, two minutes of extinction, and a two-minute reconditioning period. For group R+, the bottle was given for each right turn. Group C, controls matched with R+ subjects for number of milk presentations, received reinforcement that was not contingent upon head rotations. Group L+ received the bottle contingent on left head rotations only. After each head rotation occurrence, the subject's head was repositioned at center.

Figure 9-15 shows the mean cumulative head-turns (always of at least 45°), both left and right, for the three groups over 30–second intervals. Although there were no reliable differences during baseline, group R+ showed a significant increase in right turns from baseline through conditioning, a decrease between first and second minutes of extinction, and subsequently an increase during reconditioning. Similar comparisons for right head turns in groups L+ and C showed no such effects, as expected. Group L+, however, shifted significantly in number of left turns on each of the pertinent comparisons. Considering that no control of the deprivation circumstances of the subjects was possible in this study, the results bode well for the use of the procedure at other ages within the first year of life, to examine more closely both the external and the individual-difference characteristics of which such conditioning is a function.

Finally, a procedure (Lipsitt, Pedersen, & DeLucia, 1966) was recently explored with 12-month-old children. It was based upon suggestions of Lindsley (1963) and capitalized on the reinforcing effectiveness of sensory stimulation (Hunt, 1965). This procedure involved the presentation of changing illumination (rather than traditional discrete

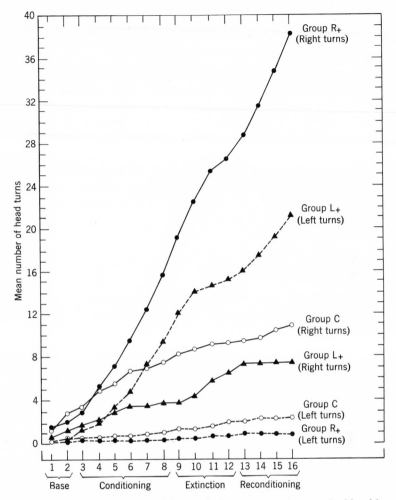

Fig. 9-15 Cumulative-curve comparisons of three groups of 4-month-old subjects, showing right and left head-turn frequencies for each (Siqueland, 1964).

reinforcing events) that was contingent upon the rate of the infant's response. The subjects were seated in an infant chair in reach of a box containing an operant manipulandum—a clear plastic 8 by 9 in. panel. Panel responses activated a power supply and an associated pulse-averaging circuit that was designed to vary the intensity of light in the viewing box according to response rate. The response-consequent, therefore, was activation of a 120-watt light in the viewing box where the subject could see through the panel whatever visual stimulus had been placed in the otherwise dark box. Reinforcement was proportionate to response rate; transition from low to high brightness (and vice versa) was gradual. In the viewing box, a colorful clown picture was mounted on a disc attached to a motor shaft that moved at a rate of 30 rpm. Cumulative response records were obtained by reading an electrical counter every 15 seconds. One procedure consisted of a 15–second baseline, followed by five minutes of conditioning, one minute of extinction, two of reconditioning, and one of re-extinction. For 10 subjects who completed the procedure, the difference between baseline rate and that of the fifth minute of conditioning was reliable, and the rate of every subject increased between these periods. Although reduction in response rate from the end of conditioning through

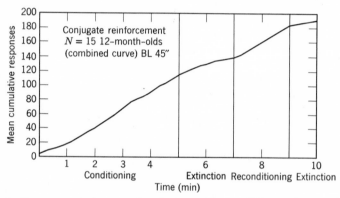

Fig. 9-16 Group cumulative curve based on 15 subjects utilizing conjugate reinforcement technique (Lipsitt, Pedersen, & DeLucia, 1966).

extinction was not reliable, 6 of 10 subjects showed a rate decline. Finally, the increase between the first extinction period and reconditioning period was not reliable, but the re-extinction procedure produced a reliable response drop.

The experimental procedure was modified to extend extinction from 1 to 2 minutes, and the nature of the baseline period was changed from a constant 15 seconds to a variable period according to the time required by the subject to make five responses. Thus, each subject began conditioning as soon as five responses were emitted, and no subject was retained who failed to make five responses in three minutes of baseline or who cried within this period. This procedure was administered to an initial group of twenty-two 1-year olds of whom 15 met the criteria for retention. Figure 9-16 shows the results for them. Reliable changes occurred as follows: Rate increased from early to late conditioning, decreased when reinforcement was withdrawn, increased when reinforcement was reinstated, and decreased again under the second extinction condition. Figure 9-17 shows an individual cumulative record for one subject under this second procedure. The control of the reinforcing circumstances over the behavior of this subject was obvious and marked. As indicated previously, the setting in which these data were collected provided little or no time for the usual shaping-up process that is brought to bear on recalcitrant subjects. For the subjects who completed the procedure, however, it is encouraging to note how effective conjugate reinforcement of a visual

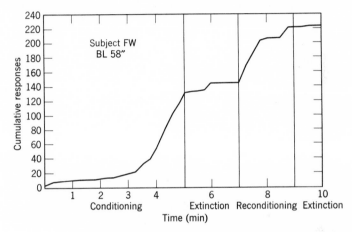

Fig. 9-17 Cumulative record of a single 1-year-old subject, through a 10-minute session. For this subject, 58 seconds were required for the first five (basal) responses to be emitted (Lipsitt, Pedersen, & DeLucia, 1966).

sort seems to be. We presume, also, that subjects who fail to meet criteria for retention are reflecting individual behavior differences that are themselves of some import and worthy of further study.

CONCLUSION

A number of studies with children in the first year of life have been reported in which experimental manipulations of environmental events have produced behavior changes, some of which may be regarded as clear-cut learning phenomena. It has been shown that the behavior of the newborn can be altered sharply through peculiarities of the sucking situation, and that new associative connections of various sorts can be induced in neonates if the appropriate stimulation is provided. Some techniques for the study of learning in the child beyond the neonate stage have also been described that show promise for further exploration. In particular, infant learning behavior must be studied in settings that afford protracted periods of observation and investigation, both within specific sessions and over the entire first-year age span and beyond. Current data on infant learning suggest that a renewed optimism is warranted with respect to the learning potential of infants, as well as to the feasibility of studying that learning potential.

REFERENCES

Anastasi, A. (1958) Heredity, environment, and the question "How?" *Psychol. Rev.* 65, 197–208.

Bartoshuk, A. K. (1962) Human neonatal cardiac acceleration to sound: habituation and dishabituation. *Percept. mot. Skills* 15, 15–27.

Bridger, W. H. (1961) Sensory habituation and discrimination in the human neonate. *Amer. J. Psychiat.* 117, 991–996.

Bronshtein, A. I., Antonova, T. G., Kamenetskaya, N. H., Luppova, V. A., & Sytova, V. A. (1958) On the development of the functions of analyzers in infants and some animals at the early stage of ontogenesis. In *Problems of evolution of physiological functions.* USSR: Acad. Sci. (U.S. Dept. of Health, Educ. and Welf., Translation Service).

Carmichael, L. (1954) The onset and early development of behavior. In L. Carmichael (Ed.), *Manual of child psychology.* New York: Wiley. Pp. 60–185.

Disher, D. R. (1934) *The reactions of newborn infants to chemical stimuli administered nasally. Ohio State Univer. stud. inf. behav.* No. 12. Columbus, Ohio: Ohio State Press. Pp. 1–52.

Engen, T., & Lipsitt, L. P. (1965) Decrement and recovery of responses to olfactory stimuli in the human neonate. *J. comp. physiol. Psychol.* 59, 312–316.

Engen, T., Lipsitt, L. P., & Kaye, H. (1963) Olfactory responses and adaptation in the human neonate. *J. comp. physiol. Psychol.* 56, 73–77.

Forbes, H. S., & Forbes, H. B. (1927) Fetal sense reaction: hearing. *J. comp. Psychol.* 7, 353–355.

Gesell, A. (1954) The ontogenesis of infant behavior. In L. Carmichael (Ed.), *Manual of child psychology.* New York: Wiley. Pp. 335–373.

Gunther, M. (1961) Infant behaviour at the breast. In B. M. Foss (Ed.), *Determinants of infant behavior.* London: Methuen. Pp. 37–44.

Hunt, J. McV. (1965) Traditional personality theory in the light of recent evidence. *Amer. Scient.* 53, 80–96.

Kaye, H. (1965) The conditioned Babkin reflex in human newborns. *Psychon. Sci.* 2, 287–288.

Kaye, H., & Levin, G. R. (1963) Two attempts to demonstrate tonal suppression of non-nutritive sucking in neonates. *Percept. mot. Skills.* 17, 521–522.

Lindsley, O. R. (1963) Experimental analysis of social reinforcement: terms and methods. *Amer. J. Orthopsychiat.* **33,** 624–633.

Lipsitt, L. P. (1963) Learning in the first year of life. In L. P. Lipsitt & C. C. Spiker (Eds.), *Advances in child development and behavior.* Vol. 1. New York: Academ. Press. Pp. 147–195.

Lipsitt, L. P., & DeLucia, C. A. (1960) An apparatus for the measurement of specific response and general activity of the human neonate. *Amer. J. Psychol.* **73,** 630–632.

Lipsitt, L. P., Pedersen, L. J., & DeLucia, C. (1966) Conjugate reinforcement of operant responding in infants. *Psychon. Sci.* **4,** 67–68.

Lipsitt, L. P., & Kaye, H. (1965) Change in neonatal response to optimizing and non-optimizing sucking stimulation. *Psychon. Sci.* **2,** 221–222.

Lipsitt, L. P., Kaye, H., & Bosack, T. (In press) The facilitation of sucking responses in human neonates through conditioning procedures. *J. exp. child Psychol.*

McKee; J. P., & Honzik. M. P. (1962) The sucking behavior of mammals: an illustration of the nature-nurture question. In L. Postman (Ed.), *Psychology in the making.* New York: Knopf. Pp. 585–661.

Munn, N. L. (1954) Learning in children. In L. Carmichael (Ed.), *Manual of child psychology.* New York: Wiley. Pp. 374–458.

Papoušek, H. (1959) A method of studying conditioned food reflexes in young children up to the age of six months. *Pavlov J. higher nerv. Activ.* **9,** 136–140.

Papoušek, H. (1960) Conditioned motor digestive reflexes in infants. II. A new experimental method for the investigation. *Cesk. Pediat.* **15,** 981–988.

Papoušek, H. (1961) Conditioned head rotation reflexes in infants in the first months of life. *Acta. Pedial.* **50,** 565–576.

Peiper, A. (1924) Sinnesempfindungen des Kindes vor seiner Geburt. *Monatssche. Kinderhk.* **29,** 236–241.

Siqueland, E. (1964) Operant conditioning of head turning in four-month infants. *Psychon. Sci.* **1,** 223–224.

Siqueland, E., & Lipsitt, L. P. (1966) Conditioned head-turning behavior in newborns. *J. exp. child Psychol.* **3,** 356–376.

Solomons, G., Hardy, J. C., & Melrose, J. (1965) Auditory reactions of the neonate. *The Journal-Lancet* **85,** 17–21.

Spiker, C. C. (1965) The concept of development: relevant and irrelevant issues. Unpublished manuscript, State Univer. Iowa.

Stanley, W. C., Cornwell, A. C., Poggiani, C., & Trattner, A. (1963) Conditioning in the neonatal puppy. *J. comp. physiol. Psychol.* **56,** 511–214.

✑ 10 ✑

Experimental Studies of Appetitional Behavior in Human Newborns and Infants

Hanuš Papoušek

Institute for Care of Mother and Child
Prague, Czechoslovakia

Probably every parent has a similar experience when seeing his newborn baby's behavior for the first time: The monotonous crying that is the only vocal manifestation and the diffuse mass activity that is often elicited by inadequate stimuli are so strikingly different from the behavior of adults that they seem to be completely incomprehensible. Yet most parents are soon able to find clues for understanding the basic meaning of the neonate's behavior and to learn to detect even the very early manifestations of developing integrated patterns of voluntary activity.

The author of this report sought to find a pattern of behavior that under experimental control might be used to study the learning abilities of newborns, and that would represent a model for the analysis of the development of intentional behavior. The motor components of appetitional behavior seemed particularly advantageous for this purpose because the need for food is a factor that is both effective and controllable. Inborn responses associated with feeding have therefore been repeatedly applied in studies of such basic learning processes as conditioning or conditioned discrimination.

Conditioning methods were first used for the systematic study of higher nervous functions in immature human subjects soon after Pavlov's basic experiments in dogs (Krasnogorskii, 1907). But until the last two decades the studies of infants dealt more often with the problems of the onset of conditioning or with the capacity for sensory

The author wishes to thank his research assistants Jarmila Melicharová and Svatava Sýkorová, as well as the staff of the research unit, for their devoted and skillful assistance in both nursing care and research investigation. Thanks are due also to our statistical consultant Dr. J. Vondráček, Institute of Mathematics, Czechoslovak Academy of Sciences, Prague, for his suggestions.

perception than with the development of learning processes. Recent surveys by Rheingold and Stanley (1963) and by Lipsitt (1963) have called attention to the fact that most studies of learning in infants have merely described the occurrence of the phenomenon; and the authors suggest that there is a need for additional studies of the processes underlying infant learning.

In the comparative physiology of infrahuman infants, attempts to analyze the development of the conditioning process have already appeared. Comparative data recently summarized by Sedláček (1963) indicated that the form and adaptive significance of temporary connections depended on the development of the CNS in individual species, and that the three main types of connections—the summation reflex (Wedenskii in 1881), the dominant center reflex (Ukhtomskii in 1911), and Pavlov's conditioned reflex—can be considered different evolutionary degrees of the same general process of synthesis in the CNS. Orbeli (1949) explained the ontogenetic development of central nervous functions by means of a similar evolutionary view. He hypothesized a genetic relation between inherited, unconditioned responses and acquired, conditioned responses, with an intermediate continuum of various transitory forms. Sedláček (1962; 1964) made a serious attempt to prove this hypothesis through studies of prenatal conditioning in relatively mature newborns, such as chickens and guinea pigs.

In man, prenatal conditioning has been studied either directly in the human fetus during pregnancy (Ray, 1932; Sontag & Wallace, 1934; Spelt, 1938; 1948), or in premature infants (Kasatkin, 1951; Irzhanskaia & Felberbaum, 1954). These studies have shown evidence of conditioned responses before the expected date of birth, but were not concerned with the mechanisms of temporary connections or with their development.

The lack of information about the earliest development of higher nervous functions in human infants stimulated the team to which the present author belongs to undertake a developmental study of individual differences in conditioning abilities. Unlike similar studies in the Pavlovian literature on typological differences in children (Ivanov-Smolenskii, 1953; Krasnogorskii, 1958) and infants (Volokhov, 1959), individual differences were defined by us in a much broader sense than the limits imposed by typological parameters. In order to maximize the generalizability of our conclusions, the same infants were exposed to several different conditioning methods—aversive, appetitional, and orientational—and to the analysis of sleep and waking, emotional and social behaviors, and EEG patterns.

Here we shall be concerned mainly with the data on learned appetitional responses and with the models for complex patterns of intentional behavior. Although the classical conditioning method of salivary response has been used with children, it is not appropriate for infants (Krasnogorskii, 1958). Therefore the analysis of conditioned sucking movements that was recommended by Bekhterev and Stshelovanov (1925) has been preferred by most authors. The first natural conditioned sucking was reported during the third week of life by Denisova and Figurin (1929), and Ripin and Hetzer (1930). The conditioning of sucking in infants to acoustic stimuli during the second or third month and to visual stimuli during the third or fourth month was reported by Kasatkin and Levikova (1935). Conditioned discrimination with vestibular stimulation was first reported by Nemanova (1935) in her study of infants 2 to 4 months old. Marquis (1931) reported much earlier conditionability; in 8 of 10 newborns she obtained conditioned oral responses to a buzzer at the age of 4 or 5 days, but her study lacked necessary controls for pseudoconditioning. On the other hand, Wenger (1936) could not establish conditioned responses before the tenth day of age with either appetitional or aversive techniques.

The problems of early conditioning continued to engage the attention of later investigators who used newer techniques and larger samples of infants (Kasatkin, 1964). Lipsitt and Kaye (1964) confirmed appetitional conditionability in 3- to 4-day-old newborns. Sucking movements were also used for testing the influence of hunger on conditioning (Kantrow, 1937), for detecting neonatal brain injuries (Dashkovskaia, 1953), and for studying premature infants (Polikanina, 1955; Polikanina & Probatova, 1957).

Until recent years, methods using other motor components of appetitional behavior were not employed adequately; Irwin (1930) discussed general motor activity, and Kriuchkova and Ostrovskaia mentioned head-turning (1957).

For the purposes of our studies, the sucking method appeared inconvenient, particularly because of the regressive changes in sucking movements that are in contrast to the progressive development of higher nervous functions (Papoušek, 1960). With increasing age, anticipatory sucking movements gradually disappear, perhaps because they are nonfunctional or nonadaptive.

Head-turning, therefore, was chosen by the author as another conditionable motor component of infantile appetitional behavior. As an inborn response, head-turning has been studied by many neurophysiologists since the first observations published by Darwin (1886) and Preyer (1895). According to Minkowski (1928), head movements appear in the human fetus by the third postconceptional month and are fully functional at birth. They can be elicited by various stimuli and during periods of hunger, occur without any discernible stimulation (Prechtl, 1953). According to Babkin (1953), an inborn rooting reflex, probably coordinated in the diencephalon, should be differentiated from the purposive movements that develop gradually, probably under cortical control, into various learned behavioral patterns such as orientational, aversive, or appetitional movements.

Natural conditioning of head movements to a visual (bottle) stimulus by the first month of life was described by Peiper (1958). After satiation, both conditioned and unconditioned food-seeking activity was suppressed.

For several reasons, head-turning seemed advantageous for conditioning studies. The movement matures earlier than do movements of the extremities, and its intensity and latency can be more easily quantified. It can be used with different kinds of reinforcement: appetitional or aversive, incidental or intentional. Thus it is suitable for molding a simple inborn reflex movement into a complex purposive or voluntary response. Finally, because head-turning involves bilateral response, and differential reinforcement can be applied for responses to the left or right, it can be used for the simultaneous study of two symmetrical responses in a single subject.

A method was devised for appetitional conditioning with milk reinforcement (Papoušek, 1959, 1961a, 1961b). For orientation conditioning with visual reinforcement the method was modified by another member of our team (Koch, 1962) and, within an operant framework, has been successfully explored by Siqueland (1964) and Siqueland and Lipsitt (in press).

METHOD

Subjects

For our investigations infants up to 6 months of age were reared in a special unit under relatively standard conditions. As far as possible, we tried to keep their life conditions comparable, at the same time meeting the demands of individual infants. Between 1956 and 1965, more than 130 infants were observed. They were healthy, full term, and without any evidence of pathology in the mothers' pregnancies or deliveries. The infants were cared for by their mothers and by specially trained nurses who could substitute for the mothers if necessary. Our team included a pediatrician who watched over the infants' health, nutrition, and somatic development, and a psychologist who was concerned with their mental development and educational care. If an occasional break in experimentation exceeded five days, the procedure being investigated during the period was eliminated from consideration.

The infants were also used by other members of the team for other experimental conditioning studies, such as conditioned eye-blinking (Janoš, 1965) and orientational head-turning (Koch, 1962).

Stimuli and Apparatus

The sounds of an electric bell (CS_1) or a buzzer (CS_2) were the conditioning stimuli. The unconditioned reinforcement (UCS) was milk presented from one side or the other through a rubber nipple connected to a thermos bottle.

Electronic equipment enabled the experimenter to program the kind and duration of both conditioning and reinforcing stimuli and to operate them and the timing mechanisms by a single button, thus freeing the experimenter to make detailed observations of the infant's behavior.

A seven-channel polygraph recorded the presentation of the stimuli

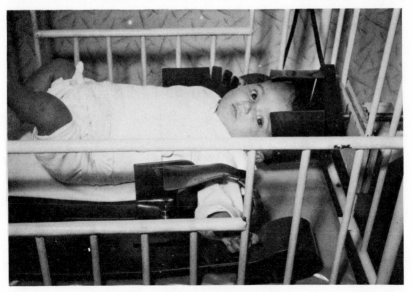

Fig. 10-1   The stabilimeter crib.

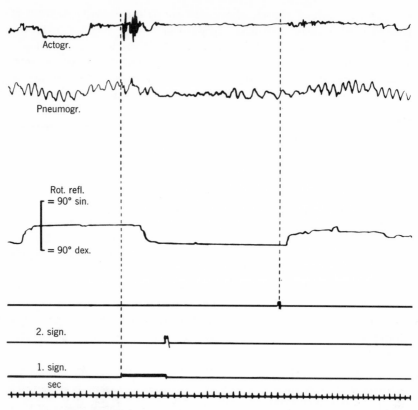

Fig. 10-2 Polygraph recordings from an experimental session.

and the infant's head-turning, breathing, and general motor activity. On a protocol, the experimenter recorded, by means of codes, intensity and latency of head-turning, changes in general behavior, and vocal, facial, and oral responses.

The infant lay in a stabilimeter crib, partially immobilized, in order to eliminate any disturbing activity of his upper extremities (Fig. 10-1). An elastic pad oscillated with the infant's movements; the oscillation was transmitted to the polygraph through a pneumatic system. This system also included a special calibrator allowing actograms of infants of different body weights to be compared. Breathing movements were recorded by means of a pneumatic pick-up.

The infant's head was placed in a plastic head cradle lined with plastic foam. The cradle's rotations on a horizontal axis changed the potential in a two-potentiometer circuit, and these changes were recorded as deflections from the baseline on the polygraph (Fig. 10-2).

The attachment of the head cradle to the axis could be shifted vertically to balance the cradle and eliminate the influence of head weight, enabling even a newborn to turn his head or keep it in a central position without difficulty.

Thus information was gathered not only on the specific response—head-turning—but also on concomitant changes in general activity (decrease or increase in general motor activity), vocalization, facial responses, eye movements, and breathing. Records of such changes were essential for estimating the general state of wakefulness during the experiment and the inhibitory or excitatory effects of the experimental stimuli.

Procedure and Measures

Infants were tested in the late morning, approximately 10 minutes after their regular sleep in the fresh air. The routine schedule of feeding and sleep in the sequence of sleep, feeding, and waking enabled us to examine the subjects in comparable states of hunger and wakefulness.

First, a baseline measure of head-turning prior to experimental stimulation was recorded. Then, all Ss received five pre-experimental trials of CS_1 and CS_2 without reinforcement. The source of the stimuli was in the midline behind the infant's head so that the sounds by themselves did not elicit head-turning. The first presentation of milk occurred prior to the conditioning trials and from the midline so that Ss might adapt to the experimental situation. Interruptions in feeding did not result in problems, particularly if the interruptions followed spontaneous breaks in the infant's sucking.

The development of the conditioned reflex to the bell (CR) was then initiated with the milk (UCS) being presented from the left side. The UCS was presented by the assistant, who sat screened behind S's head. If S responded to the bell and turned to the left, milk was offered to him immediately. The bell continued ringing until S started sucking the milk. If S did not respond to the presentation of the CS within 10 seconds, the assistant (nurse) tried eliciting the head turn by tactile stimulation, touching the left corner of his mouth with the nipple. If this stimulation was ineffective, she turned his head to the left and placed the nipple in his mouth. At the end of reinforcement the nurse turned his head back to the middle, leading it with the nipple, and then took the nipple from his mouth.

Ten such trials occurred during one session, which covered one normal feeding period of 10 to 15 minutes. The intertrial interval was one minute, on the average, but was intentionally changed to avoid temporal conditioning. A head turn of 30° or more from the central position was considered a positive response. The criterion of conditioning was five consecutive positive responses in the 10 trials of one daily session.

There was, therefore, considerable biological significance to head-turning under this procedure. The hungry infant had to rotate his head to obtain milk, and the sooner he did so, the sooner he was fed. Under these conditions, the gradual shortening of the latency of response could be considered a parameter of the process of conditioning.

Extinction was the next procedure. CS_1 was presented without the UCS for 10 seconds; as in the conditioning procedure, 10 trials were given in one session. After the criterion of five consecutive negative responses was reached, reconditioning took place. The process was the same as the first conditioning procedure.

Next, the Ss were trained to discriminate between the two stimuli; CS_1 (bell) was reinforced from the left and CS_2 (buzzer), from the right. In any one session, five CS_1 and five CS_2 were presented in random order. Six consecutive correct responses (three bell and three buzzer CR's in random order) represented the criterion of learning for this phase of the procedure. After reaching criterion, the signals were reversed: CS_1 was reinforced from the right, CS_2 from the left. The criterion for concluding this portion of the procedure was analogous to that employed in the trials for the first discrimination.

In addition to these basic procedures, other experiments were designed for the analysis of stimulus influence and for the shaping of more complex forms of learned behavior, such as the conditioned emotional behavior or the development of intentional behavior. These experiments are discussed later.

STUDIES OF BASIC LEARNING ABILITIES

The data given first demonstrate the early development of learning abilities in infants, their age peculiarities, and the individual differences among them. These data were gathered from the basic six conditioning procedures that were studied with three independent groups of Ss: newborns (A), 3-month-old infants (B), and 5-month-old infants (C). The variability of initial age within each group was reduced to a minimum. The results for the 44 infants in the three groups are summarized in Table 10-1. In this table are presented the means and standard deviations for initial age, rapidity of learning as measured by the number of trials necessary to achieve criterion, and latency of CRs.

In addition to the analysis of these data, attention was also paid to

TABLE 10-1

Means and Standard Deviations of Responses of Three Groups of Infants to the Six Basic Conditioning Procedures

Groups of infants	N	Initial age in days Mean	S.D.	Trials to criterion Mean	S.D.	Latency in seconds CR 1 Mean	S.D.	CR 2 Mean	S.D.
Conditioning:									
A	14	3.42	1.01	177.14	93.40	4.95	0.74		
B	14	85.78	1.76	42.28	18.38	3.92	1.08		
C	16	142.50	2.63	27.75	13.70	3.55	1.29		
Extinction:									
A	12	31.83	13.89	26.83	12.90	5.49	1.01		
B	14	94.14	4.58	25.07	10.39	3.70	0.94		
C	16	149.06	4.07	27.31	15.29	3.25	0.99		
Reconditioning:									
A	12	37.25	13.34	42.83	29.88	4.90	0.93		
B	14	100.35	1.45	31.64	19.84	2.73	0.65		
C	16	153.93	3.43	22.37	11.88	3.28	0.85		
Discrimination:									
A	11	43.90	15.68	223.54	99.23	4.00	0.58	3.90	0.63
B	13	105.92	6.48	176.23	82.52	2.62	0.66	3.03	0.71
C	14	159.92	5.46	68.14	28.72	2.10	0.77	2.66	0.87
Reversal 1:									
A	11	76.36	18.68	195.18	86.85	3.43	0.65	3.47	0.81
B	12	135.58	11.57	120.00	66.01	2.58	0.66	2.48	0.60
C	10	170.00	4.81	79.40	79.83	2.83	1.01	2.56	0.83
Reversal 2:									
A	11	107.54	23.81	94.63	35.51	3.29	0.91	2.91	0.74
B	12	155.41	19.08	82.41	37.74	2.34	0.91	2.15	0.74
C	10	182.80	13.50	77.60	63.60	2.29	0.97	2.72	0.97

A = newborns   B = 3-month infants   C = 5-month infants

the appearance of typical phases in the course of learning and to the various concomitant patterns of behavior. In these observations the group of newborns deserves more attention, particularly in comparison with group B, because a marked qualitative change in the development of higher nervous functions occurs during the first three months of life (Janoš, Papoušek, & Dittrichová, 1963).

Conditioning in Newborns

In newborns we had a rare opportunity to study experimental motor learning before spontaneous natural learning substantially interfered. Slow conditioning permitted an easier analysis of its phases that in older infants often passed too quickly and could be interpreted as accidental deviations.

In newborns the baseline before conditioning usually showed no head movements. Even tactile stimulation with the nipple elicited head-turning only in three of the 14 newborns on the first reinforcement, whereas three to 22 trials were necessary for the remaining 11 Ss (mean = 6.57). In group B the tactile stimulation itself elicited head-turning more quickly, usually after one or two trials (mean = 1.23). This difference was highly significant ($p < 0.001$).[1]

The rate of conditioning, as shown in Table 10-1, was very slow in newborns. On the average, 32.21 trials preceded the first conditioned head turn in group A, whereas only 9.43 trials were necessary in group B. Such a significant decrease ($p < 0.001$) indicates a rapid development of conditionability during the first three months of life. A similar decrease of the mean number of trials to criterion also supported this conclusion; the difference between groups A and B was highly significant ($p < 0.001$), whereas the difference between groups B and C was significant at the .05 level. The mean number of 177 trials for group A represented approximately three weeks of conditioning, and shows that during the 28 days of the neonatal period most newborns can achieve even a relatively severe criterion of conditioning. But wide individual differences in the newborns were apparent; the fastest conditioners needed only 7, 10, 11, or 12 days, the slowest ones, more than a month.

The latency of the CR is here considered in the behavioral sense, rather than in the physiological. Latency was defined as the interval between the onset of CS and a head turn of 30° or more. It depended, therefore, not only on the interval preceding the onset of CR, but also on the rate at which the head was turned. An analysis of variance

---

[1] The following statistical procedures were employed, depending on the particular data being analyzed: the Mann-Whitney U test; the Kruskal-Wallis one-way analysis of variance for k-sample cases; for large samples, the Snedecor F test with logarithmic transformation of scores and, if necessary, with Scheffé's (1959) method of multiple comparison; and Spearman rank-order correlation coefficients.

showed significant age differences for the three groups ($p < 0.005$), indicating that newborns carry out the CRs more slowly than older infants. For newborns, there was also a significant correlation during conditioning between latency and speed of conditioning, indicating longer reaction times in slower conditioners ($r = 0.68$, $p < 0.01$).

Several different stages could be distinguished during the course of conditioning. To a certain degree they were comparable to the four stages of conditioned sucking described by Kasatkin (1948): indifference to the CS, inhibition of general activity, unstable CR, and, finally, a stable CR.

During the first phase the CS usually elicited nonspecific orientational behavior (wider opening of the eyes, inhibition of other activities, changes in breathing) that was quickly extinguished. After a period of indifference to the CS, this phase was succeeded by one during which partial responses and later the first CRs were manifested. In newborns this phase was relatively long and had several features that should be noted. Its main features were gradual coordination of individual components of CR, such as head-turning and unilateral mouthing or eye turning (Fig. 10-3), increased general motor activity, and concomitant vocal and facial responses that are generally accepted as signs of distress (Fig. 10-4). Before a good coordination developed, the newborn could be seen to be upset, fussing, and grimacing, turning his eyes and contracting his mouth to the left, but not yet turning his head. Marked signs of such an insufficient coordination were present in 50% of the Ss in group A, but only in .7% of the Ss in group B.

The next phase was that of unstable conditioning. The frequency of correct responses increased, but the responses were isolated or appeared in small groups with fluctuating intensity and latency. Insufficient coordination was still evident in two characteristic features: (a) a generalized form of CR (the S responds with the whole body), and (b) an increased frequency of unilateral or bilateral intertrial head turning. The first feature, considered a sign of increased irradiation of central nervous processes in immature organisms, was more frequent in group A. The second feature, indicating central dominance, usually appeared only in the unilateral form in group A and was less frequent (50%) than in group B (71%).

The gradual consolidation of the CR, that is, the increasing ability to carry out more CRs consecutively, also appears to be a function of age. The analysis of the first 10 CRs (Table 10-2) showed that in group A, 60.7% of the responses were isolated, whereas in group C, 60.6% appeared consecutively in groups of three or more. It is evident that the main development of this ability again occurs during the first three months of life.

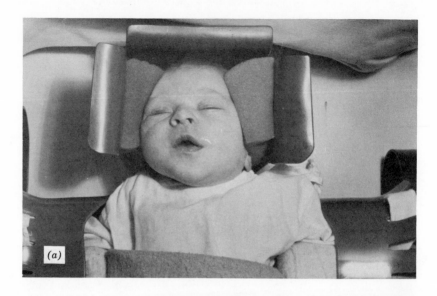

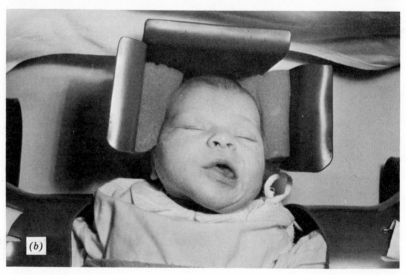

Fig. 10-3   Head-turning and unilateral mouthing.

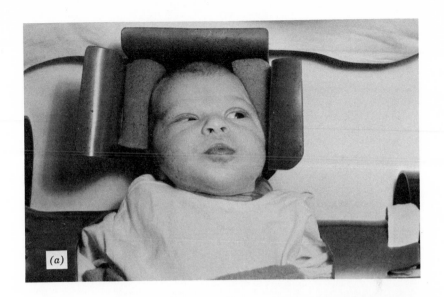

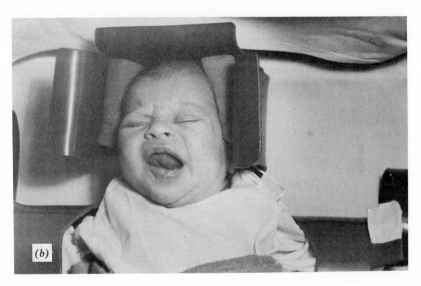

Fig. 10-4 Facial signs of distress.

TABLE 10-2

Grouping of Conditioned Responses of Three Groups of Infants, in Percentages

Group of infants	N	Isolated	The first 10 positive conditioned responses	
			In groups	
			2	3 or more
		%	%	%
A	14	60.7	32.9	6.4
B	14	34.9	17.2	47.9
C	16	18.7	20.6	60.6
		A:B $p < 0.001$	A:B $p < 0.01$	A:B $p < 0.001$
		B:C $p < 0.025$	B:C $p > 0.05$	B:C $p > 0.05$

A = newborns
B = 3-month infants
C = 5-month infants

Three main types of cumulative curves appeared to characterize the course of conditioning in the infants: (a) relatively constant increase of percentage in CRs, (b) increase of percentage with several gross waves, and (c) increase of percentage after a retarded onset. The second type may indicate a functional lability of the CNS, typical of immature organisms, and the third, a phasic maturation of the CNS (Janoš, 1965). It can be seen in Table 10-3 that the relative frequency of the three types differed in the three age groups, and that the last two types were more characteristic of the newborns.

TABLE 10-3

Frequency of Occurrence of Different Types of Conditioning Curves in Individual Age Groups

Types of acquisition curves	Age groups		
	A	B	C
Relatively constant percentage increase	6	12	16
Several gross waves	6	2	—
Retarded onset	2	—	—
Total:	14	14	16

The final phase is that of stable conditioning. The frequency of CRs approaches 100%, and the CRs are stronger, faster, well coordinated, and carried out economically with shorter and more regular latencies. They were no longer accompanied by emotional signs of distress; on the contrary, the older infants often showed vocal or facial patterns of pleasure (Fig. 10-5). In this phase the Ss reached the criterion of 5 successive correct CRs and, at the same time, the average number of CRs in three successive days usually exceeded 50%.

Even in this phase, the stability of conditioning was only relative, particularly in the younger groups in which a sudden decrease sometimes appeared after a period of consistent responses. Alternation between increased excitation and inhibition seems typical for newborns and probably caused the limited occurrence of consecutive CRs. Polygraphic records of breathing and general motor activity provided more sensitive indications of increased excitation or inhibition than the apparent state of wakefulness.

No relation was found in newborns between the occurrence of the first CR and the number of trials to criterion, but there was a significant correlation between the occurrence of the first group of two CRs and the criterion ($r = 0.71$, $p < 0.01$) or between the first group of three consecutive CRs and the criterion ($r = 0.86$, $p < 0.01$).

All these indices of age characteristics in the higher nervous functions of newborns confirm the hypothesis that the immaturity of the CNS manifests itself in the functional lability of higher centers and in the weakness of the basic central nervous system processes of excitation and inhibition. A similar conclusion was drawn from the analysis of developmental changes of sleeping and waking states in these infants (Dittrichová, 1962; Dittrichová, Janoš & Papoušek, 1962). Even under conditions involving relative immaturity of the CNS, it is apparent that a basic pyramidal response can be learned which, in later weeks and months, develops into a more complicated pattern of behavior. Our data suggest, in fact, that learning does occur in humans within the first days of life.

Further Development of Conditioning Capacity

In the older infants, as compared with the newborns, developmental changes were observed of both a quantitative and a qualitative nature. The significant increase with age in the speed of conditioning was discussed in the preceding section on newborns. This finding is important for developmental studies since experimental evidence, in spite of many ontogenetic studies, is still equivocal. As shown recently (Janoš et al., 1963), during the first half-year of infancy an age

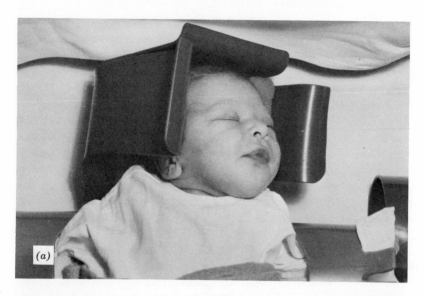

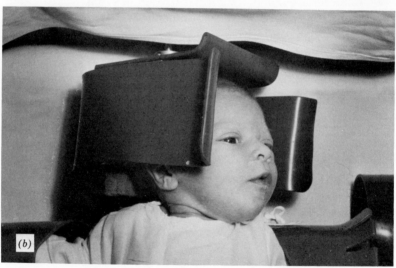

Fig. 10-5   Facial signs of pleasure.

difference of one month may produce significant differences in both aversive and appetitional conditioning.

With increased speed of conditioning, the individual phases in the conditioning process that are characteristic of newborns become shorter, and often such phases are detected only fleetingly, particularly in fast conditioners. Nevertheless, several qualitative differences could still be observed in groups B and C. Incoordination of partial components of the CR, associated with the appearance of the first CRs in newborns, was absent or appeared in a slight form only in a few trials. The generalization of the CR, observed in the phase of unstable conditioning, was also different. In newborns the CR was preceded or accompanied by increased movements of the whole trunk and extremities, and by changes in breathing and vasomotor responses, etc. These changes can be considered the result of nonspecific diffuse irradiation of the central excitatory process. It was observed that older infants showed more specific generalization, which was expressed in the specific vocal or facial signs of emotional arousal frequently shown by older children or adults in solving difficult problems.

An increase in the number of head turns during the intertrial intervals was more frequently found in older infants during the phase of unstable conditioning, and, unlike what is found in newborns, here the bilateral form of the intertrial head turns prevailed. It is difficult to estimate the proportion of maturation and extraexperimental learning in the qualitative differences found between newborns and older infants.

Extinction and Reconditioning

The main purpose of our extinction and reconditioning procedures was to confirm the critical feature of the CR—its temporary character —and thus to differentiate it from pseudoconditioning. According to previous experience (Papoušek, 1961a, 1961b) and to analogous findings in aversive conditioning (Janoš, 1965), we did not expect to gain as much information about the development of learning abilities from the study of extinction and reconditioning as we found in the use of other procedures.

Table 10-1 shows that extinction occurs more quickly than conditioning but no significant difference in the speed of extinction was found among the three groups. This finding is difficult to explain. The experiments dealing with extinction may have involved an age span different from that in which the main development of extinction ability occurs; or the role of age may have been obliterated by the level of conditioning necessary to achieve the relatively severe criterion of conditioning employed. It is interesting that in group A, a negative correlation between trials to conditioning and trials to extinction was found ($r = -0.66$, $p < 0.05$), indicating faster extinguishing in slower conditioners. Moreover, the newborns had a significantly longer latency of the CR ($p < 0.001$) than did groups B and C.

To a certain extent, the course of extinction is a mirror image of conditioning. The CRs gradually cease to be made and their latencies become longer. The negative responses appear first as isolated events and later in consecutively larger numbers. The individual components of the CR do not extinguish simultaneously, particularly in younger Ss. For example, in response to the CS_1, the S may stop turning his head to the left but may continue to turn his eyes to the left or contract the left corner of his mouth for some time. A negative response to the CS still does not mean that the CS is totally indifferent to the S. Particularly during the phase of unstable extinction, the CS obviously exerts an inhibitory influence upon the S's behavior, sometimes to such an extent that it can elicit a catatoniclike state in the S for several seconds.

Reconditioning may be considered a repetition of the first conditioning process. Here, however, the differences between individual age groups were at the limit of significance, according to a Kruskal-Wallis analysis of variance ($p > 0.05$).

Only in younger groups is reconditioning significantly faster than conditioning. The difference in speed between conditioning and reconditioning can be the effect of either maturation or relearning. The first seems more plausible since the difference was highly significant in group A ($p < 0.001$), in which the Ss were 34 days older during reconditioning than they were during conditioning, but was at the limit of significance in group B ($p < 0.05$), and nonsignificant in group C ($p < 0.05$), in which the Ss were only 15 and 11 days older. Within the total sample (but not within individual age groups), the correlation between trials to conditioning and trials to reconditioning was significant ($r = 0.38$, $p < 0.01$).

Discrimination

There is a lack of data in the literature on the development of discriminative abilities in man. It was not the goal of this study to answer the question of the age at which human infants begin to discriminate different acoustic stimuli. The Ss had to proceed through several other procedures before the discrimination tests were begun.

But even under these conditions evidence was found that in the fastest conditioners the ability to discriminate was functional as early as the second month of life. In group A, the mean age at which the Ss reached the criterion of discrimination between bell and buzzer was $2\frac{1}{2}$ months.

During the following months of the first half year of life the ability to discriminate improves substantially and the speed of differentiation increases. An analysis of variance among groups A, B, and C, showed significant differences dependent on age ($p < 0.005$). Furthermore, the latencies of response to both CS_1 and CS_2 were significantly lower ($p < 0.005$) for group A than for groups B and C.

Individual variability in the speed of acquisition of prior procedures results in a gradual increase of the variability in the age at which Ss begin subsequent procedures. Ranking according to age is in this case identical with ranking in order of decreasing speed in the preceding procedures; within individual groups the slower the Ss were in preceding tests the older they were in succeeding tests. Therefore, the correlation between age and speed of discrimination or its reversals was not significant within individual groups, although in some procedures the span of the initial age exceeded one month. It has been reported by Janoš et al. (1963) that such an age difference may be associated with significant differences in the speed of conditioning.

Several main phases may be distinguished in the course of discrimination and particularly in the reversal of discrimination. There is first a disintegration of the previously learned ability that is followed by a gradual adaptation leading to successful acquisition of the new discrimination. Secondary phases were also present, such as alternating dominance of left or right CRs in Ss' responses to both kinds of CSs. The frequency, sequence, and expressiveness of these secondary phases were, however, less constant.

Developmental differences were evident in the course of discrimination. In group A, a marked decline in both CRs was observed in 6 of the 11 Ss soon after CS_2 was introduced. After the period of decline, a gradual increase in both CRs occurred simultaneously, with gross waves as the dominant type of acquisition curve. In groups B and C, such a general decline was never observed. A gradual increase in responses to CS_2 usually occurred with a stable or only a transitory decrease in the level of responses to CS_1. The periods of alternating dominance of left or right responses were less frequent in groups B and C. In all groups the stability of discrimination was only relative even after reaching criterion; a marked decline could be easily produced by various interfering factors.

Reversals of Discrimination

In the last two procedures included in Table 10-1, the variability of the age at which the procedures were introduced increased to such an extent that the group limits overlapped, but the differences between mean ages still remained highly significant.

The speed of learning significantly increased from discrimination to the second reversal in groups A and B, but not in group C. It appears that by 6 months of age further improvement based upon age alone was not in evidence. For the first reversal, a one-way analysis of variance showed a reliable age trend reflecting a decrease in the number of trials to criterion ($p < 0.005$). In the second reversal, however, this trend was no longer significant. Similar relations were observed in the latency data. Within individual age groups there was no significant correlation between age and speed of the reversals. A possible interpretation was discussed in the previous section on discrimination. The speed with which the first reversal was acquired was positively related to the speed of discrimination ($r = 0.37$, $p < 0.025$).

The first reversal was established, on the average, in group A by the third month of life, and the second reversal by $3\frac{1}{2}$ months. We may conclude, therefore, that during the first trimester there has developed not only the capacity to discriminate but also the capacity to reverse a discrimination.

DETERMINANTS OF INDIVIDUAL DIFFERENCES

Individual differences in addition to those based upon age were found in all groups and in all of the quantitative and qualitative indices. The literature contains different opinions on the detectability of differences in higher nervous function during early infancy. Chesnokova (1951) and Krasuskii (1953) assumed that differences in higher nervous activity continued to develop until adulthood and could not be assessed definitely at earlier ages. Troshikhin (1952) and Volokhov (1953), on the other hand, recommended that they be studied as early as possible. Kriuchkova and Ostrovskaia (1957) and, in a project similar to ours, Kaplan (1963) reported stable individual differences in higher nervous function from the first months of life through later infancy.

In the present study, marked individual differences were found to be present in newborns according to all indices. As an illustrative example, acquisition curves of conditioning for groups A and B are presented in Fig. 10-6. Whether or not the observed differences represent permanent characteristics of individual Ss cannot be answered because our studies have not yet been oriented toward this problem. It should be noted, however, that studies on aversive conditioning in the same infants have also shown marked individual differences in learning abilities at early ages (Janoš, 1965).

In Table 10-1, the standard deviations for the trials-to-criterion measures of conditioning and discrimination decreased from group A to group C, indicating a developmental change in the variability of these functions. The F tests comparing groups A and C indicated that the decrease in variability was significant in both instances ($p < 0.001$).

Other determinants of the individual differences found in learning abilities were also investigated, for example, sex differences, nutrition, somatic differences, seasonal influences, etc. A preliminary analysis of our data showed no significant sex differences in any procedure between 19 girls and 25 boys of the present sample. Seasonal difference was not significant either when performances were compared for the

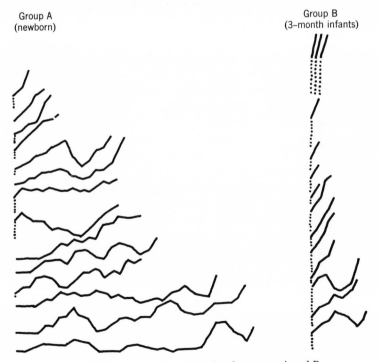

Group A
(newborn)

Group B
(3–month infants)

Fig. 10-6   Acquisition curves of conditioning for groups A and B.

first and the second halves of the calendar year, or for the spring through the summer with the autumn through the winter.

It did not appear that the individual differences in learning ability that were found could be attributable to somatic or constitutional factors studied, such as birth weight and birth length, head and chest circumference, or gain in weight or length during the first trimester. Only in newborns did some parameters of learning abilities seem to be related to some of the mentioned determinants. A significant correlation was found, for example, between the CR latency and chest circumference ($r = -0.67$, $p < 0.05$), indicating that a conditioned head turn was carried out more quickly in stouter newborns.

Since appetitional behavior can be substantially influenced by nutritional factors, the mean caloric quotient (daily intake in calories per kilogram of body weight) was calculated during each experimental procedure and was correlated with the conditioning parameters. In groups A and B, significant correlations of .59 ($p < 0.05$) and .63 ($p < 0.02$), respectively, indicated that conditioning proceeded more quickly in infants with a lower daily intake of milk, that is, they indicated an excitatory effect of a mild degree of hunger that can appear in younger infants during, for example, the period of additional feeding when a supplementary formula is kept slightly reduced in order to maintain adequate sucking at the mother's breast.

Similarly, a breast-to-cow-milk ratio was calculated during conditioning to test the influence of breast feeding and, indirectly, also of mother's presence, since mothers usually stayed at our unit as long as they could nurse. No significant correlation was evident between this ratio and the parameters of conditioning. It was the practice, however, to compensate for the mother's absence by providing substitute mothering and adequate emotional stimulation.

Thus, in general, we can conclude that this preliminary analysis of the potential determinants of individual differences in performance during the procedures employed did not contradict the hypothesis that with the conditioning procedures considered here, we were testing differences in higher nervous functions.

ROLE OF ENVIRONMENTAL STIMULATION

In the preceding sections it has been shown that various indifferent external stimuli may play an important role if they become conditioned stimuli, particularly in connection with a significant form of reinforcement such as that used in these studies of appetitional conditioning. Acoustic signals can elicit striking changes in general motor activity, in the general state of excitation or inhibition, and in emotional and other forms of behavior. Although the effect sometimes can be too slight to be observed in general behavior, it can still be detected during the process of conditioning.

Such an example is illustrated in Fig. 10-7. In a 5-month-old infant with an established discrimination between the bell, reinforced with milk from the left, and the buzzer, reinforced from the right, the reinforcement associated with the buzzer was stopped in order to reverse the buzzer to an inhibitory stimulus. After a period of training, the buzzer ceased to elicit the CR, but an inhibitory after-effect appeared in an increased latency in succeeding CRs to the bell. The more inhibitory stimuli were applied consecutively, the greater was the increase in latency.

In infants of the second trimester, further observation illustrated the effectiveness of the CSs, and, in addition, an interesting interrelation between learned and unlearned behavior. For instance, in several Ss, after completing a normal conditioning session with 10 trials and after a normal amount of milk had been presented as reinforcement, another 10 or 20 CSs were applied to test the influence of satiation upon the emission of CRs. Under these conditions the Ss did not stop responding to the CSs, even when they were fully satiated.

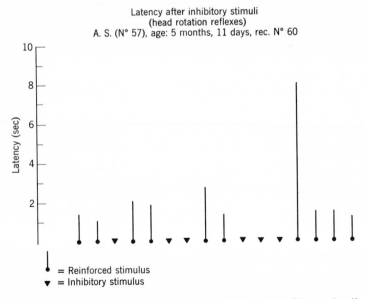

Fig. 10-7 Latencies of responses after presentation of inhibitory stimuli.

At every sound of the bell they turned to the left, even though they refused the milk presented. Any attempt to feed them elicited avoiding head turns.

Other experimental situations for studying the interrelation between learned and nonlearned behavior were undertaken by using different tasting fluids. These situations used 15 Ss, aged 88 to 201 days, in whom a left-right discrimination in head-turning had already been established. For instance, sweet milk was used as the UCS presented from the left in CS_1, and a weak solution of the quinine tincture was presented from the right in CS_2. Soon the concomitant emotional responses appropriate to the kind of UCS became differentiated, so that the Ss responded to the CS_1 with quiet sucking and head-turning, but to the CS_2 with arousal, grimacing, increased salivation, and aversive tongue movements. When in this situation the discrimination was reversed, the Ss sucked the bitter solution from the left with CS_1 without any signs of displeasure, and refused the sweet milk from the right with CS_2. For some period, this maladaptive behavior indicated that the effectiveness of conditioning stimuli was stronger than the effects of unconditioned reinforcement. Finally, a readaptation appeared and led to a new, adequate differentiation. These studies indicate that even emotional behavior, like other kinds of behavior, can be conditioned and thus put under experimental control.

Natural conditioning procedures, similar to those described above, can normally occur in the infant's life. Various environmental stimuli can in this way become conditioned stimuli of great effectiveness. It is not difficult to realize that under unfavorable conditions, for example, in various frustration situations in which many CSs remain unreinforced and become inhibitory stimuli, a cumulative inhibitory influence can produce undesirable effects in the infant's behavior.

MODELS OF VOLUNTARY BEHAVIOR

We attempted to mold a simple example of voluntary behavior in 12 infants of whom four were newborns aged 4.5 days on the average, and eight were in the second trimester, with an average age of 130.1 days. The Ss were trained in a discrimination and one or two reversals of it with only one kind of CS. The CS was reinforced with either sweetened milk from the left or unsweetened milk from the right. If he did not carry out a head turn himself, tactile stimulation with a rubber nipple was applied with the restriction that equal numbers of tactile stimulations were applied to both sides. Otherwise, the S was allowed to choose the kind of milk himself.

An exact quantitative analysis was not possible since different kinds of stimulation were used, but several general conclusions seem warranted. All Ss preferred the sweetened milk, and this preference gradually developed in a manner similar to the discrimination described in the basic conditioning procedures. The criterion of five consecutive CRs to the same side was reached in an average of 290 trials (ranging from 246 to 390) in the newborns and in 38 trials (9 to 109) in the older infants.

After achieving the criterion, the UCSs were reversed—the sweetened milk was presented from the right side and the unsweetened milk from the left. A gradual reversal in CRs occurred, consequently, and its course was analogous to that of the reversal described earlier. During the disintegration phase of a previously learned ability, accidental head turns to the side of sweetened milk helped the Ss to find the source of the preferred UCS. Concomitant emotional responses, gradual grouping of CRs to the preferred side, and other signs indicated that this simple model of voluntary behavior was learned in the same way as in the basic conditioning procedures. In the younger infants 108 trials (15 to 185) were necessary for achieving the criterion, whereas only 70 (10 to 162) were necessary in the older infants. In a schematic form, one typical case is illustrated in Fig. 10-8.

When I speak of voluntary behavior in infants of prelingual age, I do not assume that I am thereby simplifying a difficult problem. I wish only to emphasize that the chosen pyramidal movement, brought under experimental control at a very early stage of postnatal development, can be molded to patterns resembling voluntary behavior. Perhaps it would be better to say that through conditioning processes, the organism can be brought to the beginning of a long and complicated pathway of structuring, at the end of which there are patterns

Z.C. (no 51), age: 5 months 22 days, rec. no: 1–8

Fig. 10-8   Latencies of responses in initial learning and following reversal of the UCSs.

of behavior as highly coordinated as those generally designated as voluntary behavior.

SUMMARY

Head movements were chosen as a conditionable motor complex of infantile appetitional behavior to study the early development of learning abilities and the molding of a simple response to a pattern of intentional behavior.

A method was developed for appetitional conditioning with milk reinforcement in newborns and infants. The basic conditioning procedures—conditioning, extinction, reconditioning, discrimination and its double reversal—were studied as early forms of learning in three independent age groups of healthy full-term infants (newborns, 3-month infants, and 5-month infants).

Quantitative and qualitative differences among these groups were analyzed with particular attention to the peculiarities of the learning processes in newborns, and evidence was found that learning occurs during the first days of life. In the course of investigating various procedures in the study of conditioning in newborns, different phases of learning became apparent. The immaturity of the central nervous system manifests itself in the functional lability and in the infirmity of the basic central nervous processes of excitation and inhibition. The evidence for this appears in the slow grouping of consecutive CRs, gross waves in the acquisition curves, and instability in the percentage, intensity, and latency of CRs.

In several indices the comparison among individual groups indicated that major developmental changes occur during the first three months of life. During this period there develops not only the capacity to discriminate between various acoustic stimuli but also the capacity to reverse such a discrimination.

Marked individual differences are present from the neonatal period on in all parameters of conditioning employed. An analysis of the correlation between these differences and various potential determinants such as sex, somatic development, nutrition, mother-infant interaction, or seasonal influence support the hypothesis of independent variability in higher nervous function as a cause of the observed individual differences.

Further studies helped to elucidate the interrelation between learned and nonlearned behavior, indicating increasing effectiveness of conditioning stimuli in comparison to unconditioned ones. A left-right differentiation of head-turning reinforced by two as different and as emotionally effective taste stimuli as sweet and bitter solutions indicated that even emotional behavior can be put under experimental control and can be conditioned in young infants.

Finally, there is reported the attempt to design experimental conditions under which the learned response can be considered as the earliest precursor of later intentional or voluntary behavior. Here, head-turning was conditioned to one CS, and that CS was reinforced either with sweetened or unsweetened milk, depending on the side to which S turned his head. All Ss appeared to prefer the sweetened milk and to be able to find its source on the opposite side when the two variants of UCS were reversed. Learning of such a response proceeded on the same principles as conditioned discrimination or its reversal.

REFERENCES

Babkin, P. S. (1953) Head-turning reflexes in infants. (Rus.) *Zh. Nevropat. Psikhiat.* **53**, 692–696.

Bekhterev, V. M., & Stshelovanov, N. M. (1925) The principles of genetic reflexology. (Rus.) In *Novoie refleksologii i fiziologii nervnoi sistemy.* USSR: Leningrad-Moscow.

Chesnokova, A. P. (1951) Dynamism of higher nervous activity in puppies during their individual development. (Rus.) *Zh. vys. nerv. Deiat.* **1**, 555–565.

Darwin, C. (1886) Biographische Skizze eines kleinen Kindes. (Germ.) *Kleinere Schriften* (Leipzig) 2.B., 134.

Dashkovskaia, V. S. (1953) The first conditioned responses in newborns under normal and pathologic conditions. (Rus.) *Zh. vys. nerv. Deiat.* **3**, 247–259.

Denisova, M. P., & Figurin, N. L. (1929) The question of the first associated appetitional reflexes in infants. (Rus.) *Vopr. genet. Refleksol. Pedol. Mladen.* **1**, 81–88.

Dittrichová, J. (1962) Nature of sleep in young infants. *J. appl. Physiol.* **17**, 543–546.

Dittrichová, J., Janoš, O., & Papoušek, H. (1962) Characteristics of higher nervous activity in newborns. (Czech.) *Sb. čsl. lékař. kongresu.* Prague. Pp. 254–255.

Irwin, O. C. (1930) The amount and nature of activities of newborn infants under constant external stimulating conditions during the first ten days of life. *Genet. Psychol. Monogr.* **8**, 1–92.

Irzhanskaia, K. N., & Felberbaum, R. A. (1954) Some data on conditioned activity in premature infants. (Rus.) *Fiziol. Zh. SSSR* **40**, 668–672.

Ivanov-Smolenskii, A. G. (1953) Studies on the types of higher nervous activity in animals and in man. (Rus.) *Zh. vys. nerv. Deiat.* **3**, 36–54.

Janoš, O. (1965) (Czech.) *Age and individual differences in higher nervous activity in infants.* Prague: SzdN.

Janoš, O., Papoušek, H., & Dittrichová, J. (1963) The influence of age upon various aspects of higher nervous activity in the first months of life. (Czech.) *Activ. nerv. super.* **4**, 407–410.

Kantrow, R. W. (1937) Studies in infant behavior. IV. An investigation of conditioned feeding responses and concomitant adaptive behavior in young infants. *Univer. Iowa Stud. Child Welf.* **13**, No. 3, 1–64.

Kaplan, L. I. (1963) To the question of the development of individual typologic differences of higher nervous activity in infants. (Rus.) *Mater. 6th scient. conf. devel. morphol., physiol., biochem.* Moscow: Izd. APN. P. 354.

Kasatkin, N. I. (1948) (Rus.) *Early conditioned reflexes in the ontogenesis of man.* Moscow: Medgiz.

Kasatkin, N. I. (1951) (Rus.) *An outline of the development of the higher nervous activity during early infancy.* Moscow: Medgiz.

Kasatkin, N. I. (Ed.) (1964) (Rus.) *From the simple to the complex.* Moscow-Leningrad: Izd. Nauka.

Kasatkin, N. I., & Levikova, A. M. (1935) On the development of early conditioned reflexes and differentiation of auditory stimuli in infants. *J. exp. Psychol.* **18**, 1–9.

Koch, J. (1962) Die Veränderung des Exzitations Prozesses nach der Nahrungseinnahme und nach dem Schlafe bei Säuglingen in Alter von 5 Monaten. (Germ.) *Z. arztl. Fortb.* **55**, 219–223.

Krasnogorskii, N. I. (1907) An experience with establishing experimental conditioned reflexes in infants. (Rus.) *Russkii vrach* **36**. In (Rus.) *Studies in the research of higher nervous activity in man and animals.* (1954) Moscow: Medgiz.

Krasnogorskii, N. I. (1958) (Rus.) *The higher nervous activity in the child.* Leningrad: Medgiz.

Krasuskii, V. K. (1953) Methods of studying the types of nervous system in animals. (Rus.) *Trudy Inst. Fiziol. Pavlov* **2**, 111–119.

Kriuchkova, A. P., & Ostrovskaia, I. M. (1957) Developmental and individual differences of higher nervous activity in infants. (Rus.) *Zh. vys. nerv. Deiat.* **7**, 63–74.

Lipsitt, L. P. (1963) Learning in the first year of life. In L. P. Lipsitt & C. C. Spiker (Eds.) *Advances in child development and behavior.* Vol. 1. New York: Academic Press. Pp. 147–195.

Lipsitt, L. P., & Kaye, H. (1964) Conditioned sucking in the human newborn. *Psychon. Sci.* **1**, 29–30.

Marquis, D. P. (1931) Can conditioned responses be established in the newborn infant? *J. genet. Psychol.* **39**, 479–492.

Minkowski, H. (1928) Neurobiologische Studien an menschlichen Früchten. *Abderhalden's Handb. biolog. Arbeitsmeth* (Berlin) **5**, 5b, 511–618.

Nemanova, C. P. (1935) The earliest positive and negative aversive and nutritive conditioned responses to vestibular stimuli in infants. (Rus.) *Vopr. Pediat. Okhran.* **7**, 278.

Orbeli, L. A. (1949) On the mechanism of the development of cerebrospinal coordinations. (Rus.) In *The problems of higher nervous activity.* Moscow-Leningrad: Izd. AN SSSR. Pp. 7–20.

Papoušek, H. (1959) A method of studying conditioned food reflexes in young children up to the age of six months. (Rus.) *Zh. vys. nerv. Deiat.* **9**, 136–140.

Papoušek, H. (1960) Conditioned motor alimentary reflexes in infants. I. Experimental conditioned sucking reflexes. (Czech.) *Cesk. Pediat.* **15**, 861–872.

Papoušek, H. (1961) Conditioned head rotation reflexes in infants in the first months of life. *Acta Paediatr.* **50**, 565–576. (a)

Papoušek, H. (1961) (Czech.) *Conditioned motor nutritive reflexes in infants.* Thomayer. Sb., Prague: SzdN. P. 409. (b)

Peiper, A. (1958) Unbedingte und bedingte Reflexe der Nahrungsaufnahme. (Germ.) *Kinderäerzt. Prax.* **26**, 507–515.

Polikanina, R. I. (1955) Origin and development of a nutritive conditioned response to sound in premature infants. (Rus.) *Zh. vys. nerv. Deiat.* 5, 237–246.

Polikanina, R. I., & Probatova, L. J. (1957) Development of an orienting response and a conditioned motor nutritive response to color in premature infants. (Rus.) *Zh. vys. nerv. Deiat.* 7, 673–682.

Prechtl, H. F. R. (1953) Die Kletterbewegungen beim Säugling. (Germ.) *Mnschr. Kinderhk.* 101, 519–521.

Preyer, W. (1895) *Die Seele des Kindes.* (4th ed.) (Germ.) Leipzig.

Ray, W. S. (1932) A preliminary report on a study of fetal conditioning. *Child Developm.* 3, 175–177.

Rheingold, Harriet L., & Stanley, W. C. (1963) Developmental psychology. *Ann. Rev. Psychol.* 14, 1–28.

Ripin, R., & Hetzer, H. (1930) Frühestes Lernen des Säuglings in der Ernährungssituation. (Germ.) *Z. Psychol.* 118, 82–127.

Scheffé, H. (1959) *The analysis of variance.* New York: Wiley.

Sedláček, J. (1962) Functional characteristics of the center of the unconditioned reflex in elaboration of a temporary connection in chick embryos. (Czech.) *Physiol. Bohemoslov.* 11, 313–318.

Sedláček, J. (1963) Problems of the ontogenetic formation of the mechanism of temporary connections. (Rus.) *Acta Univer. Carol. Medica* 4, 265–317.

Sedláček, J. Hlaváčková, V., & Švenlová, M. (1964) New findings on the formation of the temporary connections in the prenatal and perinatal period in the guinea pig. (Czech.) *Physiol. Bohemoslov.* 13, 268–273.

Siqueland, E. R. (1964) Operant conditioning of head turning in four-month infants. *Psychon. Sci.* 1, 223–224.

Siqueland, E. R., & Lipsitt, L. P. (In press.) Conditioned head-turning behavior in newborns. *J. exp. child Psychol.*

Sontag, L. W., & Wallace, R. F. (1934) Study of fetal activity. (Preliminary report on the Fels Fund) *Amer. J. Dis. Child.* 49, 1050.

Spelt, D. K. (1938) Conditioned responses in the human fetus in utero. *Psychol. Bull.* 35, 712–713.

Spelt, D. K. (1948) The conditioning of the human fetus in utero. *J. exp. Psychol.* 38, 338–346.

Troshikhin, V. A. (1952) Some tasks in the research of higher nervous activity in ontogenesis. (Rus.) *Zh. vys. nerv. Deiat.* 2, 561–571.

Ukhtomskii, A. A. (1952) The principle of dominant center. (Rus.) In I. M. Sechenov, I. P. Pavlov, & N. E. Wedenskii (Eds.), *Physiology of the nervous system.* Vol. 1. (3rd ed.) Moscow: Medgiz. Pp. 262–266.

Volokhov, A. A. (1953) Typologic differences of nervous system in infants. (Rus.) *Med. Rabot.* 16, 2–3.

Volokhov, A. A. (1959) Typologic differences in higher nervous activity in infants and their reflection in some autonomic functions. (Rus.) *Mater. 7th Congr. Soviet. Pediat.* 77–80.

Wedenskii, N. E. (1952) Relationship between rhythmical processes and functional activity of an excitated neuromuscular apparatus. (Rus.) In I. M. Sechenov, I. P. Pavlov, & N. E. Wedenskii (Eds.), *Physiology of the nervous system.* Vol. 2. (3rd ed.) Moscow: Medgiz.

Wenger, M. A. (1936) An investigation of conditioned responses in human infants. *Univer. Iowa Stud. Child Welf.* 12, 9–90.

~ 11 ~

A Comparative Psychology of Development

HARRIET L. RHEINGOLD

University of North Carolina

Now that the reports are assembled, it is appropriate to ponder the value of the collection as a whole, beyond the value of each individual report. What justified the collection of the research reports in this book was the committee's wish to draw attention to an interesting and, in its opinion, important area of investigation. The same diversity of the reports that was the committee's goal makes a summary difficult. Not only is a variety of species reported on, but equally various are the ages of the organisms, the responses studied, the questions asked, the methods used, and the theoretical orientations of the. individual investigators.

Despite the diversity of the reports, several issues of consequence for the study of early behavior do emerge. What is the nature of early behavior? What are the special problems of conducting research on the development of behavior? What are the advantages of presenting in one collection studies of the human child with studies of the weanling rat, the kitten, and other infrahuman infants? Can the different theoretical orientations of the ethologist, the zoologist, and the psychologist be resolved when all focus on a common area of investigation? These questions will be considered on the basis of the research findings themselves.

SOME CHARACTERISTICS OF EARLY BEHAVIOR

The behaviors studied by the investigators range from sucking in the human newborn to playing in the juvenile chimpanzee; different as they are, some characteristics of early behavior stand forth. The characteristics are, (a) the organism possesses well-organized responses

Preparation of this paper was supported by a Public Health Service research career program award (No. K6-HD-23,620) from the National Institute of Child Health and Human Development.

279

even at birth; (b) it is able to discriminate among stimuli and shows a preference for some; (c) with repeated stimulation it responds less often and finally not at all; and (d) certain of its responses are very quickly modified by experience. In the following sections the research findings that suggested these principles will be reviewed. Since these characteristics are not unique to immature organisms, but are in fact common to organisms of all ages, they serve to unite the study of development with the science of all behavior.

The Presence of Well-Organized Responses

In the studies of neonatal organisms Fantz, Lipsitt, and Mason presented considerable evidence of responses that are efficient at birth. These responses are complex in the sense of being analyzable into components. They can be measured; they regularly occur to certain stimuli; and they have demonstrable effects upon other responses. Specifically, Fantz reported on the presence of pecking at small objects by newly hatched chicks and of visual regard for certain displays in human infants less than 24 hours of age. Kessen studied sucking and looking, and characterized them as "organized congenital patterns of behavior." By "congenital" he meant that the behavior was present at birth, and by "organized patterns of behavior," that the behavior could be "reliably described in metrics of space and time." He affirmed the tendency of the just-born human neonate to suck when presented with a suckable object. Not only is the sucking response a highly stable pattern of behavior but it can be analyzed into two components, "expression and suctioning." By day 3, feeding almost immediately resulted in a general lowering of the infant's activity; in fact, there is evidence that sucking by itself reduces movement even before the first feeding. From these findings Kessen concluded that the relation between sucking and movement is congenital. Lipsitt, too, characterized the complete sucking act as a complex pattern of response: "it is executed by the newborn with rhythm and grace." (p. 231)

In subjects only a little older other responses were sufficiently well organized to yield to analysis; these included head-turning in human infants during the first month of life (Papoušek), vocalizations of distress in infant chimpanzees (Mason), and reaching in 2-month-old kittens (Warren).

Stimulus Discrimination

Many of the reports provide evidence that the young organism can discriminate among stimuli; in some of the reports, preference is inferred from measures of the frequency, duration, or latency of a response to one of two or more stimuli.

Lipsitt's studies show that human neonates can not only distinguish between two olfactory stimuli, but even between two components of different compounds. The infants can also discriminate between two "intra-oral stimuli," as indicated by their sucking more frequently on a nipple than a tube; and they can discriminate between two auditory signals, a bell and a buzzer, when one serves as a positive cue for reinforcement, the other as a negative cue.

Papoušek, too, found that infants discriminated between auditory stimuli; some infants as early as the second month of life turned their heads to the left when a bell was sounded, and to the right when a buzzer was sounded. He also reported that infants in the first month of life turned their heads more often to the side from which they could obtain sweetened, rather than unsweetened, milk.

In studies of visual regard Kessen reported that newborn infants looked least at a panel of low brightness, more at a panel of high brightness, and most at one that was of intermediate brightness; they looked less at a complex checkerboard pattern than at a simple checkerboard pattern; and they looked more at random shapes of 10 independent turns than at random shapes of 5 and 20 turns. Shown a drawing of a triangle, they directed their gaze to its vertices.

Fantz reported that newborn infants looked longer at more complex patterns, and therefore he concluded that they could discriminate visual patterns. Under 2 months of age, the infants looked longest at a "highly linear" pattern; thereafter, up to 6 months of age, they preferred a circular or random pattern.

Two other classes of data also show the ability of very immature organisms to discriminate between stimuli. Fantz reported that newly hatched chicks pecked more often at circular than at angular targets. Mason found that newborn chimpanzees gave fewest distress vocalizations to ventral contact and more to other kinds of tactile and kinesthetic stimuli.

Response Decrement

Response decrement as a result of repeated stimulation is a common phenomenon. Given that a particular stimulus elicits a response, response decrement occurs in a wide variety of responses in many organisms. Attention is drawn to the phenomenon here simply to show that it occurs in the immature as well as the mature organism.

Fantz reported a marked drop in length of fixation for a frequently presented visual array in infants 2 to 6 months of age. In another study the infants looked less and less often at a repeatedly exposed pattern, longer and longer at a novel pattern, during the session.

Lipsitt found that changes in the movement and respiration of newborn infants decreased during repetitive stimulation with two different olfactory stimuli; that stimulation by one odor tended to decrease sensitivity to the other; that the response recovered to the second stimulus after habituation to the first, and recovered a second time when the first stimulus was reintroduced following habituation to the second. The same results were also observed with the individual components of mixtures. On the basis of these findings he concluded that "one of the most easily observed behavioral attributes of the human newborn is that with repetitive stimulation by an initially effective or unconditioned stimulus, response diminution tends to occur." (p. 228)

Modifiability of Early Behavior

There is much evidence in this book to show that early behavior is modifiable. There is also evidence to suggest that even in young organisms certain responses may not be easily modifiable. Any conclusion about the nonmodifiability of a response, however, can be stated only with reference to the procedures used; history teaches, and caution warns, that with some other procedure modifiability may subsequently be demonstrated.

The modifiability of infant behavior can be noted by even the casual observer, but its demonstration by experimental procedures is relatively recent. The youngest organisms on whom data are reported in this book are the newly hatched chick and the human neonate.

The form of grain first offered chicks modified their subsequent pecking responses; also, the early opportunity to peck at certain patterns for a short period of time increased the likelihood that they would peck at similar patterns (Fantz).

The object, whether tube or nipple, on which human newborns sucked modified their initial sucking rate on the other object. Further, rate of sucking on a tube was increased by pairing it with a dextrose solution. Head-turning to tactile stimulation was also increased in infants 2 and 3 days of age when it was followed by a dextrose solution. Infants of a similar age could be trained to turn their heads to the side from which they received the solution, or to turn their heads on the one of two auditory signals (paired with tactile stimulation) that was followed by the dextrose solution (Lipsitt). From these findings Lipsitt concluded that "the human neonate is not only a learning organism but may be remarkably sensitive to environmental events, . . ." (p. 241).

In somewhat older, although still immature, organisms Papoušek demonstrated that human infants learned to turn their heads on an auditory signal to the side from which milk was available. Although infants younger than 1 month of age conditioned more slowly than infants in the third and fifth months of life, even some of the youngest infants learned the response in less than two weeks of training. In the youngest infants, moreover, stages could be detected in the conditioning process that suggest early sensitivity to environmental events. By 2 and 3 months of age, some infants also learned to turn their heads to the left when the bell was sounded and to the right when the buzzer sounded, and subsequently to reverse the discrimination. In Papoušek's words, ". . . during the first trimester, there has developed not only the capacity to discriminate but also the capacity to reverse a discrimination." (p. 268)

Further evidence of the modifiability of responses may be seen in Fantz's study of the effects of light deprivation on rhesus infants. Infants with less than eight weeks of light deprivation looked longer at patterned than unpatterned targets; those with more than eight weeks of deprivation did not. Subsequent experience in light did not modify the visual responses of the animals deprived for the longer period. When both groups of subjects were 15 months of age, and had had many intervening months of visual experience, those that had been deprived for shorter periods of time solved more discrimination problems. Fantz concluded that "rearing in darkness can have a pronounced, long-lasting effect on attention, perception, and accompanying responses which is not due simply to lack of opportunity for visual learning." (p. 216)

Campbell reported that guinea pigs 20 to 24 hours of age learned to escape shock in three successive days with only 15 training trials a day. The same response was learned by 25-day-old rats. Rats of this age also learned to avoid shock and to press a bar for food. It is noteworthy that in the acquisition of these responses their rate of learning was comparable to that of mature organisms.

The behavior of birds also shows the possibility of early modifiability. Specifically, Klinghammer reported lasting effects of hand-raising on ring and mourning doves. Birds removed from the nest before 8 days of age and hand-raised were always tame with humans; in contrast, birds removed after 8 days of age were always fearful of humans.

Impressive and significant as these indications of early modifiability are, there is also evidence that some responses resist modification. In this category belong Fantz's finding that bottle-fed human infants did not look longer at a nursing bottle than at other stimuli; Eibl-Eibesfeldt's finding that young squirrels raised on a liquid diet in wire-mesh cages tried to bury nuts in the same way as squirrels raised in a normal fashion; and Warren's finding that lateral preferences in kittens and immature macaques not only appeared early but changed little as a result of extended practice.

Taken as a whole, the findings in this book show that a number of responses in very immature organisms were relatively quickly altered by experience. The investigators would be the first to point out that their findings are specific to the response under study, the organism, the age at which practice was begun or withheld, and the stimulating conditions. The same considerations must also be applied to findings that the response did not yield to modification. As was stated earlier, it is indeed premature to declare that any response cannot be modified, although it is of great value to learn under what conditions modification is not produced. Nevertheless, the possibility always exists that the next experiment using some different technique may find that the behavior can indeed be modified.

Summary

The findings indicate that the behavior of immature organisms, even from birth, share many important traits with the behavior of mature organisms. Many of their responses are sufficiently well organized to permit measurement; they are not only specifiable but already are so complex that components can be defined. Responses are given selectively to certain stimuli. They decrease under repeated application of the same stimulus and also recover spontaneously. They are modifiable as a result of associations formed with preceding or subsequent events. Together, these traits of the young seem sufficient to warrant a significant place for the study of immature behavior within a comprehensive science of behavior.

RESEARCH DESIGNS FOR THE STUDY OF DEVELOPMENT

The experimental procedures used by the investigators in this book varied considerably. Each seemed most appropriate to the investigator for the questions he sought to answer. It may be instructive to examine the nature of their procedures as designs for the study of the development of behavior because in their variety they illustrate designs characteristic of this area of endeavor and because some of the problems of design are special to it.

The most obvious distinction may be drawn between research designs that study the behavior of an organism at one age (to be referred to as the first method) and those that study it at two or more ages. A further distinction may be drawn between research designs that study the behavior of *different* organisms at different ages (the second method) and those that study the *same* organisms at different ages (the third method). These distinctions raise the question of whether by definition the study of the development of behavior requires comparison between ages. There are some investigators who feel strongly that it must. When the behavior under investigation, however, is that of an immature organism, the case can be made that a comparison between that organism and a more mature one is implied and need not be made explicit.

Among the chapters in this book three investigators used the first method. Kessen reported studies on two classes of responses during the first few days of the human infant's life. Lipsitt also reported some studies on the same period, as well as on others, on infants at 4 and 12 months of age, drawing no comparisons between results at the different ages. Eibl-Eibesfeldt also concentrated on behavior at one age in his investigations of nut-hiding and opening in the immature squirrel. These investigations, in my opinion, qualify as studies in the development of behavior; they provide information on the characteristics of an organism at the very beginning of independent life, as well as techniques for subsequent age comparisons.

A second type of study in this collection did compare behavior between two or more ages in different groups of subjects. Campbell traced the acquisition, extinction, and retention of learned responses in rats and guinea pigs at ages ranging from a few days to adulthood. Mason, although concentrating most of his efforts on an analysis of social responsiveness in adolescent chimpanzees, also presented some comparable data on infant and adult chimpanzees. Fantz, too, presented age comparisons; in different studies he used similar sets of stimuli to measure pattern vision in human infants over the first six months of life. Lastly, Papoušek compared the performance of human infants, under various conditioning procedures, at three different ages during the first year of life.

Both methods, that of investigating behavior at one age and that of investigating behavior at different ages in different groups of subjects, are, of course, cross-sectional designs. When, in the second method, no unusual change in genetic strain or the environment has occurred to cause differences between the populations of different ages, differences in performance may be reasonably related to differences in ages. We can assume that Campbell's rats and guinea pigs at the different ages came from the same genetic stock and experienced closely similar environmental conditions in the laboratory until time of testing. It is clear, however, that the wider the age span covered, and the more heterogeneous the stock from which the organisms come and the environmental stimuli to which they have been exposed, the more caution one needs to exercise in attributing any difference in performance to age alone.

An interesting variation of the second method may be seen in Warren's study of laterality in two groups of rhesus monkeys. Not only were the groups widely different in age, one immature and the other adult, but they differed also in genetic stock and life experiences; the immature monkeys had been born and raised in the laboratory; the adults had been born in the wild and, in addition, had participated in many experiments in the test apparatus. From the results of this and other experiments Warren concluded that handedness appeared early in the immature macaque and changed little as a result of further development or experience. When no difference in performance is found, despite wide differences in age and other characteristics of the groups, the reliability and generality of the findings are increased.

The remaining reports employed the third method; they investigate responses of the same organism at different ages. Papoušek, who compared the performance of different groups of infants at different ages, also charted the performances of each group through successive conditioning procedures. Fantz deprived infant rhesus monkeys of visual experience for varying periods of time and measured the effect of age at deprivation and the duration of deprivation on pattern and object discrimination. Warren measured paw preference in kittens at 60 days of age, gave some of them practice until 180 days of age, and then tested preferences at 180, 210, and 360 days of age. When 15 months of age, some of these animals were given forced practice with the nonpreferred paw to measure the effect upon subsequent behavior in different types of reaching tasks. Similarly, in a study of rhesus monkeys, Warren compared the performance of a group of animals when they were 2 years old and experimentally naïve with their performance two years later after much experience in the test apparatus.

Although it falls into the same class, that of investigating responses at different ages in the same organism, Klinghammer's design deserves separate attention. It differs from the others in spanning a longer period in the life of the organism, and in measuring in maturity a behavior that was not present at the time of experimental intervention. Although the crucial test of the intervention came in maturity, the necessary precondition, tameness to human beings, occurred when the organism was immature.

The third method is of course the longitudinal method. It is a powerful research design but is always confounded with whatever effects may result from repeated measurements of the same individuals (see Schaie, 1965).

Special mention should be made of Campbell's efforts to insure equally motivating conditions across ages. Although his efforts had special relevance to his problem, this nicety of procedure serves as a model for all work that attempts to compare behavior at different ages.

THEORETICAL ORIENTATIONS

The comments on the book to this point have been written as though all the studies belong to the discipline of psychology and as though all the investigators are psychologists. Not so! Surely Eibl-Eibesfeldt and Klinghammer would call themselves ethologists. This distinction suggests that it might be instructive to compare their theoretical position with that of the others. And, even among the others, differences in theoretical position are apparent. For example, Fantz argued the need for some theoretical framework other than conventional learning theory to make sense of his findings; Kessen came out strongly for a study of the organism's behavior at birth; and Papoušek worked within the classical Pavlovian framework, although his procedures contained elements of both classical and instrumental conditioning.

Although differences in theoretical orientations cannot easily be resolved, there need not be an unresolvable dichotomy between studying the development of the behavior of an organism in its natural environment and the development of behavior of that organism in the laboratory. The tasks are different, but they complement, rather than negate, each other. Sometimes, to be sure, the laboratory study is designed to discover a *principle* of behavior rather than to chart a particular organism's behavior under a particular set of circumstances. Still, no contradiction exists once it is agreed that all types of study may contribute to the understanding of behavior.

The first task of the ethologist is to become thoroughly acquainted with the natural behavior of the organism he wishes to study. Not only is this task explicitly stated as an aim but the findings are also presented as a contribution to knowledge. Although it may sometimes *seem* that the psychologist does not know his animal before he begins his study, such ignorance is only illusory. No organism can be studied in the laboratory until the investigator knows how to maintain it, how to motivate it, to what stimuli it is sensitive, and of what responses it is capable. These facts are seldom reported in their own right, but obviously must be entirely known. It is true, of course, that after years of investigating one organism (the laboratory rat is *the* example) many of these facts have been learned and are passed on to successive generations of investigators as laboratory lore. When the organism has not been much studied, a large portion of the investigator's efforts must first be devoted to discovering its special characteristics.

The special characteristics of organisms of different species, and even of different subspecies, are thus of concern to all investigators of that species' behavior, to the behavior theorist, the learning theorist, the zoologist, and the ethologist. To label the behavior as species-specific or species-characteristic adds no new knowledge, but the labeling stimulates interest in comparing the behavioral characteristics of different species. The labeling does indeed serve to pinpoint the problem.

The psychologist long ago adopted the strategy of learning about behavior by finding out how it could be modified. Assessment studies (for example, normative studies in children) are judged to reveal less knowledge about the causes of behavior than experimental studies. Experimental studies, especially those carried out in the laboratory, exercise control over stimulating conditions. One may criticize such studies on the grounds of incompleteness or artificiality, but not on the grounds of logic; control is the heart of the scientific method. The experimental method seeks to understand behavior by asking which responses can be modified by which stimuli provided at what ages, and for how long. These same questions, one may note, and these same procedures have been used in the experimental studies carried out by Klinghammer and Eibl-Eibesfeldt.

The deprivation experiment, so characteristic of ethological study, fits very well the procedure outlined above as a typical one for the experimental psychologist. In this book examples of the deprivation experiment are to be found in the reports by Eibl-Eibesfeldt and Fantz. Of all the investigations here included, only Kessen and Fantz, in other studies, come closest to studying the normal behavior of the normal organism under relatively normal conditions. Thus distinctions between methods and theoretical orientations that one might make in the abstract become blurred in the execution.

Ethologists, stemming from a background in zoology, draw attention to the phylogenetic basis of behavior. Psychologists in general shy away from the topic. Some find in it no answer to the kind of questions they ask, since their questions relate to the ontogenetic course of behavior. Others are put off by what seems to them a too easy recourse to biologic adaptiveness as an explanation. The evolution of behavior is still a new subject. Wherever ethology calls attention to it, a welcome stimulus is provided to broaden the scope of our understanding. Surely it is important for us to know how the capacities to learn, to communicate, and to live socially were modified by evolutionary pressures.

THE NEED FOR HUMAN SUBJECTS

In these chapters a sharp difference may be seen in the periods of life during which the behavior of the various organisms has been studied. In part, the difference reflects the shorter life span of some organisms. For example, Klinghammer hand-raised mourning doves from a few days of age and measured the effect upon choice of mate when the doves were mature. Similarly, Campbell in one of his experiments compared the acquisition of an avoidance response in weanling and mature rats, as well as the retention of the response 50 days later.

By contrast, the studies of human infants reported here are limited to a very much smaller fraction of the organism's life span. Kessen, for example, studied infants only during the first three or four days of life. No one can question an investigator's limiting his study to any period of time, no matter how short; the period he chooses depends, of course, upon the questions he asks. But the possibility exists that an investigator might have continued his investigations of human infants beyond 4 days of age if the infants had been available past this customary hospital lying-in period. To pursue their study the investigator would have had to follow the infants to their homes, a procedure that not only presents mechanical problems but also demands parental cooperation.

Lipsitt's studies also show the marks of being designed, at least in part, in accordance with the availability of subjects. He and his colleagues studied infants during the first few days of their residence in the newborn nursery and then again at 4 and 12 months of age, ages required by the larger study with which their efforts were coordinated. Fantz studied infants at different ages during the first six months of life; most of them were residents of an institution. Papoušek alone had the same subjects available for daily study during the first year of life; they too were residents of an institution.

These comments are not meant to be critical of any study but to point out a problem. Nor are they a plea for repeated measures over time. Surely it is conceivable that a single measure obtained in a few seconds may be sufficient to answer a particular question. Studies of learning, however, usually demand more than a few minutes. Lipsitt's results show what impressive modifications of behavior could be obtained in the relatively few minutes at his command, but successive sessions would be required to show how lasting are the modifications.

Although much has recently been said about the competence of the human infant, it is nevertheless true that he is alert and content in the same situation for only a matter of minutes. The human infant by nature or training appears to require frequent changes in stimulation to maintain behavior, and this is especially apparent in the controlled laboratory situation. Here Papoušek has come closest to solving the problem. The subjects lived in an institution under his control, they lived by a precise schedule of waking, sleeping, and feeding; they became adapted to the experimental situation over days; they were trained and tested on only 10 trials a day; and a normal feeding was used as the reinforcer.

Research on human infants and children is already limited by ethical constraints on depriving them of normal experiences and by practical problems of motivating them to perform. Further limitations are imposed by their relative unavailability for study. These limitations stem first from the technical problems of bringing children to the laboratory and adapting them to the strange environment, or of bringing the laboratory to them. Conducting experiments in institutions remains a solution, but a limited one because of the small number of institutions in this country now caring for young babies. Day-care centers will offer new possibilities as they become more numerous. These problems are mechanical; they can be solved in a variety of ways by the experimenter's ingenuity.

A second and perhaps more difficult problem must be met: obtaining the easy and confident cooperation of parents. The study of the development of behavior requires human infants, in numbers and over considerable periods of time. Yet we cannot study infants without involving their parents, their time, their efforts, and their good will.

So far, many investigators have succeeded very well in obtaining the cooperation of parents but often only by a considerable expenditure of time and effort.

There still lingers in our culture the notion that the behavior of young children should develop without intervention of any kind. Surely such an opinion rates too highly the ordinary home environment of the ordinary infant. Many psychological studies would, of course, chart only what naturally occurs, but we also need studies that measure the effects of new stimuli and the formation of new associations.

We hear, too, that the study of human infants entails an invasion of privacy. Our privacy is always being invaded; what matters is not the invasion but the nature and the purpose of the invasion. Of course, no human being should be studied without his informed consent; by extension, no infant should be studied without the informed consent of his parents. The scientific study of human behavior is also criticized on occasion because it treats the subject impersonally. When an individual serves as a subject, however, his need for privacy is best served by his anonymity.

I propose that behavioral scientists make known their need for human subjects. As scientists we shun publicity for many good reasons; yet for other good reasons we should inform the public of our procedures, our results, and our needs. In the process we may discover what I suspect to be true—that the public would join in the venture. Parents would then come to regard participation of themselves and their children in scientific studies of behavior as the duty, even as the privilege, of responsible and altruistic citizens.

MAN AMONG THE ANIMALS

Behavior develops in man and animal, in birds and fishes, as well as in mammals. Yet often the line is drawn between man and animals, and that line is drawn more often by the student of animal behavior than by the student of human behavior. Thus in textbooks and journals on zoology, ethology, and comparative psychology, data on man's behavior are seldom to be found. In contrast, in textbooks and journals on human psychology, data on the behavior of animals are common. In part, psychology pays attention to the behavior of animals because it is concerned with general principles of behavior, and in part because some experiments can be carried out only on infrahuman subjects.

In this book several reports are truly comparative. Warren employed the same method to study the same response class, laterality, in cats and monkeys. Campbell, too, compared the acquisition and retention of escape behavior in rats and guinea pigs. Fantz covered the widest range and included the human organism; he used a consistent method to chart the nature and course of visual discrimination in chicks, monkeys, and human infants.

Not only is the human infant included in this volume but four of the nine reports, almost half the book, are devoted to studies of his behavior. When the topic is behavior in immature organisms, it is perhaps easier to include the human infant; he, like the other animals, is nonverbal. In addition, he possesses the advantage of being larger than many other infant organisms and hence is easier to observe and, maturing more slowly, provides the investigator with more time for the analysis of behavior. The final question is whether man's enormous capacity for learning and his ability to communicate by sounds and symbols set him so far apart that no advantage can be gained by relating his behavior to that of infrahuman animals. Intuitively one feels that there may be certain advantages in thinking of him as one of the animals, as in fact he is. Only in surveying behavior wherever it appears, however, and by noting similarities and differences can the unique characteristics of man, or of any other species, be known.

A UNIFIED SCIENCE OF DEVELOPMENT

The variety of theoretical orientations in this book, of questions asked and methods used, and of behavior studied in different animals at different ages shows how many forms the study of behavior can assume. Despite diversity, the common topic is the development of behavior in immature animals.

Divisions between knowledge are arbitrary, arising from history, not truth. They record our ability to discriminate differences as well as similarities. Even as new areas of study are staked out, old areas are combined. The contents of this book clearly show how closely related the topics of developmental psychology are to those of general psychology. They also suggest the possibility of a common area of knowledge: the behavior of all living organisms, man and animal. More specifically, they demonstrate within that common area the possibility of a new division of knowledge: the development of behavior in immature organisms.

As matters now stand, the study of behavior is pursued and taught in several different departments of a university. Zoology presents courses in animal behavior, omitting man; psychology presents courses in animal and human behavior; physical anthropology presents courses in the behavior of free-ranging primates. To these may be added the disciplines of cultural anthropology, educational psychology, and sociology. Although worthy achievements arise from parochial settings, still other achievements can arise from more catholic settings. The attempt to see behavior as a characteristic of living organisms, and therefore as biological, may provide fresh insights.

The need for caution in extending generalizations beyond the species under study remains. The findings reported in this book emphasize the need. At the same time, however, the attempt to test generalizations should be pursued. Perhaps the task will be easier when we know enough to present a collection of reports on one response class of behavior in different species or, better still, on one response class of behavior at a similar age in different species. One lives by a faith in the orderliness of the universe, a universe that includes the behavior of living organisms. It is indeed possible to envision a science of behavior that takes as its province behavior in immature as well as in mature organisms, in animals as well as in man, in natural as well as in laboratory settings.

REFERENCE

Schaie, K. W. (1965) A general model for the study of developmental problems. *Psychol. Bull.* **64,** 92–107.

Author Index

Subject Index